A Short History of Machine Tools

A Short History of

Machine Tools

L. T. C. Rolt

THE M.I.T. PRESS
MASSACHUSETTS INSTITUTE OF TECHNOLOGY
CAMBRIDGE, MASSACHUSETTS

Second Printing, June 1966
Third Printing, April 1967

Library of Congress Catalog Card No.: 65-12439
Printed in the United States of America

Foreword

In a lifetime of dealing with the production and distribution of machine tools I have been impressed by the vital part that tools have played in the history of the Industrial Revolution. Even at the risk of appearing partisan to the Industry in which I have had such an absorbing interest it does seem odd, if not unfair, that those who hail technological marvels as triumphs of ingenuity and skill fail to give any credit to those engineers whose work has made such spectacular inventions possible. But for the innovators and creators of machine tools, there would be no steam turbines, motor cars, bicycles, aeroplanes, radio, washing machines nor, indeed, most of those industrial and domestic items on which civilised progress depends. The names and the work of the machine tool builders have, for the most part, remained hidden within the four walls of the workshop and their ingenuity quite unappreciated by the public at large.

A tribute to these unacknowledged 'back-room boys' is long overdue and I am glad to see published a book which fulfils this need. This volume is, however, not a catalogue of fulsome compliments, though they be well enough merited, to the pioneers of machines for making machines. It presents for the first time a definitive short history of machine tools.

Although the development of the machine tool in the United Kingdom up to the middle of the nineteenth century is fairly well covered by Samuel Smiles as well as by Professor Roe, there the story previously ended. What was needed, therefore, was a modern Smiles to carry out the necessary research and write a book covering objectively and comprehensively the interplay of metal-working production needs and complementary development of the machine tool in both the Old and New Worlds and there could not have been found a better author than Mr L. T. C. Rolt, distinguished writer and engineer-historian, to see this task through.

It is my sincere hope, surely not without foundation, that this book's contribution to the knowledge of those machines on which our present civilisation depends will be widely welcomed.

J. B. S. Gabriel
Chairman
Charles Churchill and Company Limited

Contents

The Illustrations

Acknowledgment

The Author and the Publishers wish to thank the following for permission to reproduce illustrations appearing in this book:

Messrs W. & T. Avery, Soho Foundry, Birmingham, for fig. 24; the Bettmann Archive, New York, for figs. 61, 62, 65, 75, 78, 86 and 87; the Birmingham City Museum and Art Gallery, for figs. 26, 45, 46, 74 and 92; Messrs Brades Skelton & Tyzack Ltd, Birmingham, for fig. 5; the Brotherton Library, University of Leeds, for fig. 25; the Brown & Sharpe Manufacturing Company, Providence, Rhode Island, for figs. 76, 80 and 84; the Cincinnati Machine Tool Company, Cincinnati, Ohio, for fig. 97; the Conservatoire National des Arts et Métiers, Paris, for figs. 18 and 19; the *Engineer*, London, for figs. 32, 33, 34, 39 and 47; the Fellows Gear Shaper Company, Springfield, Vermont, for fig. 85; the Heald Machine Company, Worcester, Massachusetts, for figs. 96 and 98; Messrs Alfred Herbert Ltd, Coventry, for figs. 21 and 23; the Institution of Mechanical Engineers, London, for fig. 29; the Landis Tool Company, Waynesboro, Pennsylvania, for fig. 95; the McGraw-Hill Book Company, New York, for figs. 63, 64 and 77; the Manchester Guardian and Evening News Ltd, for fig. 57; the National Portrait Gallery, London, for fig. 44; Norton International Inc., Worcester, Massachusetts, for figs. 93 and 94; the Royal Aeronautical Society, London, for fig. 91; the Science Museum, London, for figs. 7, 8, 16, 27, 37, 38, 41, 42, 43, 51, 52, 53 and 54; Mr T. Semeijns de Vries van Doesburgh, of The Hague, for fig. 17, also reproduced on the jacket; the University Library, Utrecht, for fig. 2; and the *Wellington Journal and Shrewsbury News*, for fig. 6.

Preface

It is impossible to study the history of technology without becoming aware of the crucially important part played in that history by machine tools and their makers. It is scarcely an exaggeration to say that man's tools have governed the pace of industrial revolution. We should never have heard of James Watt, George Stephenson, Gottlieb Daimler, Rudolph Diesel or the Wright Brothers but for the tools which could alone give their ideas a practical shape. Yet although the names of such great inventors and pioneers have become household words, those of the great tool-makers on whom the success of their efforts depended are comparatively unknown. A glance through the bibliography at the end of this book will help to explain this. It will reveal that while some attention has been belatedly devoted to the subject in the United States and in Germany, not a single work on the history of tools and their makers has been published in England. Samuel Smiles, in his *Industrial Biography* published in 1882, devoted a section to the British tool-making pioneers, but that is as far as we have gone.

The reason for this neglect is that the fruits of the tool-maker's art are confined within the four walls of the workshop where their ingenuity is appreciated only by engineers. They lack the spectacular and dramatic quality of inventions such as the locomotive, the motor car or the aeroplane, which they brought to successful birth. Hence the printed record of machine-tool evolution has lain buried in many treatises, articles and papers written by specialists for specialists.

This state of affairs is a classic example of the results of too much specialisation. Because of an intense concentration upon the trees, the wood has been lost to sight. Happily, the increasing importance which educationalists now attach to the study of the history of technology shows that the great dangers inherent in this situation are becoming widely recognised. Specialisation is an essential element of technical progress in our modern world, but it can spell ultimate disintegration unless the historian and philosopher redoubles his efforts to relate the parts to the whole and so enables the specialist to understand the social significance of what he is doing. Where there is no such understanding there can be no proper sense of responsibility, no sense of purpose and direction.

All down the ages the rate of man's material progress has been determined by his tools, because all tools represent synthetic extensions of the human hand, being designed to magnify its cunning or its power. When that hand first used a tree branch as a lever or a stone as a hammer, an evolutionary process began which has led logically to the fully automatic power-controlled machine tool of today. As we follow that process step by step its logicality is such that it appears inevitable; it is as though the end was implicit from the beginning. But this is one of the errors into which the historian's hindsight can lead us. The historian's desire for order always tempts him to over-simplify so as to make past events form a neat pattern. To some extent this is inevitable if history is to be written coherently, but it can lead the reader into the error of supposing that the logical pattern created by the historian was evident to those taking part in the particular sequence of historical events he is recording. This is never the case; if it were we should all be soothsayers. Nevertheless, man should always endeavour to foresee the consequences of his acts and in the advance of technology such an effort is particularly vital at the present time. Man's creative enthusiasm is such that he has frequently launched new discoveries upon the world with scant regard for the possible consequences. If those consequences have been ill, scientist or technician have assumed a God-like pose, blaming politician or entrepreneur for misusing their priceless gifts. Such an irresponsible attitude is no longer tenable today. Man must learn to control the development of his technology and, notwithstanding the errors into which hindsight can lead us, the best way he can do this is to study the past history of that technology.

In machine-tool history, one reason why an evolutionary process which now seems obvious to us was not obvious to the pioneer tool-makers is the remarkable propagating power of tools. One man constructs a new or improved tool in order to solve a particular production problem, but others speedily discover that this same tool makes practicable inventions such as its inventor never dreamed of. Moreover, such a tool at once makes possible the construction of still better tools of a similar or different kind. This cycle of cause and effect repeats itself endlessly through the chapters of this book and with each repetition the evolutionary process accelerates. Again, inventions made possible by improved tools pursue a parallel but separate course of development for a time, until they reach a stage when they can be seen to offer something of value to the tool-maker, who then assimilates them with profoundly significant results. Electrical power and hydraulic engineering are but two examples of this.

Man's tools faithfully reflect that increasing tendency towards specialisation which has accompanied the growth of knowledge. The most versatile of all tools is the human hand, but it is feeble and fallible. The aim of all tool-makers from first to last has been to overcome these defects by enhancing the power of the hand and reducing its fallibility. All hand tools and the simpler machine tools give enhanced power to the user, but so long as the tool is controlled by the skill of the user fallibility must remain. So the tool-makers attacked human fallibility by 'building the skill into the tool', a process which culminated—inevitably as it now seems to us—in the fully automatic tool, totally emancipated from the possibility of human error in the unwearying precision of its motions. Yet this elimination of human error has been purchased at the price of a corresponding loss of versatility in the tool. How to combine versatility with automation—to use the current term—is a problem which has not yet been solved. The power, the speed of operation and the infallible precision of the automatic tool can only be harnessed to advantage in the manufacture of a uniform product in large quantities, that is to say, in mass production. But man has varying needs. Consequently the automatic tool is only applicable to certain industries and even in them its lack of flexibility can be disadvantageous. In the case of the logical successor to the automatic tool—the fully automated production plant—this difficulty is even more formidable, although the latest developments in tape-controlled machine tools indicate how the problem of flexibility may be met in the future.

No aspect of the Industrial Revolution has provoked more controversy, more violent social and economic stresses and strains than the process of building the skill into the tool. The days of the machine-wrecking Luddites are over, but although they manifest themselves in different ways, the same problems which provoked the Luddites exist today. They are likely to become more acute as the techniques of automation are more widely applied. The inventors of improved tools have ever been bitterly attacked. Champions of the working man have accused the tool-makers of robbing him of his livelihood by reducing the need for hand labour. By humanists the tool-makers have been sternly criticised for debasing and degrading the workman by robbing him of his skilled craft and turning him into a mere machine-minder, condemned to the performance of a simple repetitive task of soul-destroying monotony.

There is substance in both these criticisms, but they have had very little influence on the progress of technology because, though passionately sincere, they were uninformed. Sociologists and reformers must remain powerless to influence the direction of technological progress so long as they concern themselves solely with the social effects of technology and remain ignorant of the causes which produced those effects. Only the study of the history of technology can amend this ignorance, and it is hoped that in this way the following chapters may be of some value. They have been deliberately confined strictly to the realm of technology, that is to say they tell a straight story of machine-tool evolution. They include some account of the influence of these tools on the general progress of technology, but are not concerned with their social and economic effects. But the book has not been written for specialists and it is hoped that it may help to dispel certain illusions.

One of the hoariest of these illusions is that the human dynamic behind machine-tool development and the mass production process has ever been the capitalist greedy for gain and prepared to disregard every human consideration in his pursuit of maximum profits. It is true that new tools have been exploited by entrepreneurs in this way but, as this book reveals, it has been the skilled craftsman and not the entrepreneur who has supplied the original dynamic in the story of machine tools. It is an illusion to suppose that the machines evolved in Britain in the first half of the nineteenth century by the first great generation of tool-makers rapidly dispossessed a nation of craftsmen. On the contrary, these tool-makers, Maudslay, Nasmyth, Whitworth and their fellows, were themselves high craftsmen who evolved their improved tools primarily to satisfy their own exacting standards of workmanship. They found that both existing tools and the existing level of human skill fell lamentably short of the standard they set, and the process of building the skill into the tool which they initiated was their answer to this dilemma. James Nasmyth is quite explicit on this point. Moreover, the first machine tools were not designed to replace traditional craft methods but to solve novel production problems which could not be surmounted in any other way.

Similar illusions surround the origins of the techniques of mass production. These were eagerly seized upon and exploited by entrepreneurs, but these men did not supply the incentive which originated such methods. Interchangeability of parts in a complex assembly was the advantage which inspired the originators of modern mass-production methods. In America the commercial possibilities of such methods were quickly grasped and exploited, yet here again it is significant that the technique was first applied to the manufacture of such novel and complex inventions as the sewing machine and the typewriter which could not have been produced commercially in any other way.

The scope of a short book on so large a subject must necessarily be limited. Practically every article we use or consume today has been manufactured or processed by large, intricate, highly specialised machines which could, in the wider sense of the word, be called tools. Here we are concerned only with what might be called the basic tools, the engineer's machines that make machines. As such, they are the Adamite machines, possessing the oldest ancestry and the greatest influence. When an engineer talks about a machine tool he usually means a metal-cutting tool, and this book is confined to the history of tools which comply with this definition. Wood-working tools, or machines which process metal before it is cut, are mentioned only when they have had some influence on the evolution of metal-cutting tools.

It is impossible to tell the story of machine tools without a certain amount of technical description, but I hope this will not deter the layman. As far as possible technicalities have been restricted to the descriptions of machines which were outstanding landmarks in design and, with the aid of the illustrations, these should not prove very difficult to follow. The emphasis throughout is on the broad pattern of evolution. I can only hope that the result may lead to a wider appreciation of the great tool-makers—what they strived for, what they achieved and the momentous results of the techniques they perfected.

Finally, I must record my gratitude to Charles Churchill & Co. Ltd. for inviting me to write this book. It has been for me a fascinating voyage of discovery which I could not have undertaken without their generous sponsorship. My thanks are also due to members of the staffs of Charles Churchill & Co. Ltd., Alfred Herbert, Ltd., the Lapointe Machine Tool Co. Ltd., the Machine Tool Trades Association, the Institution of Mechanical Engineers, the London and Birmingham Science Museums, Het Nederlands Leger en Wapenmuseum at Leyden, the Manchester College of Science and Technology, the Machine Tool Industry Research Association, the Derby County and Borough Libraries, and to members of the Newcomen Society. Their help has been invaluable. The book also owes much to the splendid drawings by my friend, Max Millar, particularly that of the Clement lathe, which is a masterpiece of careful reconstruction. Of the sources listed at the end of this book I must mention especially the series of four monographs written by Professor Robert S. Woodbury of the Massachusetts Institute of Technology on the history of the lathe, the milling machine, the grinding machine and the gear-cutting machine. Without the aid of these, plus the work of Professor J. W. Roe, the section of this book dealing with developments in the United States could not have been written.

L. T. C. ROLT

CHAPTER 1

Machines in the Craftsman's Workshop

THE STORY OF MACHINE TOOLS can be said to have begun when man, in the effort to extend the power of his hands over stubborn materials, first constructed a rigid, ground-based frame supporting a bearing or bearings in which either a tool or a workpiece could be rotated on a spindle. An irregular workpiece fixed upon such a spindle and rotated could, by the application of a hand-held tool, be reduced to a perfectly circular form the diameter of which could be varied at will. Alternatively, if a crude bit was fixed to the end of the rotating spindle it would bore a hole through a stationary workpiece that was pressed against it. In this way the lathe and the drilling or boring machine, the Adam and Eve of machine tools, were born.

Precisely when and where that birth took place we shall never know. It has been said that the lathe was derived from the potter's wheel, but this is pure speculation of doubtful validity. Because such an adaptation seems blindingly obvious to us it does not follow that it would have been so obvious to our remote ancestors. Although it bears no marks or grooves, the lip shape and the centre hole of a shallow wooden bowl found in a pit-grave at Mycenae (*c.* 1200 B.C.) suggest that it may have been turned. The oldest indisputable example of the turner's art so far discovered is a fragment of an Etruscan wooden bowl found in the 'Tomb of the Warrior' at Corneto (*c.* 700 B.C.), while beautiful and elaborate wooden bowls and beads and other ornaments in amber have been found to prove that by the sixth century B.C. highly accomplished turners were at work among the Etruscan and Celtic peoples.

By the second century B.C. the use of the lathe was known throughout Europe and the Near East and as the turner's proficiency increased so the range of lathe-turned products widened to include spokes and hubs for wagon wheels. Unfinished or spoiled pieces of turnery have been preserved in the peat of the Glastonbury Lake Village site to reveal that the La Tene Celts had by then (100 B.C.–A.D. 50) become remarkably versatile turners. Thus an unfinished wooden wheel hub has spindles or 'deadheads' at each end to prove that it was turned between centres, the earliest known example of this technique. These Celtic turners at Glastonbury also turned bracelet rings from the soft Kimmeridge stone and here again spoiled

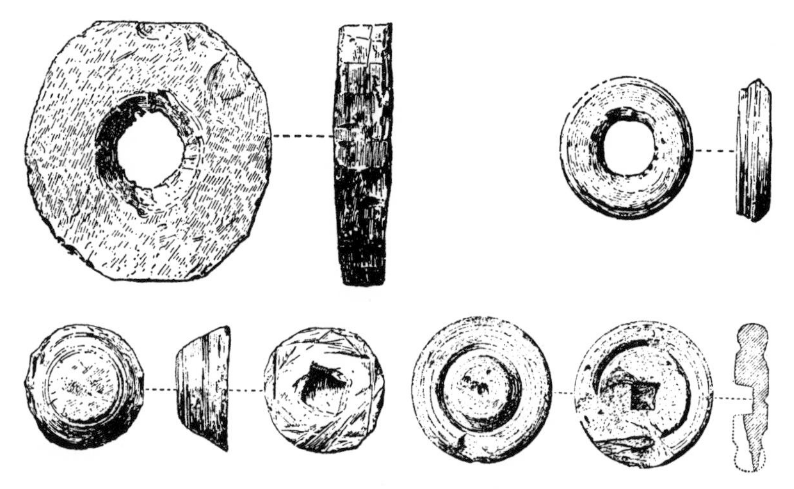

1 *Glastonbury Lake Village bracelet rings,* c. *100* B.C. (*Bulleid and Gray*): (top left) *Blank prepared for turning on mandril;* (top right) *Blank from which ring has been parted off;* (bottom left) *Blank with squared driving hole;* (bottom right) *Spoiled workpiece with ring partly turned and showing driving square and centre pop*

pieces have been found which show that these were produced in one of two ways from a roughly circular blank fashioned by hand. In some cases the blank has a circular hole in its centre to show that it was either driven onto the end of the lathe spindle or onto a mandril held between centres. Other blanks have a blind square hole formed on one side and an indentation or 'centre pop' on the other. Clearly, such a blank was fitted over the squared end of a lathe spindle and then retained there by a dead centre-point attached to a tailstock. In both cases the periphery of the blank was trued, rounded and undercut on both faces until the finished ring was finally 'parted off' from the centre of the blank.

The fact that these Celtic craftsmen were accustomed to turn in stone leads naturally to the argument as to whether or not the cylindrical drums of the stone columns with which the men of the ancient world adorned their buildings were lathe-turned. The idea that they were rests on a statement made by Pliny in the first century A.D., but this is vague and retrospective and the consensus of modern opinion is that they were not turned. The notion that so massive a machine existed in the ancient world is inherently improbable.

Historically, the most important result of the ability to turn stone in the lathe was that it led to the birth of the grinding machine. The increasing use of iron, and later steel, for weapons and edge tools focussed attention upon the abrasive properties of stone as a means of producing a cutting edge on metal. It soon became evident that a stone, bored in the centre and turned true like the bracelet blanks of the Glastonbury Celts, could, when rotated upon a spindle, produce a keen cutting edge more rapidly and efficiently than a whetstone. Again we do not know when this significant step was first taken. The first known representation of a grinding wheel occurs in the Utrecht Psalter of A.D. 850, but it was most probably in use earlier than this. Its value not merely as a sharpener but as a burnisher of metal was evident and armourers were soon making extensive use of it for this purpose.

2 *Sword grinder, Utrecht Psalter,* A.D. *850* (*Library, University of Leiden*)

As we shall see, the history of the grinding machine has been completely different from that of its parents the lathe and the boring machine. Whereas the latter continued to evolve, slowly at first but with gathering momentum, the grinding machine, once conceived, remained completely static. Power might be applied to it, but the machine itself retained its simple basic form unchanged, the operator continuing to hold the workpiece against the periphery of the wheel, or more rarely against its side, with or without the use of a rest. The grinder in the Utrecht Psalter is depicted sitting on a pole whose height above the axis of the machine is equal to the radius of the wheel. While his assistant rotates the wheel by a crank, the grinder leans forward and, between extended arms, runs the sword he is sharpening to and fro across the top of the wheel's periphery. The grinder can bring his weight to bear upon the job and at the same time control the workpiece most readily from such a position. In England, the practice persisted for more than 900 years.

In 1944 the writer watched a scythe-grinder plying his trade in a Worcestershire village. He sat astraddle on his 'horse'—a high-mounted seat formed out of half a tree-trunk—and, leaning forward arms astretch, worked the scythe blade across the top of the big grinding wheel of Permian sandstone. Except for the fact that his wheel was turned by water power instead of by an assistant with a crank, the scene so vigorously portrayed by the artist of the Utrecht Psalter was precisely re-enacted. This remarkable example of the continuity of primitive craftsmanship typifies the story of the grinding machine. It is only within the last 80 years that the development of synthetic abrasives has transformed the antique grindstone into the self-acting and self-regulating machine tool of supreme accuracy and precision which the engineer uses today.

The assistant manning the crank-handle in the Utrecht Psalter illustration gave the grindstone its essential rotative motion, but many years passed before such a unidirectional form of drive was applied to the lathe or the drilling machine. The earliest known form of lathe drive consisted of a length of cord wound round either the lathe spindle or the workpiece itself. The turner's assistant then worked the two ends of the cord to and fro. The alternating rotative motion which this cord imparted to the work called for great skill and dexterity on the part of the turner because he could only apply his cutting tool to the job when the workpiece was rotating towards its edge. The craftsmanship evident in early specimens of turnery becomes all the more remarkable when this difficulty is appreciated.

The earliest form of drill drive was similar except that the two ends of the cord were attached to the ends of a wooden rod, called for obvious reasons a bow. By working this bow to and fro with one hand, the operator could dispense with an assistant. This principle of the bow drill, as it is called, was also applied to the lathe, but it is obvious that only a supremely skilful craftsman doing light work could operate a bow lathe successfully without an assistant.

To this day in the East turners can be seen working primitive lathes by sitting on the ground and using the foot and toes as a movable tool rest, the right hand propelling the spindle and the left holding the tool. This technique, however, is peculiarly oriental and it is extremely unlikely that it was ever used by turners in the Western world. Such a use of the feet has never been natural to Western man who prefers to stand to his work. Consequently the first development of the lathe drive in the West took an opposite course by making the operator's foot do the driving so as to leave both hands free for the work. This development was the pole lathe, illustrations of which first appear in the thirteenth century. It retained the same principle of cord drive, but one end of the cord was now attached to a foot treadle and the other to the free end of a well-sprung ash pole overhead.

The pole lathe dispensed with the need for an assistant but it still called for a very high degree of skill on the part of the operator. The direction of rotation of the workpiece still alternated, while the action of the spring-pole could only perform what might be called the idle stroke. The pressure of the foot on the treadle had to provide the power for the cutting stroke. To combine this vigorous action of the foot with the precise and simultaneous application of the hand-held cutting tool to the workpiece demanded perfect physical co-ordination such as only the true craftsman can achieve.

A German illustration of a pole lathe dated 1395 shows that by this time the first essential of the machine tool—rigidity—was appreciated. Although they are made of wood, the bed of this lathe and its head and tailstocks are very substantial. The illustration also shows that the tailstock could be adjusted to the length of the workpiece, a wedge being then driven between the two longitudinals of the bed to hold it in position. Yet there is no form of rest for the tool; the turner is shown holding it up to the work with both hands while he depresses the treadle with his left foot. The tool shown has a short handle; more usually the handle was made long enough to bear against the turner's right shoulder. This enhanced his control over the tool and enabled him to bring more pressure to bear upon it if required.

3 *A German pole lathe of 1395* (Mendelesches Brüderbuch)

The use of primitive appliances among a primitive people is to be expected, but one of the remarkable features of machine-tool history is the way the use of primitive tools has persisted in the midst of an advanced technology. The example of the rural scythe-grinder has already been mentioned. The writer has also watched a craftsman in the Birmingham jewellery quarter using a bow drill, while shortly before the last war in a small shed on Bucklebury Common in Berkshire he saw George Lailey, last of the Berkshire bowl-turners, turning his elm bowls upon a pole lathe which differed scarcely at all from its medieval ancestors. The strength of an established tradition of craftsmanship and the high capital cost of more sophisticated machine tools are closely associated reasons for the survival of such ancient methods in rural workshops or in trades where quantity production methods do not apply.

It was only as a light wood-turning tool that the pole lathe persisted so stubbornly. Even the most expert craftsman found it extremely arduous, if not impossible, to carry out heavier wood-working and especially metal-turning on such a machine. The demand for such work increased during the later Middle Ages with the effect that by the mid fourteenth century the lathe had been provided with continuous drive to the spindle by an endless rope which passed round the grooved rim of a large flywheel. This flywheel was rotated by the turner's assistant, using a crank handle, but before the century was out the assistant had been replaced in some cases either by a horse-engine or a waterwheel. Once this unidirectional motion had been applied to the lathe the transfer of the tool from the hand of the turner to a fixed rest on his machine became a practical possibility, but 400 years had still to pass before this step was achieved with complete success on a heavy-duty metal-turning machine.

That it should have taken four centuries to make an improvement which now appears to us so obvious seems at first thought the more strange when we realise that during these centuries many of the distinguishing features of the modern machine tool were anticipated on a small scale in the clock-maker's workshop and by the drawings of that extraordinary genius of the Renaissance, Leonardo da Vinci. Complex social factors account for this seemingly inexplicable time-lag between conception and large-scale realisation.

We should expect the clock-maker to be a pioneer of advanced techniques because the mechanical weight-driven clock was the first complex piece of mechanism to be evolved by man. The origin of the mechanical clock is not known but it is believed to have been developed by Italian craftsmen towards the end of the thirteenth century. By 1364 Giovanni De' Dondi (1318–1389), professor of astronomy at the university of Padua, had completed, after 16 years' work, a planetarium clock of astounding complexity. The original was destroyed, but De' Dondi left a sufficiently detailed description of his work to enable a replica to be constructed recently. The fact that its planetary motions were based on the fallacious geocentric Ptolemaic system need not lessen our admiration for the way De' Dondi solved the incredibly complex mechanical problems involved. Thus, in order to simulate the supposed elliptical orbit of Mercury about a fixed point slightly removed from the earth, he constructed a gear train which included elliptical gearwheels and sun-and-planet motion. According to a contemporary report De' Dondi fashioned his clock entirely from brass and copper. The teeth of its innumerable gearwheels would have been laboriously cut by hand with the aid of some form of dividing engine to ensure sufficient accuracy of pitch. The clock was thus an almost miraculous feat of manual craftsmanship and its interest in this context lies in the way it anticipated motions such as the sun-and-planet gear over 400 years before they were adopted by mechanical engineers and tool-makers for industrial applications.

From Italy the use of the mechanical clock spread through France and the Low Countries to England. The clock installed at Salisbury in 1386 and now preserved in the nave of the cathedral is certainly the oldest in England, and possibly the oldest in the world, to survive in reasonably complete original form. It is therefore an excellent example of metal-working technique at that time. The small pinions are of the lantern type, that is to say their 'teeth' consist of a series of round iron pins held between two end-plates. The lantern pinion was derived from the medieval mill where the exclusive use of wooden gearing prohibited the adoption of pinions of toothed or 'leaf' pattern. The large gearwheels of forged iron have hand-cut teeth of a very square profile. The most significant feature of the Salisbury clock, however, is that not a single screw thread was used in its construction, the iron framing of the mechanism being held together either by rivets or wedges. It is clear that large clocks of this date were the work of highly skilled blacksmiths. A turner was obviously responsible for producing the wooden barrels on which the driving ropes were wound, but apart from this machine tools do not appear to have played any part in construction. Even the holes in the framing for arbor pivots, rivets or wedge bolts were evidently punched by the smith through the hot metal.

The De' Dondi clock was an exceptional tour de force. The first demand for clocks which could be described as commercial came from the medieval church. This demand was for clocks of a size which, as at Salisbury, a skilled blacksmith could construct. It was when the laity began to demand clocks of a size practicable for domestic use that clock-making became a specialised craft. It was evident to the clock-maker that he could not look for custom beyond an extremely restricted circle of kings and a few wealthy nobles unless he could produce with reasonable facility and economy clocks of much smaller size. The smaller the clock the wider the market, and so there was a great incentive to evolve new and more precise production techniques: accurately turned arbors, machine-cut gears and screw threads. This process of refinement and 'scaling down' began at the end of the fourteenth century and proceeded continuously thereafter until by the seventeenth century the clock-maker's craft had progressed far beyond the general level of contemporary technology.

The origin of the screw thread goes back to the days of Archimedes when it was introduced as a means of raising water. The wine press probably represents the earliest application of the screw and nut principle. The wooden-threaded barrels of such presses were laboriously marked out and cut by hand and the first metal screws were produced in the same way at the cost of much greater labour and pains. The first recorded mechanical means of producing a screw thread was most probably inspired by the needs of the clock-maker and appears as an illustration in the *Mittelalterlichen Hausbuch* of about 1480. This shows a very remarkable little lathe indeed. Not only does it possess a tool rest which can be slid along the bed of the lathe and held by a wedge in the required position, but the tool itself is held by a screw and bridge-piece in a socket on a cross-slide which can be moved to and fro by a screw mechanism. It is therefore a true compound slide rest. As can be seen from the illustration, the driving spindle of this lathe, which is turned directly by a crank-handle, is threaded through the head stock. The workpiece on which the thread is to be cut engages in a deep socket in the end of the lathe spindle, being free to revolve in, and to slide through, the tailstock. When the tool was brought up to its work by the cross-feed and the crank-handle was turned it would cut upon the workpiece a thread of the same pitch as that on the lathe spindle.

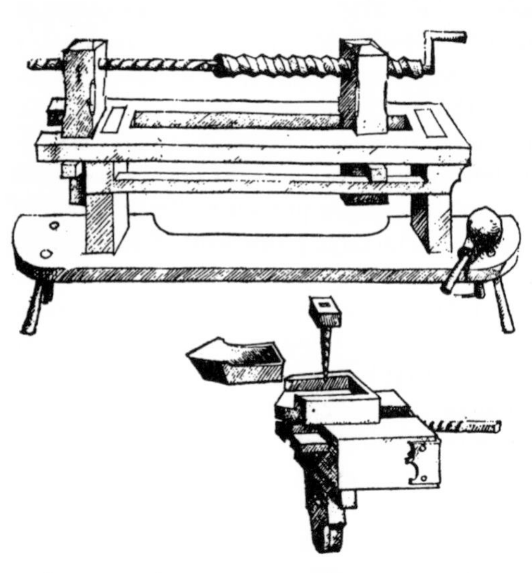

4 *German clock-maker's screw-cutting lathe, c. 1480, showing* (below) *the tool-holder on cross slide* (Mittelalterlichen Hausbuch)

The first reference to what is evidently a form of mechanical gear-cutting device is dated about 1540, that is to say, sixty years after the screw-cutting lathe. This occurs in a book by the Spaniard Ambrosio Morales in which he describes the work of an Italian craftsman, Juanelo Torriano of Cremona (1501–1575), who came to Spain in 1540 to build a

5 *Grinding scythe blades at Belbroughton, Worcestershire*

THE PERSISTENCE OF ANCIENT METHODS

6 *Turning elm bowls on the pole lathe*

7 *Clock-maker's wheel-cutting engine, c. 1672 (Crown Copyright. Science Museum, London)*

8 *Model of Leonardo da Vinci's boring mill, showing the self-centring chuck (Crown Copyright. Science Museum, London)*

great planetary clock for Charles V. According to Morales, Torriano completed the clock in $3\frac{1}{2}$ years notwithstanding the fact that it contained more than 1,800 gearwheels. He accomplished this feat, we are told, because he used a machine which enabled him to produce an average of more than three wheels a day. Morales' description of this device reads as follows: '. . . Even more astounding is a most ingenious lathe that he invented (and we see them today) to carve out with a file iron wheels to the required dimension and degree of uniformity of teeth.' The inference here is that Torriano must have adapted a lathe to act as an accurate dividing engine and used it in conjunction with a form of hardened rotary file cutter. The reference in brackets suggests that Torriano's machine had been adopted by other clock-makers by the time Morales' book was published in 1575. It was doubtless the parent of the 'wheel-cutting engines' used by clock-makers in England and France in the seventeenth century. One of these machines dating from about 1672 is to be seen in the Science Museum at South Kensington in London. This has a horizontal indexing plate, the wheel to be cut being mounted on the top of its vertical spindle. The formed rotary file cutter is driven by gearing from a hand-crank and the depth of cut can be adjusted by screw.

A drawing by Leonardo da Vinci dated about 1500 shows another remarkable screw-cutting machine. This consists of a broad table with a cutter block of equal breadth sliding upon it. The workpiece on which the thread is to be cut passes through the centre of this block and engages directly with a spindle rotated by a crank-handle. The two lead screws which propel the block and its cutter along the table are driven by gears from this spindle and the most interesting detail of all is that Leonardo depicts under the table an alternative set of gear wheels which would enable a screw of different pitch to be cut using the same lead screws. This is the earliest record of the use of change wheels for screw cutting and in this respect it represents an advance upon the screw-cutting lathe of 1480.

9 *Screwing machine by Leonardo da Vinci,* c. *1500. Note change wheels under table* (*Institut de France manuscript*)

Whether the lathe of 1480 and Leonardo's no less advanced machine were ever actually built is doubtful. If they were, they had no direct successors. Another sketch by Leonardo in the *Codex Atlanticus* shows a treadle lathe in which a bow has been substituted for the overhead spring-pole, the driving rope being attached to the centre of the bowstring. A partly threaded workpiece is shown mounted between the lathe stocks and although the sketch is not very clear the idea seems to be to cut the first portion of a thread by hand and then to use this portion as a lead screw in order to cut the rest. Yet a third lathe drawing by Leonardo shows a plain turning lathe in which the interesting feature is the method of obtaining unidirectional motion of the spindle from a foot treadle. The lathe spindle incorporates a single-throw crank supported between bearings, the cord from the treadle being looped round the journal of this crank. The spindle is prolonged to carry a large flywheel and the end of this extension is supported by a third bearing. This is not only the earliest illustration of the use of a treadle to provide unidirectional motion for a lathe spindle but also the first to show the drive applied between two bearings at the headstock, an arrangement which ensured much greater rigidity under heavy cutting loads and consequently greater precision. The machine has a fixed tailstock, but the cranked dead-centre is threaded through it to allow for workpieces of varying length.

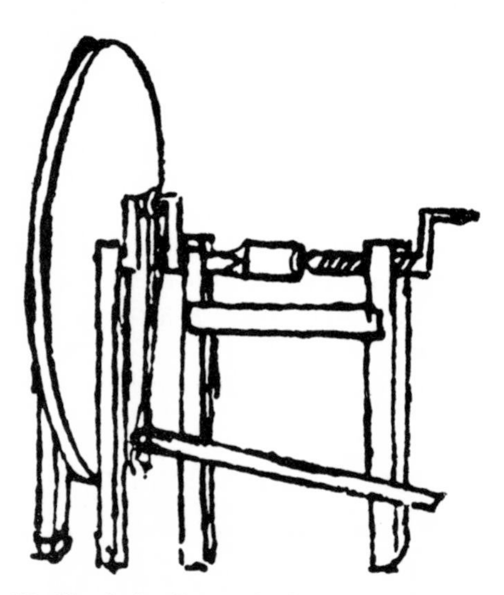

10 *Sketch by Leonardo da Vinci,* c. *1500, showing lathe with three-bearing headstock and drive by treadle, crank and flywheel* (*Codex Atlanticus*)

Jacques Besson, Leonardo's successor as engineer to the French court, described and illustrated a weird and wonderful screw-cutting lathe which, though it cannot be taken seriously as a practical machine tool, embodies one important feature of the lathe for the first time. This is the use of a lead screw and nut to advance the cutting tool along the face of the workpiece. The alternating drive to both workpiece and lead screw by cords, pulleys and weights, plus the fact that the tool was held up to its work by still more pulleys and weights, positively ensured that Besson's device could not work satisfactorily—certainly not upon the massive scale which he depicted. Compared with the work of his great predecessor, Besson's lathe and his style of drawing shows that machine-tool development was not always a forward march but could sometimes be retrogressive.

The lathe drawings already mentioned by no means exhaust Leonardo da Vinci's extraordinary fertility of invention in the field of machine tools. His drawing of a proposed pipe-boring mill is so detailed that it was

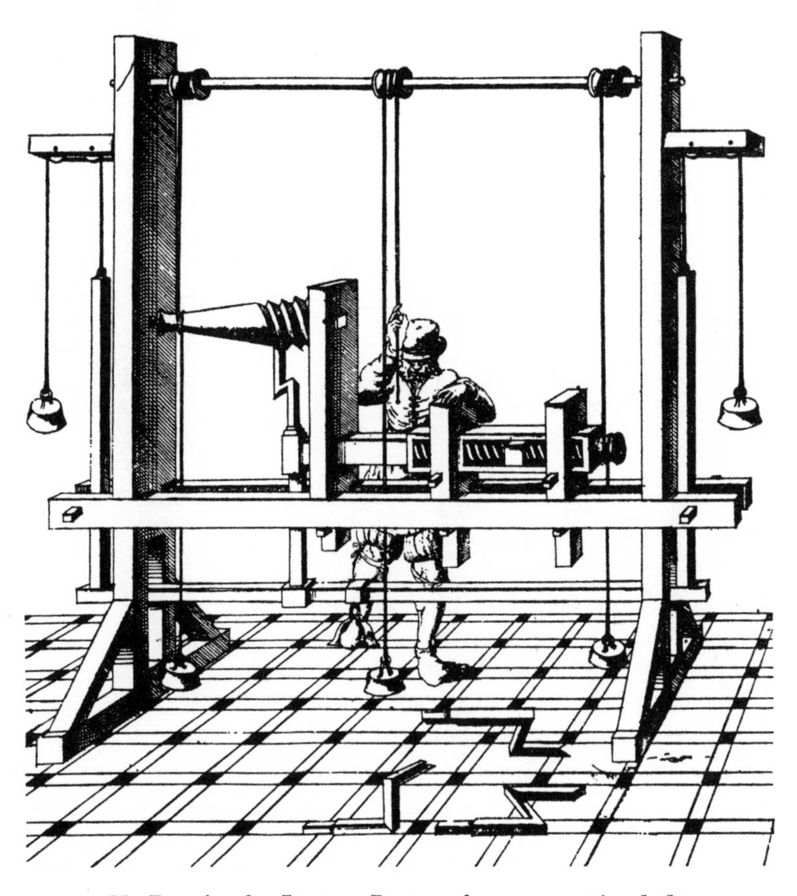

11 *Drawing by Jacques Besson of a screw-cutting lathe with lead screw, 1578*

possible to make a model of it which can be seen in the Science Museum in London. The most remarkable feature of this machine is that the screw clamps which hold the workpiece in position for boring are interconnected by pinions with a ring gear so as to be self-centring. This arrangement anticipates the self-centring chuck. Leonardo also designed a whole series of grinding machines the like of which would not be seen again for 400 years. His drawings show horizontal and vertical disc grinding machines with table support for the work, these being the first to use the face of the wheel for grinding instead of the periphery. Instead of a natural stone, Leonardo specified a wooden wheel faced with leather, using a mixture of emery and tallow as the grinding medium. Also shown in the *Codex Atlanticus* is a heavy-duty external grinder obviously intended to be driven by

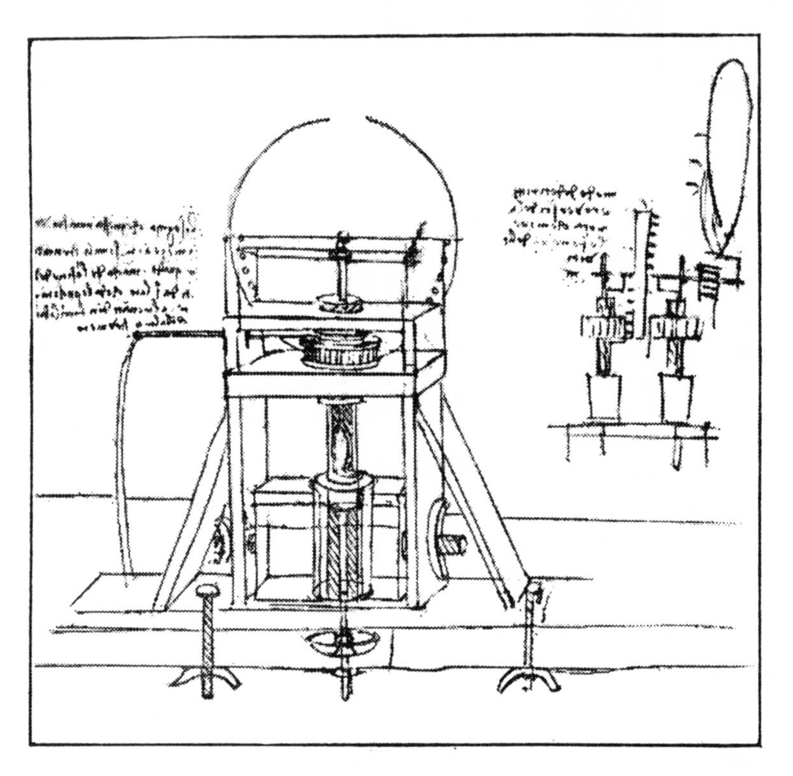

12 *Design for an internal grinding machine by Leonardo da Vinci,* c. *1500* (*Codex Atlanticus*)

water power, a machine for grinding curved mirrors, which anticipates the idea of form grinding by the use of multiple wheels, and a most ingenious belt grinding machine, this last being one of a series of special-purpose machines intended for the mass production of needles.

Perhaps the most remarkable of all Leonardo's designs, however, is his internal grinder which resembles the honing machine used for reboring the cylinders of automobile engines today. The clamp for holding the workpiece is provided with screw adjustment so that it can be accurately centred under the grinding head. This head consists of a wooden cylinder, fluted to allow the oil and emery mixture to reach the grinding surfaces. The spindle of the grinding head carries a threaded portion which engages with the internal thread in the hub of a lantern pinion in the upper part of the machine. A large crown wheel, pin-toothed over half its circumference, meshes with the lantern pinion. For half a revolution, therefore, the rotation of the crown wheel raises the revolving grinding head while during the second half-revolution, when the lantern pinion is disengaged, the grinding head is lowered by a spring-loaded cord wrapped round a pulley secured to the pinion. This cord is clearly shown anchored to the end of a vertical spring-pole to the left of the machine.

Today we can but marvel at the universality of the genius of Leonardo da Vinci, at the intellect that could range with such assured brilliance over the whole field of the arts and sciences. But—and it is a large but—he ranged too far. He conceived man's highest aim to be the acquisition of knowledge and the communication of knowledge, but this he only partially fulfilled because his towering intellect took him into realms far beyond the ken of his contemporaries and successors. Walter Pater said of the Renaissance that it was 'in many things great rather by what it designed or aspired to do than by what it actually achieved'. And because Leonardo was the very embodiment of the spirit of the Renaissance, Pater's words are particularly applicable to him. It is most unlikely that any of Leonardo's more complex machine-tool designs were ever constructed. It was not until 1797[1] that the contents of his notebooks became known to the world, but even if this had not been so it is doubtful whether they would have influenced future development to any marked degree. It was not so much that their construction was beyond the technical competence of Leonardo's contemporaries as that the world did not want them. For example, what conceivable industrial purpose could his internal grinding machine have served in sixteenth-century Italy? A long, slow process of change, social, political and economic, had to take place before machines such as this could come into their own.

The work of the great masters of the Italian Renaissance has that timeless quality which is the mark of true genius. Examples of such work can be found in any age but never before or since has there been a flowering so rich, so widespread and so precocious; precocious because it suddenly

[1] The bulk of the material was looted from Italy by Napoleon. This enabled the French scholar, J. B. Venturi, to publish in 1797 his *Essai sur les ouvrages physico-mathématiques de Léonardo de Vinci.*

threw upon the world a new, bright intellectual light which proved too dazzling, too disturbing for eyes only just emerging from centuries of medieval twilight. As T. S. Eliot put it—'Human kind cannot bear very much reality.' Hence this brief, bright light of the Renaissance was followed in Europe by the age of the baroque which, despite its splendours and its achievements in art and science, seems to us a strangely ill-lit stage by contrast with the brilliance that preceded it. Once lit, the lamp of intellectual inquiry could not be put out, but it was certainly dimmed for a time by customs, traditions and habits of thought which were the legacy of the Gothic world and which sought to reimpose a darkness and a certain archaic and formalised rigidity where before, for a brief space, all had been light and energy.

In this baroque world of the seventeenth and early eighteenth centuries, uncertainly poised between the ages of faith and reason, the scientist, or natural philosopher as he would prefer to call himself, remained for the majority a slightly suspect figure, heir of medieval alchemist and necromancer and, like Faust, prepared to barter his immortal soul to satisfy his insatiable thirst for knowledge which a wiser man would forgo. For him, as for Faust, the pursuit of knowledge was a sufficient end in itself and although in the course of this pursuit he made discoveries of profound significance for the future, his influence upon the everyday life and work of his contemporaries was negligible. In other words his realm was that of pure science; the age of applied science had not dawned.

With rare exceptions baroque art is instantly recognisable as such; it is the art of a period, lacking the universal quality of the art of the High Renaissance. What is true of art is also true of science. Much of the scientific writing of the seventeenth century is wilfully obscure, its stilted high-flown language being designed not to instruct but to convey the impression that the author is the master of mysteries too profound for lesser men. When such writings are embellished by illustrations of mechanisms these are executed in a stiff and formalised style, strangely archaic in its misuse of perspective, which is characteristic of its period and of no other. To appreciate the truth of this it is only necessary to contrast the machine-tool drawings of Leonardo da Vinci with those of his successor Jacques Besson or of that other court engineer Saloman De Caus. The former are so essentially lucid and practical that they would not appear out of place in any engineer's notebook from the end of the eighteenth century onwards, whereas the latter convey to our eyes a strange impression of unreality. They suggest to us, sometimes quite wrongly, that such machines never existed in fact and that if they did they could not have worked.

During the baroque age scientists and engineers depended upon royal and aristocratic patronage. This was seldom inspired by a genuinely disinterested desire to improve the lot of the common man by the advancement of science. The necromantic aura which still clung about the exponents of the new knowledge—and which some of them deliberately fostered—attracted a sophisticated and jaded minority ever searching for excitement in novelty. Hence, a great deal of ingenuity and craftsmanship was dissipated in devising scientific instruments, apparatus and mechanisms for the entertainment of wealthy dilettanti.

Now all this has an important bearing on the course of machine-tool history. It explains why the promise implicit in the designs of Leonardo da Vinci was not fulfilled in the industrial workshop for more than two centuries. In that workshop the primitive pole lathe continued in use virtually unchanged while technical ingenuity was concentrated upon two specialised forms of machine, the ornamental turning lathe or 'rose engine' and the small precision tools which were developed to meet the needs of the makers of clocks, watches and scientific instruments. Both these forms represent by-paths in this evolutionary story. Despite the ingenuity that was lavished upon them, they had little direct influence upon the design of the heavy-duty industrial machine tool with which we are primarily concerned and therefore they need not detain us long.

The earliest illustration of an ornamental lathe comes, appropriately, from Jacques Besson in 1569. The hand tools used with this machine are forked, one arm having a cutting edge and the other designed to engage with a guide bar resting in extended stocks above the workpiece. A templet slot in this guide bar enables a given form to be reproduced on the work. Adjustable circular or non-circular cams on the lathe mandril can be used to give the guide bar a vertical reciprocating motion and so enabled the turner to produce work that was elliptical or irregular in cross section. The design is entirely typical of its period. The bloated bulbosities that characterise the furniture which we call in England Elizabethan or Jacobean were the unfortunate result of the over-enthusiastic employment of machines such as this.

Subsequent hands transformed this crude tool into an ornamental lathe of great refinement and complexity in which arrangements of templets and cams controlling the movements of the tool and the workpiece generated intricate motions enabling ornamental work in wood, ivory or soft metals of great variety and beauty to be carried out. In the eighteenth century ornamental turning became a fashionable hobby, particularly in France. In order to satisfy the fastidious taste of aristocratic hobbyists the ornamental lathe became an ornament in itself, an exquisite piece of craftsmanship as may be judged from the finish of the early French medallion lathe in the Science Museum in London, which is believed to have been the property of Louis XVI.

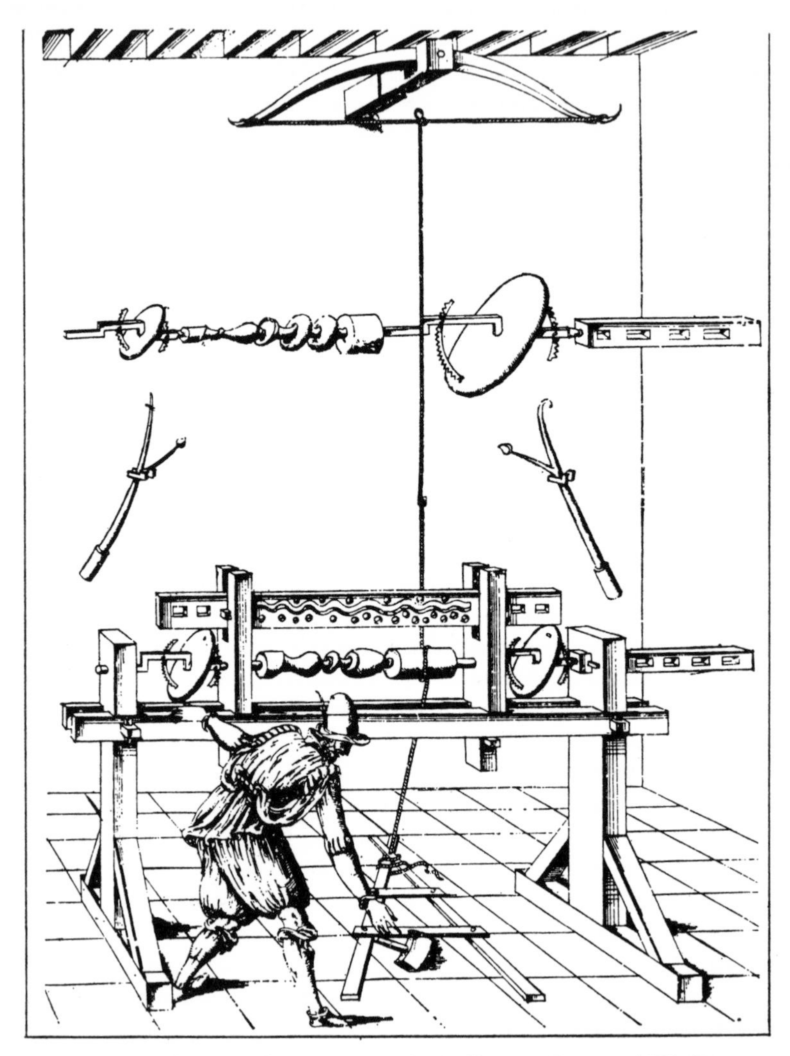

13 *Ornamental turning lathe with templet by Jacques Besson, 1578* (*Besson*)

Control of the cutting tool in the ornamental lathe was exercised by cams working against weights or springs. Although this method served its special purpose admirably it was not adaptable to industrial metal cutting which required a rigidly mounted tool positively controlled in order to achieve true accuracy under heavy duty. The only feature of the ornamental lathe which influenced industrial practice was the method of generating screw threads. A series of master threads of different pitch was cut upon the spindle of the lathe which was free to slide through its bearings unless retained by a catch and groove. With this catch released, any one of a series of fixed followers could be brought into engagement with the master thread required, whereupon the lathe spindle and workpiece would begin to traverse longitudinally, enabling the turner to cut upon the latter a screw thread of equivalent pitch using a hand tool and steadying rest. This became the standard method of mechanical screw cutting until the end of the eighteenth century. Although France was the true home of ornamental turning, one of its greatest latter-day exponents was a Londoner, Charles Holtzapffel, the son of a German who migrated to England in 1784. Charles Holtzapffel and his son, John Jacob, were together responsible for a massive work in five volumes (a sixth was intended but never published) entitled *Turning and Mechanical Manipulation* which became the ornamental turner's bible.

It is in the workshop of the clock- and instrument-maker that the precision lathe of all metal construction first appears, albeit upon a very small scale. It was developed to meet the demands of wealthy customers for timepieces and other instruments of ever-increasing accuracy and delicacy of workmanship. Its simplest form was the clock-maker's 'turn', a miniature lathe designed to be held in a bench vice and driven by a hand-bow. With such a simple tool a skilled craftsman could turn small shafts and spindles with great precision. More specialised machines were evolved to produce the more intricate components of clocks and watches, and coincident with this development certain craftsmen began to specialise in the production of a particular component for their fellows in the trade. This specialised production of components logically follows from the use of a complex and highly specialised machine tool and it was in the making of clocks and watches that this form of organisation first emerged.

Such a tool was the so-called 'fusee engine' which was really a special-purpose lathe. The fusee made the spring-driven clock practicable, being the first successful means of compensating for the progressive weakening of a coiled steel spring as it unwinds. It consists of a taper barrel carrying a spiral groove. The power of the mainspring is communicated to the going train of the clock by a gut cord wound on the fusee, the effect of its taper barrel as the gut unwinds from it being to compensate for the spring's weakening pull. The fusee was an Italian invention and has been credited to da Vinci. By 1741 a fusee engine had appeared in France which was semi-automatic and was, in effect, a miniature lathe with a traversing tool rest driven from the hand-cranked spindle by change gears and a lead screw. The use of such a machine called for great skill because although the traverse of the rest was automatic the cross-feed of the tool required to follow the hyperbolic taper of the fusee barrel had to be applied manually. In 1763, however, Ferdinand Berthoud showed a fully automatic fusee engine which is a remarkable early example of the process of 'building the skill into the machine'. This machine, like its predecessor, has a slide rest but instead of being traversed by a lead screw and change gears, the rest is held by a cord and spring-loaded barrel against the inclined face of a straight edge mounted on a cross-slide moved by rack and pinion from the hand-cranked lathe spindle. An indexed screw adjustment enables the inclination of the straight edge to be varied to suit the different pitches required. The operator applied cross-feed pressure to the tool by means of a plunger on the slide rest, but in this case the feed is accurately controlled by a cross-pin in the spindle of the plunger which follows the curved face of a templet fixed to the rest. The hyperbolic curve of the templet is thus accurately reproduced on the fusee.

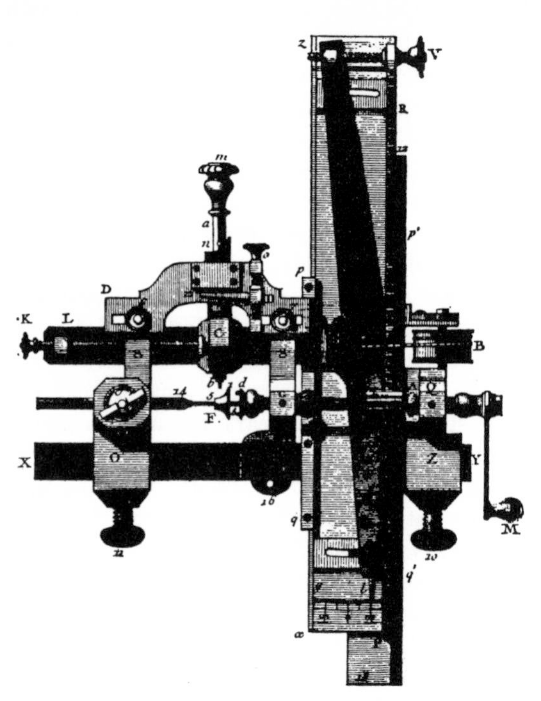

14 *Improved automatic fusee engine by Ferdinand Berthoud, 1763* (*Berthoud*)

When Charles Plumier published his *L'art du tourneur* in 1701 (the earliest known treatise on the lathe, which he is believed to have completed in 1689) he illustrated a watch-maker's screw-cutting lathe which is a miniature version of the machine previously described. But instrument-makers began to demand greater precision than was possible with a machine of this type. Thiout took the first notable step forward in 1741 by rejecting the sliding spindle in favour of a sliding rest in which the cutting tool was rigidly mounted with a cross-feed adjustment. This slide rest was traversed via a system of levers by a single lead screw on the lathe spindle. Variations in pitch could be obtained by altering the adjustment of the lever linkage.

The ultimate in eighteenth-century screw-cutting accuracy stands to the credit of the English instrument-maker, Jesse Ramsden (1735–1800). The mathematical and astronomical instruments which Ramsden was required to make called for linear scales of great accuracy. In order to scribe such scales with the necessary precision, Ramsden needed for his dividing engines long, fine-thread screws of the utmost accuracy. He constructed a series of screw-cutting lathes with the greatest labour and pains and by incorporating the product of one machine in its successor he was able to achieve a progressively higher standard. In his final machine the workpiece on which the thread was to be cut was rotated through gearing by a hand-crank and was mounted in bearings parallel with a bar upon which a rigid tool-holder could be traversed. This tool-holder was traversed in the following way. One end of a flexible steel strip was attached to the holder and the other wound round a pulley which formed the boss of a very large wormwheel. A short worm, cut as accurately as possible to a pitch of 20 threads to the inch, meshed with this large wheel and was turned directly by the hand-crank. This short worm was, in effect, the lead screw. The ratio between the worm and wheel and the diameter of the pulley were so determined that 600 turns of the hand-crank traversed the tool-holder five inches. With this machine Ramsden was able to produce fine-thread screws of extreme accuracy and of any desired length.

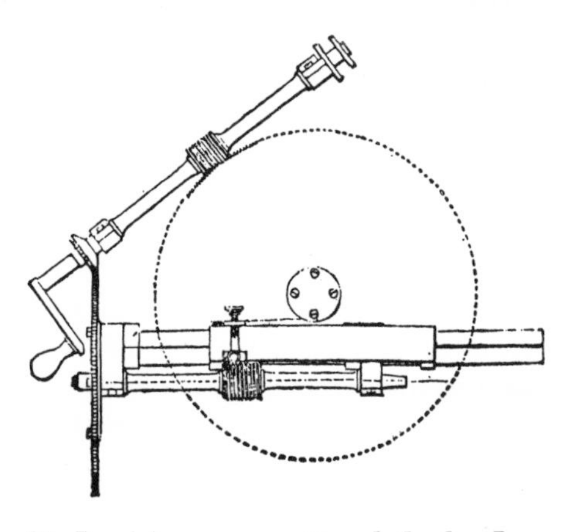

15 *Precision screw-cutting lathe by Jesse Ramsden, 1778* (*Ramsden*)

In the second half of the eighteenth century the precision techniques evolved in the workshops of the clock- and instrument-makers produced results of great significance in human history. First and foremost was the production of a marine chronometer. As long ago as 1530 it had been appreciated that if a ship could carry a timepiece of sufficient accuracy, the problem of determining its longitude at sea would be solved. To enable longitude to be fixed within half a degree, however, such a timepiece must not gain or lose more than three seconds a day throughout a long ocean voyage. In 1714 the British Government offered a reward of no less than £20,000 to anyone who could produce a timepiece of this accuracy. Other countries offered similar awards, but the problems of achieving such a result, particularly under shipboard conditions, appeared insuperable. In 1759, however, the English horologist, John Harrison, succeeded in producing a chronometer the accuracy of which actually surpassed the required performance. His work was followed by that of Pierre Le Roy in France (1766) and in England by John Arnold and Thomas Earnshaw who, working independently, had evolved by 1780 a design of marine chronometer which has remained in use to this day. The value of this achievement in precision workmanship has been incalculable.

The makers of precision instruments influenced the history of technology in many other ways. Their craftsmanship placed in the hands of the scientists accurate instruments of measurement unknown before. This enabled the latter to formulate theories which engineers, no longer working empirically, were able to apply towards the end of the eighteenth century with momentous results. For example, accurate heat-measuring instruments alone enabled Joseph Black to formulate his theory of latent heat upon which James Watt's improvements to the steam engine were based

In 1759, when Harrison produced his miracle of precision, the divorce between the new science and everyday life and work was still almost complete. The shift from pure to applied science had scarcely begun and consequently the influence of scientific discovery on practical technology was negligible. Moreover, the contrast between the instrument-maker's precision equipment and the crude ancestors of the machines which we find in the modern heavy machine shop was still extreme. As the youthful James Watt discovered in 1755 when he tramped the streets of London seeking in vain for an instrument-maker willing to employ him, the trade was a jealously preserved 'closed shop' to which entry was extremely difficult. Even if this had not been so, however, the situation would have been little changed. At the level of technology then prevailing, machine-tool precision could only be achieved upon a miniature scale. It was not possible to 'scale up' an instrument-maker's lathe into an industrial tool of equivalent accuracy.

Yet the most momentous revolution in human history was now gathering momentum in Britain with astonishing and ever-increasing speed. By the time Jesse Ramsden produced his ultimate screw-cutting lathe in

1778 the old barriers were fast breaking down. Scientists were leaving their studies and laboratories to hob-nob with a new generation of engineers in workshop and engine-house. There was a positive ferment of new ideas, the fulfilment of which called urgently for new methods. The traditional crafts of millwright, carpenter and blacksmith that had held sway in the industrial workshop for so long would no longer serve. 'Never use iron where wood will do' had been the unspoken rule in such workshops for centuries, but now the world was moving into a new iron age and required tools which could cut and shape that intractable metal with speed and precision. Hence the work of Jesse Ramsden may well have influenced Henry Maudslay, greatest of the early makers of engineering machine tools.

It was, above all, the tireless driving power of the steam engine that called the engineer's heavy machine tools into being. It was to build more efficient steam engines with greater facility that the first heavy machine shops were laid out, but first the engineers had to bring the steam engine to birth without such improved mechanical aids. How this was achieved will be considered in the next chapter.

CHAPTER 2

Industrial Machine Tools of the Eighteenth Century

A MACHINE TOOL is an expensive item of equipment. It represents an investment of capital which can only be justified if its capacity for greater productivity can be fully exploited. This condition cannot be met unless the flow of raw material to the machine and of the finished product away from it can be cheaply and reliably maintained by an efficient transport system.

In the light of this evident truth the reason why the development of precision production methods was for so long confined to the workshop of the horologist and instrument-maker becomes easier to understand. The miniature machines he used were generally made in his own shop and represented only a small capital investment. The stocks of raw material he required were small in bulk, while his finished products were also small in bulk but of high monetary value. Consequently contemporary transport problems touched him but lightly, if at all.

With heavy industry in the seventeenth century and throughout the greater part of the eighteenth century it was quite otherwise. Indeed there could be no heavy industry in the sense of the large industrial concentrations with which we are familiar. Even if contemporary technology had been capable of producing industrial machine tools, the necessary capital for so heavy an investment would not have been forthcoming, while the few navigable rivers were the only means of transporting heavy indivisible loads and rarely tapped the sources of the necessary material supplies. A dependence on water power, the only known means of driving heavy machinery, was another handicap. It restricted the location of industry requiring such power to sites in the immediate vicinity of streams and rivers where a suitable fall could be obtained. Such sites were often inconvenient from a transport point of view. On navigable rivers the needs of mill owners and barge owners conflicted and were a constant source of dispute, while on the smaller streams, lack of water frequently brought the mill wheels to a stand during the summer months. No wonder, then, that the small workshop, using methods of traditional hand-craftsmanship unchanged since medieval times, persisted for so long.

Such workshops employed wood for heavy work wherever possible not only because it was easier to work by hand or machine but because its availability minimised the transport problem. The use of iron was restricted as far as possible to small components which could be most readily transported either as raw material for the blacksmith or in the finished state. Local resources of coal and ore made the Black Country a great centre of the metal trade in the seventeenth century, but lack of water-transport facilities and water power on that high Midland plateau ensured that for years it would remain a light cottage industry. Hundreds of smiths working in forges behind their homes produced from bundles of bar iron carried to their doors on the backs of pack-horses such things as nails, locks, light chains and hand tools which could be readily transported.

In such an economy there was no room for the heavy metal-cutting machine tool, but then as now there was one trade to which normal commercial sanctions did not apply. This was the production of weapons of war. It is a sorry commentary on human nature that the only one of man's diverse activities which has never been inhibited by considerations of expense or practical difficulty is the development of more potent means of mutual destruction. It is precisely because armament production has always been so uninhibited that the industry has contributed so much to the general progress of technology. Though we have not yet acquired the wisdom to convert the one into the other, by producing better swords we certainly learn how to make better ploughshares. We should therefore expect to find the first heavy metal-cutting tool in the armament-maker's workshop and we should not be wrong.

Vannoccio Biringuccio in his *Pirotecnica* of 1540 not only illustrates a water-powered cannon-boring mill, but also shows us three types of radial boring tool which were used with it. A water wheel drives a long horizontal boring bar and the cannon to be bored is mounted on a moveable carriage. This method of gun boring continued with very little change until the early years of the eighteenth century. Crude though it appears, it sufficed so long as guns were cast upon a core. It was simply a method of cleaning up the cored hole in the barrel; the boring tool would follow the hole and for such an operation little driving power or accuracy in setting up was required to produce an adequate result provided the cored hole was reasonably true. The majority of Sussex mill ponds, though we refer to them all indiscriminately as 'Hammer ponds', were not in fact used to drive tilt hammers at all, but to power cannon-boring mills of a kind not dissimilar from that pictured by Biringuccio.

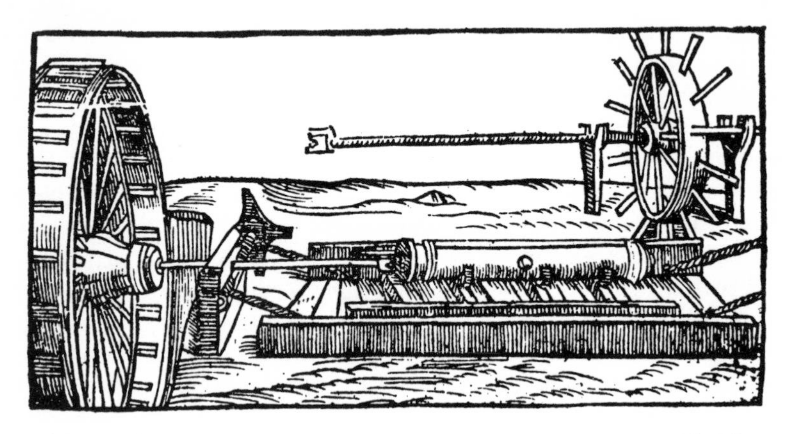

16 *Water-powered cannon-boring mill of 1540 from Biringuccio's* Pirotecnica, *and* (below) *the tools used*

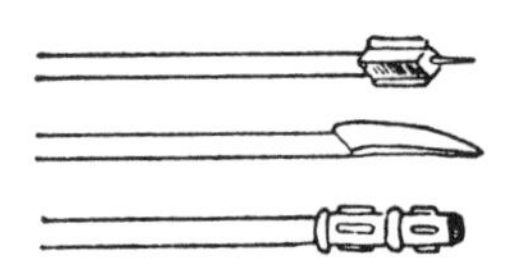

The making of a mould for the casting of a cannon called for great skill, the most difficult operation being to position the core so that it was truly concentric. Failure in this respect, which was not infrequent, resulted in a barrel of unequal thickness in cross section, a fault which the boring mill then in use could not rectify. Guns with this defect generally failed to pass proof and sometimes burst. To counter this difficulty a Swiss named Maritz, who was Commissaire des Fonts at Strasbourg, invented a vertical boring mill of sufficient accuracy to enable gun barrels to be bored from the solid casting. The date of this invention is said to have been 1713, but, if this was the case, many years passed before it was perfected and brought into use. Maritz moved from Strasbourg to the Netherland States Gun Foundry at the Hague, where he worked on his invention to such purpose that in 1747 the States Privy Council issued an order stating that in future all guns were to be cast solid and then drilled. The fact that the

17 *A remarkably detailed drawing by Peter Verbruggen of his father's mortar-boring mill at Woolwich Arsenal, 1770*

18 *Vaucanson's lathe,* c. *1775*

19 *Senot's lathe, 1795*

TWO PIONEER FRENCH MACHINE TOOLS

machine was the subject of the strictest security precautions indicates that Maritz must have improved it considerably because by that time his original invention was well known in Europe. Diderot illustrates a mill of this type, but it is not clear whether he depicts Maritz's original invention or the improved version used at the Hague. It shows the gun mounted upright on a carriage moving between two vertical slide bars of vee section. The boring bar is rotated by a horse engine beneath the machine and the feed applied by using two triple-fall tackles, a winch barrel and reduction gears to lower the carriage. An illustration of the type of boring bit said to have been used on machines of this kind shows a tool not unlike a milling cutter in appearance, consisting of a series of steel cutter blades keyed into an iron core.

In 1755, Jan Verbruggen, previously gun founder to the Dutch Admiralty at Enkhuizen, was appointed Master Founder at the Hague. He was dissatisfied with Maritz's vertical machine and, working in association with a Swiss engineer named Jacob Ziegler, he produced in 1758 a very remarkable horizontal boring mill which was a great advance on anything known before. An original inscribed plate[1] from this machine and a replica model of it may be seen in the Dutch Military Museum at Leiden. As the model shows, Verbruggen and Ziegler adopted a stationary horizontal boring bar and rotated the cannon between bearings. The cannon was rotated by means of capstan bars, a large-diameter crown wheel and a lantern pinion on the axis of the cannon. The boring bar had rack teeth which engaged a second lantern pinion, feed being applied by crank-handles on the axis of this pinion. The machine was easier to set up than Maritz's vertical mill and would produce more accurate work than any type using a rotating boring bar.

As a result of alleged irregularities, Jan Verbruggen was discharged from the Hague Foundry in January 1770 and on the recommendation of the British Ambassador at the Hague, he was immediately appointed Master Founder at the Royal Arsenal at Woolwich. It appears that his son, Peter, was already working at Woolwich by this time. In this way Verbruggen's methods were introduced to England. The large sum of £214 19*s* 4*d* that was paid for the transport of his equipment from Holland suggests that Verbruggen may have brought one of his improved mills with him.

Two heavy boring mills of Verbruggen type were at work at the Arsenal

[1] The inscription is in rather curious Latin. A free translation reads: 'This horizontal cannon-boring machine is established by the care and industry of Jan Verbruggen, General Superintendent of the casting of bronze cannon in the country of Holland. The first stone [was] placed by his son, Peter Verbruggen, on 8th March 1758.'

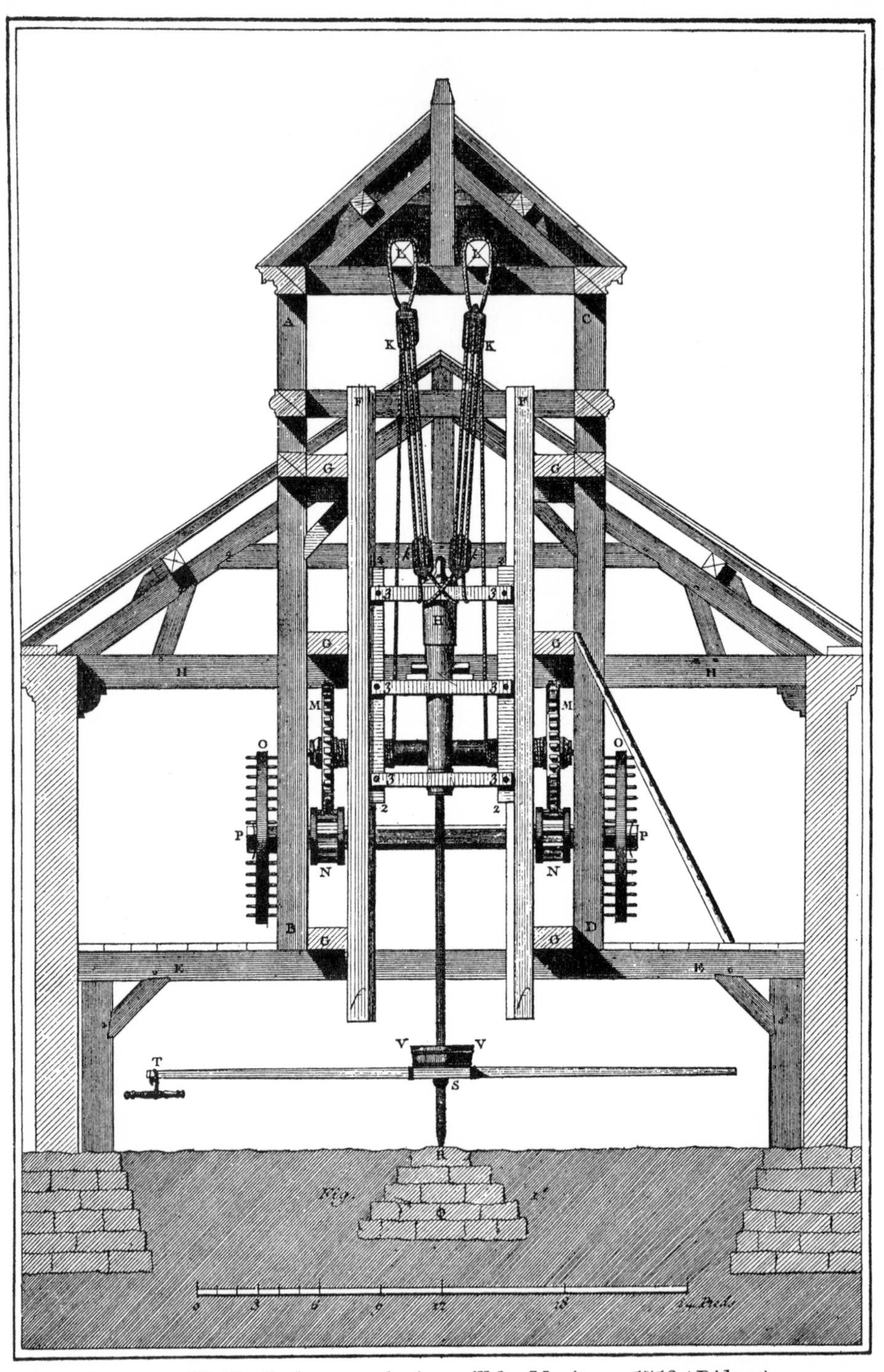

20 *Vertical cannon-boring mill by Maritz,* c. *1713* (*Diderot*)

by the end of 1770 and a third smaller mill on the same principle was built to bore mortars. They replaced an earlier mill built by Verbruggen's predecessor, Andrew Schalch. The only thing we know about this earlier mill is that in 1717 material was issued to Schalch for 'the female of the great screw for the engine at the Royal Foundery'. This suggests that the mill may have had a form of lead-screw feed, in which case it is by far the earliest known application of this principle to a machine tool of such size.

Fortunately, Peter Verbruggen has left us a drawing (see Fig. 17) of his father's Woolwich mortar-boring mill that is so masterly and so accurately detailed that it deserves careful examination. After all, what he portrays is the first heavy machine tool in the world that was capable of working to a reasonable standard of accuracy and the parent of the machine that made Watt's steam engine possible. By means of the sheer-legs, a mortar has just been lifted onto the machine and, with the help of a crowbar, the workman on the left is positioning it between the bearings in which it will rotate. The cap of the machine's tail bearing has not yet been replaced but lies on the shop floor in the foreground. In a rack behind this workman appear boring tools, sizing callipers and set-square. Above them hang what look like profile templets, suggesting that the machine may have been adaptable for external turning also. The massive timberwork of the bed supporting the boring bar reveals Verbruggen's concern to ensure rigidity. The workman on the extreme right leans on the handwheel controlling the rack feed for a fine finishing cut. For additional purchase when advancing a heavy cut, the long bar, shown in rests on the wall below the windows opposite, would be used instead. The drive to the machine is taken through the end wall of the shop. It has always been said that the Woolwich boring mills were powered by horse-engines, but the provision of two cords, leading over pulleys through the wall, to enable the operator to start and stop the machine at will, suggest water rather than horse power. They resemble the sluice controls used on contemporary water-powered tilt hammers.

In 1774, Verbruggen was ordered to prepare comparative estimates of the cost of producing cored guns and guns bored from the solid, with the result that the Board of Ordnance issued instructions to the effect that in future all guns produced at Woolwich should be cast solid. Jan Verbruggen remained in practical charge at the Royal Arsenal until his death in 1786. His boring machines remained in use till 1842. As a youth, Henry Maudslay worked at Woolwich Arsenal and legend has it that it was the sliding carriage of a Verbruggen-type boring mill which first gave him the idea of his lathe slide rest. This is doubtful. What is certain is that the cannon-boring mill played a very important part in bringing the steam engine to successful birth.

Britain has been called with truth the cradle of the Industrial Revolution. What brought about this spectacular advance in technology? Why did the seeds which had been slowly germinating for centuries suddenly flower so prodigally in eighteenth-century England? The interaction of events was so complex that there is no simple answer to such questions. Cause cannot be distinguished from effect. The accumulation of capital and the improvement of the transport system during the eighteenth century in Britain undoubtedly gave the Revolution tremendous impetus, but to some extent these developments were products of the Revolution. A growing timber famine was probably the most potent fertilising agent. Growing demands from the shipwrights, from an iron industry dependent on charcoal, from industrial workshops and from a vast number of private and commercial consumers who still used wood as a fuel, all pressed upon the dwindling timber resources of a country in which the process of clearing forest lands for agriculture had been going on for centuries. By the end of the seventeenth century the timber shortage had become acute. It was forcing ironmasters to migrate from the cradle of the industry in the Sussex Weald to the west Midlands, to the Welsh Marches, to south Yorkshire and to Cumberland where there were still great areas of woodland and where they did not have to compete with the shipwrights for supplies as was the case in southern England. But it was clear that this was no long-term solution to the problem, for despite heavy imports of iron from Sweden and the planting of new coppice woods, the consumption of charcoal for smelting was such that it outstripped the rate of woodland regeneration. It became essential to substitute coal for wood as a fuel and iron for wood as a structural material. These two aims were closely interlocked because more iron could not be produced unless a way could be found of smelting iron with coal. This was the necessity which proved so fertile a mother of invention; which began an interesting series of developments that set the great wheel of the Revolution revolving with ever-increasing momentum.

The answers to the two basic questions which necessity posed—how to smelt iron with coal, and how to obtain more coal from the mines—came almost simultaneously. Abraham Darby may have begun smelting iron with coked coal at his ironworks at Coalbrookdale, Shropshire, in 1709 and was certainly doing so by 1711. In 1712 Thomas Newcomen set his first successful mine-pumping engine to work at a coal pit near Dudley Castle in Staffordshire. Darby's discovery, momentous though it was, was slow to take effect. Coke smelting was at first confined to the production of cast iron and for many years British production of wrought iron had to be augmented by substantial imports from Sweden. It will therefore be appropriate to consider first the story of the steam engine.

Most of the shallow coal seams had been worked out by the end of the seventeenth century so that the only way of increasing coal output was by deep mining. It was beyond the power of horse-pumps to keep deep mines clear of water, so it was only Newcomen's invention of the world's first successful steam engine which made it possible to tap these vital fuel resources and so keep the wheel of Industrial Revolution revolving. But how was it possible to make a successful steam engine so early as 1712? The answer is that, unlike Leonardo da Vinci, Thomas Newcomen did not range too far ahead of his time. A practical man, an ironmonger by trade, he designed for his time from an intimate knowledge of the capabilities of the men and the tools of his time. As early engravings show, construction of the engine was such that it could be built upon the site by a team of craftsmen, millwrights, carpenters, blacksmiths, plumbers, coppersmiths and bricklayers using their traditional skills.

There was only one major production problem and that was the cylinder. The cylinders of Newcomen's first engines were of cast brass about eight feet long and with a bore of from 21 to 28 inches. Such a diameter was far beyond the capacity of current cannon-boring mills. Moreover the thickness of the cylinder wall did not exceed one inch for thermal reasons connected with the atmospheric principle on which the engine operated. We must salute the unknown craftsmen who moulded, cored and cast successfully these great brass cylinders. It is believed that their cored bores were not machined at all but were laboriously fettled and honed by hand with the aid of whetstones shaped to the diameter. We know that the bored cylinders of a later date were often given a final finish in this way. It is obvious that the bore of the early Newcomen cylinder must have been very rough and inaccurate by our standards, but the piston was liberally packed with hemp, its speed was very low and it was connected to the beam which worked the pumps by a chain. In addition, the cylinder being open-topped, water could be introduced to the upper surface of the piston to keep the hemp packing soft and to form an additional seal. All these factors combined to make the design tolerant of error.

The next important step in the evolution of the steam engine was the introduction of bored cylinders of cast iron in increasingly large sizes. This was entirely due to the development of technique at Darby's pioneer Coalbrookdale Ironworks and for many years the Coalbrookdale Company enjoyed a complete monopoly of steam engine cylinder production. It was their unique 'know how' alone which enabled engines of much greater power to be built.

The production of iron cylinders began at Coalbrookdale in 1722, but mention of a boring mill in the Company's records does not appear until 1725, which suggests that the first few cylinders were entirely hand-finished. Cylinders up to 46 inches in diameter were bored on this first mill —heavy machining upon a scale never attempted, still less achieved, before—and it is not surprising to learn that considerable trouble was experienced with the boring bars which broke repeatedly. In 1734 a new mill was set up for which a much heavier boring bar was ordered from a Bristol anchor smith. The order specification read as follows: 'A wrought-iron spindle 12 feet long and full 3 inches in diameter; one end to be left square for 6 inches, and the remaining 10 feet [*sic*] to be left round, but to be as true as may be, and to be made of right tuff iron and right sound.' This was delivered in September 1734 at a cost of £26 10*s* and was evidently successful for a second similar bar was purchased in 1745.

Unfortunately no drawings or particulars of this Coalbrookdale boring mill have survived. The Quaker principles of the Darby family forbade the production of cannon at Coalbrookdale, but it is safe to assume, in the light of what follows, that it was a horizontal machine developed from the contemporary cannon mill and driven by a waterwheel. We can judge Coalbrookdale technique only by its results as described in this enthusiastic quotation of 1763:[1]

> A fire engine cylinder was landed at Wincomblee coal staith on the river Tyne, for the use of Walker Colliery, which surpassed everything of the kind which had been seen in the North. The diameter of the bore measured upwards of 74 inches, and it was 10½ feet in length. Its weight, exclusive of the bottom and the piston, was 6½ tons, containing altogether between 10 and 11 tons of metal. The bore was perfectly round and well polished. It was considered a complete piece of work, and did honour to Coalbrookdale foundry in Shropshire, where it was manufactured.

By this date, however, the Coalbrookdale Company no longer enjoyed a monopoly in northern Britain, for the famous Carron Ironworks, near Falkirk, had come into existence in 1759. This concern soon became noted for its cannons, particularly its speciality, the Carronade, but it also began to cast engine cylinders and that great and versatile engineer John Smeaton, who was responsible for the design and installation of the plant at Carron, laid down a special cylinder-boring mill. An illustration of this

[1] Quoted in M. A. Richardson, *The Local Historian's Table Book*, Newcastle, 1842, Vol. II, p. 109.

mill has survived. Dr. Roebuck, the founder of the Carron Company, recruited some of his key men from Coalbrookdale so that, although this machine is always referred to as Smeaton's boring mill, it doubtless followed Coalbrookdale practice pretty closely. The engraving shows the cylinder mounted on a carriage having double-flanged wheels running on edge rails and traversed by means of a rope and winch. The cutting head is constructed in the same fashion as the cannon drill used by Maritz, a series of steel cutters being keyed to the periphery of an iron disc of the required diameter. There is an alternative set of rails for the cylinder carriage aligned with a second reduction gear drive from the water wheel

21 *John Smeaton's cylinder-boring mill at Carron Ironworks, showing* (inset) *the support for the cutter head*

which provides a lower speed for the cutter bar. But the most interesting feature of this design is the attempt made to overcome the chronic defect of the long, unsupported horizontal boring bar. Obviously this defect became the more serious in its results as the weight of the boring bar and cutting head increased. A small wheeled carriage running within the cylinder carries upon a vertical pillar adjustable for height a pivoted and counterweighted lever which is linked to a ring bearing on the end of the cutter bar. It is clear that such a method of supporting the weight of the cutter and its bar cannot have been effective since it could not ensure an even depth of cut. With the object of mitigating this it was usual to run the boring head through the cylinder four times, turning the latter through

90° after each cut. Despite such efforts, however, although this machine could produce a cylinder that was truly circular at any given point along the bore, that bore was seldom or never truly parallel throughout its length. Nevertheless the work of such machines was adequate for the Newcomen-type steam engine; it was when James Watt came upon the scene that the trouble began.

James Watt is a figure of great significance in the history of technology not only for what he achieved but for what he was. He was one of the first men to apply in the industrial workshop the knowledge which had been won and the methods which had been perfected in the scientific laboratory. He found mechanical engineering an empirical craft and left it an applied science. He began his working life as a maker of scientific instruments and this not only gave him exacting standards of precision but brought him into contact with the most advanced scientific thinking of his time. He combined practical craftsmanship with speculative and methodical qualities which enabled him to assimilate scientific knowledge and apply it to practical purpose.

Newcomen's steam engine was the ultimate achievement of empirical craftsmanship and in this sense it represented, not the beginning but the end of a road. True it was the outcome of the scientific discovery that the earth's atmosphere had weight—it was this weight which Newcomen brought to bear upon his piston—but the men who built it had no idea *why* it consumed such vast quantities of fuel for a very low power output. Further development required a scientific knowledge of the properties of heat and accurate instruments of heat measurement, both of which Watt was the first to apply when he made his classic series of experiments at Glasgow. His inventions were the outcome of these experiments and he was able to demonstrate the principles of his improved engine by means of models. It was when he tried to translate the instrument-maker's model into a full-size machine that his difficulties began, for he was at once made painfully aware of the yawning gulf between his own standards of precision and those prevailing in the industrial workshop at that time.

Watt's first patron was Dr. Roebuck of the Carron Ironworks and his first full-sized steam engine was built in secrecy in a shed behind Roebuck's house at Kinneil, from components manufactured at Carron. Protracted efforts to get this engine to work satisfactorily failed miserably to Watt's bitter chagrin, the reason being that standards of workmanship which had served the Newcomen-type engine well enough fell far short of the far more exacting standard the new engine demanded. For the cold air acting upon the top of a piston in an open cylinder Watt substituted steam. This meant a steam-tight piston, a closed cylinder and a piston rod working through a stuffing-box in the cover. Watt only called for an 18-inch cylinder—a modest enough demand when we recall the huge Newcomen-type cylinders which had been produced by this date—yet Smeaton's boring mill at Carron failed to achieve a sufficiently accurate result and Watt eventually abandoned his fruitless efforts to make his piston steam-tight. The frustrated engineer was forced to seek other employment and for five years his invention hung fire solely through the lack of machine tools of sufficient precision.

In May 1774, when Watt's historic partnership with Matthew Boulton began, the Kinneil engine was dismantled and re-erected at Boulton's Soho Manufactury at Birmingham. Here Watt resumed his experiments, but with no better success until Boulton suggested that a new cylinder should be ordered from his friend John Wilkinson of Bersham Ironworks, near Wrexham.

John Wilkinson (1728–1808) was the greatest ironmaster of his generation. He was the son of Isaac Wilkinson, a Cumberland ironmaster who removed to Denbighshire when he acquired the Bersham Furnaces in 1753. At the height of his power John Wilkinson owned furnaces, foundries and forges at Bersham and Brimbo in Denbighshire, at Merthyr Tydfil, at New Willey near Broseley in Shropshire and at Bradley in the Black Country. At these works Wilkinson developed iron-working techniques which rivalled those of the Coalbrookdale Company. Unfettered by the religious scruples of the Darby family, Wilkinson cast a great number

22 *John Wilkinson's cannon-boring mill of 1774*

of iron cannon and on 27 January 1774 he obtained a patent for a 'New Method of Casting and Boring Iron Guns or Cannon'. This consisted of a machine in which the solid cannon casting was rotated horizontally between bearings and the stationary boring head was advanced by a toothed rack on the boring bar, the feed being applied by a handwheel through suitable gearing. The bar advanced through guides on a supporting table. Because Verbruggen had introduced a machine of almost identical design at Woolwich Arsenal four years earlier it is difficult to understand why Wilkinson applied for this patent, still less why he was granted it. Sure enough, the patent was challenged by the Board of Ordnance on the ground that it was not novel and in 1779 it was revoked. It seems likely that Wilkinson had seen a Verbruggen-type boring mill on his continental travels but was not aware that identical machines had been installed at Woolwich. Perhaps the latter were the subject of security.

The cylinder required for the Kinneil engine was of small size so it seems likely that when Boulton & Watt brought their problem to Wilkinson he devised a fixture which enabled him to bore the cylinder on his cannon-boring machine. The finished cylinder was delivered to Soho in April 1775 and its accuracy was such that Watt's difficulties were immediately solved.

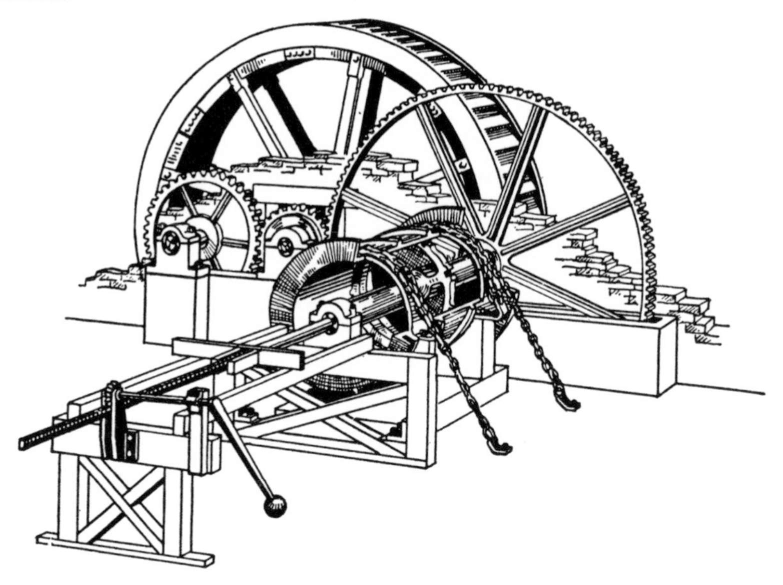

23 *John Wilkinson's cylinder-boring mill at Bersham Ironworks, 1776*

The shrewd Wilkinson was never in any doubt as to the merit of Watt's engine—he soon became the first user of it—and he at once recognised that his machine would not be suitable for the much larger cylinders which would soon be required. In the Watt design the top cover of the cylinder and the cylinder bottom were separate castings so that, unlike the muzzle-loading cannon, the cylinder itself was open at both ends. The significance of this was not lost upon Wilkinson. He proceeded to design a second boring machine in which the cylinder was fixed upon a work table and the revolving cutter bar passed right through it, being supported in bearings at both ends. In 1919 a drawing of this mill was found among a collection of early Watt drawings in Birmingham. It is headed 'Drawing of the Bersham Boreing Mill by Jno Gilpin' and must have been made before 1795 because the Bersham works closed in that year.

This drawing suggests that Wilkinson earlier used a boring mill of the Carron type since the arrangement of a single waterwheel driving two bars through gearing is similar and the drawing even shows a travelling carriage. But the older machine has been adapted to drive two of the new boring bars, one 12 inches in diameter and 15 feet long, the other 10 inches in diameter and 14 feet long. Two cylinders of 45-inch and 27-inch diameter respectively are shown fixed in position by chains between the bar bearings. The significant feature of the bars is that they are hollow. They may have been bored by the cannon-boring machine, an example of that self-propagating characteristic of machine tools which Jesse Ramsden exploited in his quest for accurate screws. The cutting head is advanced along the revolving bar by means of a toothed rack bar passing through the hollow centre, its end connecting with the cutter head by means of a longitudinal slot extending the full length of the bar. The rack is prevented from rotating by guided cross-heads and the feed is applied by a weighted lever on the axis of the pinion which engages the rack. The model of the Wilkinson machine in the Science Museum in London was based upon this drawing.

In 1913 a boring bar, traditionally believed to have come from Bersham, was presented to the Science Museum. Its dimensions almost coincide with the larger bar in the drawing, being 15 feet long and 11·875 inches in diameter, but instead of the rack it has a positive self-acting feed by an internal lead screw and nut. This is driven from the boring bar by reduction gearing, the ratio of the pinions and the pitch of the lead screw being such that the cutting head would advance 0·046 inches per revolution. According to tradition, when the Bersham works was dismantled in 1795, this bar was purchased by Messrs Rigby, Engineers of Hawarden and Sandycroft, who 'fitted it with a new screw'. Until Gilpin's drawing was discovered in 1919 it was believed that this screw feed was part of Wilkinson's invention, but it is now practically certain that what Messrs Rigby did was not to renew an existing lead screw as tradition implies, but to replace the original rack feed by a lead screw. The bar bears evidence of having been altered in this way, a fact which supports the belief that it is indeed an original Bersham boring bar and therefore a relic of one of the most important milestones in the history of machine tools.

With this machine John Wilkinson was able to produce a cylinder bore that was both truly circular and truly parallel throughout its length. It was used to bore the cylinders of the first two Watt engines to be built commercially, a 38-inch cylinder for a blowing engine for Wilkinson's own furnaces at New Willey and a 50-inch cylinder for a pumping engine at Bloomfield Colliery, Tipton. Soon after the Tipton cylinder was delivered, the Carron Company inquired about a Watt engine and must have been mortified to receive a reply from Matthew Boulton in which he wrote: 'Mr. Wilkinson has bored us several cylinders almost without error, that of 50-inch diameter, which we put up at Tipton, does not err the thickness of an old shilling at any part, so that you must either improve your method of boring or we must furnish the cylinder to you.' Watt was even more enthusiastic. Writing to Smeaton in April of the same year (1776), he declared that: 'Mr. Wilkinson has improved the art of boring cylinders so that I promise upon a 72-inch cylinder being not further from absolute truth than the thickness of a thin sixpence in the worst part.'

The thickness of a coin may seem by our standards of precision a monstrous error, yet it represented a marvellous advance in heavy machine-tool technique and it made Watt's steam engine a practical proposition with momentous consequences for mankind. The extraordinary thing is that Wilkinson failed to patent his historic machine. Can he have supposed that it was covered by his patent of 1774? This seems most unlikely, yet his boring mill was not copied elsewhere until after that patent had been revoked in 1779 which suggests that his competitors may have believed that this was so. Similar mills were then installed at Coalbrookdale in 1780, by Messrs Banks & Onions of Benthall in 1781, by the Hornblowers in 1782 and by the Eagle Foundry, Birmingham, in 1792. These rivals, however, did not succeed in robbing Wilkinson of the reward of his ingenuity for he continued to produce all the cylinders required by Boulton & Watt until his works were dismantled in 1795 as a result of a dispute with his brother.

Before pursuing this particular evolutionary thread further it is necessary at this point to go back in time in order to see what other effects a growing iron-producing industry was having on the development of machine tools. As we should expect, the use of machines first began to make headway in those metal trades producing a light, uniform product which the community required in quantity and which, having a relatively high money value in proportion to its weight, could be economically transported by the crude means available. Although their comparative rates of development might be unequal such trades usually followed the same evolutionary pattern. In the first place, production, from raw material to finished article, was a cottage craft, the necessary capital being furnished by the merchant or 'ironmonger' who supplied the cottage workshop with raw material and collected the finished goods. The next stage marks the transition from cottage to factory industry and began when the merchant took a hand in production by introducing the principle of division of labour. Production was still carried on in cottage workshops, but those engaged became 'outworkers' employed by the merchant—who could now call himself a manufacturer—and were so organised that groups of outworkers were responsible for particular specialised operations only. These might be carried out entirely by hand or with the aid of simple hand-powered machine tools. The final phase—usually violently opposed by the workers—was the substitution by the manufacturer of the specialised machine tool for the specialised outworker. This necessarily entailed the concentration of production in a power-driven mill, in other words the factory system.

The London needle-maker of the mid seventeenth century was a member of the 'Society of the Art or Mysterye of Needle Makers of the City of London' and in order to qualify for membership he must have produced 500 needles by his own hand under the eye of a master needler. A proposal to point needles by grinding on a stone instead of by filing was successfully resisted by the London needlers, but their trade ebbed away to Buckinghamshire and to Redditch in Worcestershire where, by the middle of the eighteenth century, it had expanded greatly and reached the transition stage between domestic and factory production. Division of labour split the outworkers into groups of 'soft workers', 'hammer straighteners', 'hardeners', 'pointers' and 'finishers'. The last two occupations were transferred from the home workshop to small mills as water power was applied to grindstones and polishing machines.

Needle points were dry ground on natural stones with terrible results, most pointers dying of the pulmonary disease known as 'pointers' rot' before they reached middle age. Two humanitarians named Abraham and Elliot attempted to instal a magnetic method of metal-dust extraction on the grinding machines—the earliest use of an extractor on a grinder known to the writer—but the pointers refused to use the device, arguing that if their trade was made safe their wages would be reduced. A local poet summed up the tragic situation in this fashion:

There draws the grinder his laborious breath,
There, coughing at his deadly trade he bends,
Born to die young, he fears no man, nor death,
Scorning the future, what he earns he spends.

Yet, Abraham and Elliot both in vain
Bid science on his cheek prolong the bloom;
He would not live! He seems in haste to gain
The undisturbed asylum of the tomb,
And, old at two-and-thirty, meets his doom.

The method of polishing consisted of wrapping a quantity of needles together with a mixture of fine sand, soft soap and water in buckram to make a tight roll called a 'packet' and then rolling a number of these packets between two boards. The machine version of this process consisted of a two-tier table, each fixed tier having the equivalent moving portion working to and fro upon it between guides, this motion being derived from the waterwheel by gearing, cranks, connecting rods and vertical steadying links. Machines of this kind have remained in use down to the present day and the complete mechanisation of needle making came slowly.[1]

The making of wood screws was another trade which favoured the introduction of specialised quantity-production methods and because the process of filing the thread on the blank was extremely laborious, manufacture reached the stage of complete mechanisation at a remarkably early date. In 1760 the brothers Job and William Wyatt of Tatenhill and Burton on Trent in Staffordshire took out a patent for a 'certain method of cutting screws of iron commonly called wood-screws in a better manner than had been heretofore practised'. Unfortunately this specification is not illustrated, but the description suggests two types of special-purpose lathe of a very advanced design. These produced the finished screw from the forged blank in three operations. The first machine was apparently equipped with some form of fast-and-loose pulley drive. The screw blank was placed shank foremost in a two-jaw chuck on the first lathe spindle and the head was trimmed by hand filing as it rotated. Next, with the lathe spindle stopped, the nick was cut by a revolving cutter. The screw was then centred by the head in a three-jaw chuck on the second lathe. The screw thread was then cut by two opposing cutters fixed in a frame which began to traverse when it was engaged by a follower pin with a lead screw, called a 'master screw'.

About 1776 the Wyatt brothers acquired a water-driven cornmill at Tatenhill and converted it into a screw factory. The venture was a financial failure and was sold as a going concern to Shorthose, Wood & Co. who improved the processes and expanded production to such purpose

[1] The last water-powered needle-scouring mill at Redditch ceased working in 1958 and efforts are now being made to preserve it.

that a second, larger factory was equipped at Hartshorn, nearby. In 1792 Shaw, the Staffordshire historian, described this enterprise as follows:

> ... At Hartshorn, co. Derby ... they employ 59 pairs of hands, and make on an average 1,200 gross per week, by means of 36 engines, or lathes, turned by one water wheel, each cutting, with great velocity, eight or nine screws a minute, and is stopped 18 times in the course of that short period to put in and take out the screw. They are made of various sizes from half-an-ounce to 30 lbs per gross and children can earn by the employment from 1*s*. 6*d*. to 19*s*. per week. Before the present war they could not be got up fast enough for exportation; but they still continue to make £100 worth per week and have now a large warehouse in this town, stored with about 4,000 gross; yet the sale is still pretty brisk.

This must be one of the earliest examples in machine-tool history of 'mass production' by means of special-purpose machines in which the skill had been built into the tools to such purpose that they could be operated by children. The methods patented by the brothers Wyatt were refined but not basically altered until 1854 when John Sutton Nettlefold, working under licence, re-equipped his Birmingham screw factory with American machinery for the production of the modern type of pointed taper woodscrew.

As mentioned earlier, Abraham Darby's historic discovery of the art of smelting iron with coke had no immediate effect upon the British iron industry as a whole. The success of Darby's exploitation of his discovery, which made Coalbrookdale the cradle of the new iron age, was largely due to Darby's shrewdness in the choice of a site for his ironworks. At Coalbrookdale, resources of coal and iron ore were close at hand, the stream which flowed down the valley provided water power, while at the valley foot flowed the Severn to provide transport. Nowhere else in England were these essentials so conveniently combined.

Even so the output of the coke-fired furnaces at the Dale was at first confined to the production of iron castings. Conversion of cast pig into wrought iron had to be carried out in open-hearth 'finery' furnaces using charcoal so that this process was still inhibited by the timber shortage. Moreover, there was considerable prejudice in the trade against the use of coke-smelted pig in the finery although experience at Coalbrookdale had proved that this was groundless.

For these reasons the Coalbrookdale swallow did not make a summer. Indeed for some 30 years after the date of Darby's historic discovery, British home production of iron continued to decline and in 1740 the total make was only 7,000 tons. It then increased slowly until 1780 when the spectacular expansion of the industry began. By the end of the century output had reached 150,000 tons, in 1820 it was 400,000 tons and by 1830 the figure of 700,000 tons had been reached. Three main factors were responsible for this phenomenal increase in British iron output after 1780. These were the perfection by Henry Cort of the puddling process for the conversion of raw pig into wrought iron, the construction of canals which brought cheap transport to the great coal- and iron-producing areas and the application of steam power to furnace and rolling mill.

The development of metal-cutting machine tools followed this expansion in the output of their raw material very closely. That the tool-makers were thus able to keep pace with the demands of the new iron age was due to another metallurgical development, the successful manufacture of crucible or carbon steel in Sheffield.

The Chinese and the Indians mastered the art of making crucible steel before the birth of Christ, but the secret of its manufacture was unknown to the Western world until it was re-invented in England in the mid eighteenth century. Indian Wootz steel, as it was called, was produced upon a very small scale by placing hammered iron and wood in a closed clay crucible of about one pound capacity and then subjecting it to intense heat for several hours in a small conical clay furnace blown by skin bellows. This brought about the necessary carbonisation. Strips of Wootz steel and wrought iron twisted together and then welded produced the celebrated Damascus steel and the same process was copied at Toledo. The method of steel making used in Europe and in Sheffield until the mid eighteenth century was to place iron bars upon a bed of granulated charcoal in a muffle furnace and subject them to intense heat for several days and even as long as a week, the period depending on the degree of carbonisation required. The result was called blister steel because of its appearance, but the carbonisation achieved in this way was superficial and unequal so that its behaviour when worked up was unpredictable and frequently unsatisfactory.

It was the indifferent quality of the steel springs supplied to him that induced Benjamin Huntsman, a Doncaster maker of clocks and watches, to begin, about 1743, a long series of experiments which, after many failures, ultimately led to the successful production of crucible steel in 1746. At first he continued in his trade as a watchmaker and produced steel only in very small quantities, but in 1751 he began producing his crucible steel on a commercial scale at a works which he built in Worksop Road, Sheffield. Huntsman's greatest difficulty had been to make crucibles capable of withstanding the intense heat. Having solved this problem he

24 *Boulton & Watt's Soho Foundry, Birmingham*

25 *Matthew Murray's Round Foundry, Leeds*

26 *William Murdock*

27 *John Wilkinson (Photo. Science Museum, London)*

28 *Matthew Murray*

29 *Joseph Bramah*

did not patent his process but endeavoured to keep it secret. In this he was unsuccessful although for many years the making of crucible steel remained an art confined to Sheffield where its secrets were handed down from father to son.

Benjamin Huntsman's discovery was of cardinal importance for it is obvious that the efficacy of any metal-cutting machine depends absolutely upon the ability of the actual cutting tool to do the work required of it. Indeed it would be true to say that the machine is designed round the cutting tool since its proportions, its feeds and speeds are necessarily determined by the tool's cutting ability. Thus Huntsman's carbon steel made possible and influenced profoundly the achievements of the pioneer machine-tool makers. His discovery is the more remarkable because it was made empirically. Huntsman had no clear idea *why* his crucible steel was so superior for it was not until about 1820 that Karsten established that the difference between pig iron, wrought iron and steel depended upon the amount of carbon present and not until 1831 that Liebig perfected an exact method of determining the amount of carbon in steel.

Until the expansion of Britain's iron industry took place, Sweden, with her vast timber resources, remained the great iron-producing country of Europe and Britain was dependent upon her for as much as four-fifths of the wrought iron used in manufacture. During this period Swedish iron enjoyed a reputation similar to that of English oak and whenever a piece of wrought ironwork of the highest quality and toughness was required 'best Swedish iron' was almost invariably specified. We should therefore expect to find significant developments in machine-tool design in Sweden during the first half of the eighteenth century, but with one very significant exception the evidence is lacking.

This exception is found in a manuscript on iron working by the Swede Christopher Polhem dated 1710 and preserved in Stockholm. Polhem describes how the rollers used for rolling strip and bar iron were forged and then continues: 'Thereafter, they are set aside for turning. This is best done with a turning lathe run by a small waterwheel. The cutting tool is held by means of a block, which gradually is drawn forward along the roller by a long screw and controlled by the rolling master's own hand. However, it can also be done so that the waterwheel itself is used to turn the screw.' It is unfortunate that no illustration of such a machine has been found, for the description would fit the heavy-duty industrial lathe developed in England a hundred years later.

Polhem goes on to describe how the long and heavy lead screws for such lathes were made. A replica of the screw in hard wood was first made by the hand methods used for many years to produce the patterns from which screw threads of large diameter could be cast.[1] By means of suitable couplings and carriers the wooden pattern and the blank workpiece were then placed end to end between the centres of a lathe so that they could be rotated together. What Polhem describes 'a long iron', having a cutting tool fixed in it at one end and a follower which engaged the pattern screw at the other, was then used to cut the thread on the workpiece. This method must have entailed many light cuts because even with the hardest wood a heavy cut would have caused the follower to damage the pattern threads. The iron screw was finished by mounting it in a second lathe and dressing it with a file as it rotated. Finally the screw was brought to red heat and tempered by quenching.

The rollers used in the Swedish iron mills were also hardened and Polhem later states that even after hardening they could readily be trued up by means of a grinding device invented by his son Gabriel in 1737. Again there is no illustration, and in this case no description, to tell us what this device was like.

Both Christopher Polhem and his admiring pupil Emanuel Swedenborg travelled extensively in Europe, yet there is no evidence that the advanced methods which the former describes had any influence outside Sweden. The importance of the iron trade to the Swedish economy at this time was such that many Swedish engineers made it their business to visit other countries, especially England, to study with intelligent interest—and latterly with well-founded apprehension—the latest developments in technology. But, naturally enough, they were concerned to import ideas not to export them and consequently over the rest of Europe the heavy metal-turning lathe remained a very crude tool compared with the machine described by Polhem.

A drawing of a turning shop in Diderot's Encyclopaedia (1771) features two pole lathes and a heavy metal-cutting lathe driven from a large pulley and still larger flywheel turned by a hand-crank. Apart from the fact that it is far more massively built there is little to distinguish this machine from the traditional pole lathe even at this late date. To turn iron on such a machine called for considerable muscular effort as well as skill. The hand cutting tools were about 2 feet 6 inches long, being designed to be gripped firmly in both hands and clamped under the armpit. For a heavy cut a hook was used to hold the business end of the tool on the rest. This was the type of machine most commonly in use throughout Europe before the rise of the first generation of the great British machine tool makers at the end

[1] The large-diameter screw threads used to screw the barrel to the breech in some early guns were cast from such wooden patterns.

of the eighteenth century. The only advance which such machines displayed was in the design of lathe spindle bearings in order to resist heavier loads without loss of accuracy. Detachable split cast bearings of soft metal ('brasses') for lathe spindles were illustrated by Plumier as early as 1701, while coned bearings, or a combination of cone and parallel journals, to resist end thrusts also appeared at an early date.

30 *A turner's workshop of 1771* (*Diderot*)

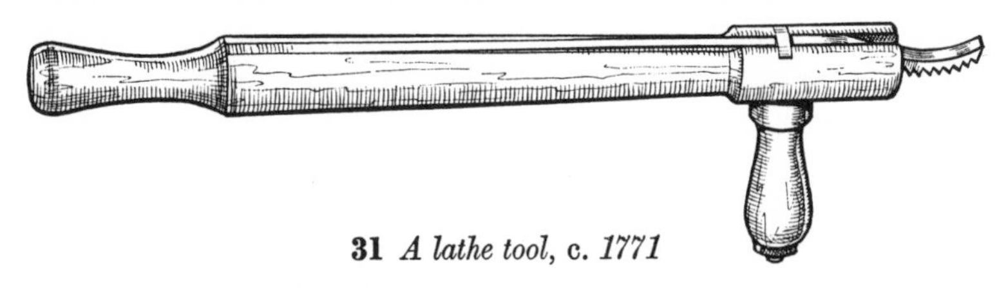

31 *A lathe tool*, c. *1771*

It must be emphasised that in the industrial workshop of this time there was no such thing as face turning for, excepting very small special-purpose machines such as those used to make woodscrews, all turning was done between centres.[1] The closest approximation to a faceplate lathe was

[1] The Gilpin drawing of the Bersham Boring Mill mentioned earlier in this chapter shows a second shaft driven from the waterwheel. Some historians have suggested that this second shaft originally carried a faceplate and was used to machine cylinder covers, but this cannot be more than conjectural. The amount of fitting which we know had to be done on site before the cylinder and covers of a Watt engine could be successfully wedded would seem to discount the idea that Wilkinson used a facing lathe.

the rose engine used for fine tool engraving or 'engine turning'. Diderot illustrates a large rose engine of this kind equipped with a compound slide rest having gibbed slides and screw traverses, which presents an appearance so surprisingly modern by contrast with his picture of the turner's workshop that it is hard to believe that the two are of the same date. But the ornamental craftsman evidently had no links with the industrial workshop.

The oldest surviving heavy industrial lathe which reveals a complete breakaway from the pole-lathe tradition and employs, like Polhem's machine, a fixed cutter on a traversing carriage was designed by Jacques de Vaucanson (1709–1782) between 1765 and 1780 and is now in the Conservatoire des Arts et Métiers. This was obviously an attempt to ensure a much higher standard of precision. Instead of the wooden bed then current its component parts are housed in a massive framework of iron bars within which the head and tailstock housings can be adjusted vertically and laterally. Because of this provision for vertical adjustment, the framework extends high above the lathe bed which must have made the machine very awkward to operate. The bed itself consists of two 1½-inch-square iron bars set on edge so that the carriage slides on two faces inclined at 45°. This is a very important feature. It shows that Vaucanson appreciated the value of prismatic guide ways which would not only free themselves from swarf but ensure greater precision by resisting the thrust of the tool. The carriage is of brass traversed by a hand-cranked lead screw and it also has a cross slide for the tool-holder though the feed screw for this has no index. The machine is something of a mystery. There is no indication as to how it was driven, while the very limited longitudinal adjustment provided between centres suggests that it was designed for some special purpose. It could have accommodated a workpiece about 40 inches long with a maximum diameter of 12 inches and may have been intended to machine the cylinders of Vaucanson's automatic loom.

Vaucanson was an engineer who was well ahead of his time. He was responsible for the oldest known formed rotary cutter of industrial size, and his lathe, despite its oddity, represents a remarkable advance. He was followed by Senot, whose screw-cutting lathe of 1795 with back gearing and workrests to oppose the thrust of the tool, is also in the Paris museum. Yet these two brilliant Frenchmen could not deflect the great currents of history. By 1795 the technological initiative was with England where the mighty surge of creative activity loosed by Watt's rotative steam engine was transforming the industrial workshop.

CHAPTER 3

The First Machine Shops

IN FEBRUARY 1769, long before James Watt joined Matthew Boulton in partnership, he received a letter in which Boulton outlined his ideas. He wrote:

> I was excited by two motives to offer you my assistance which were love of you and love of a money-getting, ingenious project. I presumed that your engine would require money, very accurate workmanship and extensive correspondence to make it turn out to the best advantage, and that the best means of keeping up the reputation and doing the invention justice would be to keep the executive part out of the hands of the multitude of empirical engineers, who from ignorance, want of experience and want of necessary convenience, would be very liable to produce bad and inaccurate workmanship; all of which deficiencies would affect the reputation of the invention. To remedy which and produce the most profit, my idea was to settle a manufactory near to my own by the side of our canal where I would erect all the conveniences necessary for the completion of engines, and from which manufactory we would serve all the world with engines of all sizes. By these means and your assistance we could engage and instruct some excellent workmen (with more excellent tools than would be worth any man's while to procure for one single engine) could execute the invention 20 per cent cheaper than it would otherwise be executed, and with as great a difference of accuracy as there is between the blacksmith and the mathematical instrument-maker. It would not be worth my while to make for three counties only,[1] but I find it very well worth my while to make for all the world.

[1] Roebuck had offered Boulton a limited concession to build engines for the counties of Stafford, Warwick and Derby.

Matthew Boulton was not, as he was often at pains to point out, an engineer himself and it may be that it was this detachment which enabled him to assess the contemporary situation so acutely. His letter is the more remarkable when we realise that at this date he had not even seen Watt's engine; indeed construction of the first engine at Kinneil had scarcely begun. As a business man and industrialist Boulton had no equal in his generation. It is easy for the industrial historian, wise after the event, to point to the shortcomings of technology at a particular period and indicate the remedies required; a diagnosis of equal accuracy made at the time requires rare genius. Boulton alone appreciated the true significance of Watt's invention. It meant that in engineering the days of the craftsman-millwright, who had reigned supreme ever since Newcomen had built his first engine in 1712, were numbered. The standards of accuracy which Watt's engine demanded could only be met commercially by large-scale production in a factory equipped with machine tools.

When Boulton and Watt applied to Parliament in 1775 for an extension of Watt's engine patent to 1800, heavy capital expenditure on the plant required to make it was chief among the supporting arguments. In the event, however, plant development upon the scale envisaged by Boulton was not embarked upon until 1795. In the meantime engine manufacture and erection proceeded on traditional lines. Engines were erected on the site, a proceeding which included a great deal of fitting and the manufacture locally of the simpler components. The more important parts were ordered from outside suppliers. Moreover, this whole operation was the responsibility of the customer, Boulton & Watt merely acting as consultants and supplying a man to superintend erection. The reputation of the firm lay in the hands of these foremen erectors and since men of sufficient skill were hard to find serious difficulties were apt to arise.

At this time when transport difficulties loomed large, the tendency in heavy engineering was to process the material close to its source in the blast furnace. Hence, as we saw in the last chapter, the first great ironworks, Coalbrookdale, Carron and Bersham, were also the first builders and users of heavy machine tools. The Butterley Company in Derbyshire founded by William Jessop and Benjamin Outram in 1790 was another celebrated example of the same type of unspecialised industrial complex. While this pattern persisted the space and plant devoted to engine production at Boulton's Soho Manufactury remained very modest indeed. All the patterns for the engine castings were made at Soho, but the only parts manufactured there from the outset were those which called for the greatest accuracy in machining and skill in fitting—the valves, valve chests and certain parts of the valve gear. These were produced from forgings and castings supplied from Wilkinson's Bradley works and as they were small components this more specialised method of production presented no transport problem and no heavy outlay on plant. We are told that the first engine shop at Soho consisted of two smiths' hearths, a fitting bench and a single lathe with the later addition of a second lathe and one or two drilling machines. These would not be heavy-duty tools since the nature of the work would not require such.

The event that precipitated the building of the famous Soho Foundry on the site beside the Birmingham Canal which Boulton had proposed 26 years before was the closure of the Bersham works. The difficulty Boulton & Watt experienced over the following months in getting cylinders and other parts accurately machined elsewhere indicates that Wilkinson had maintained his lead over his competitors. The work of the Coalbrookdale Company alone came up to Boulton & Watt's exacting standards, but the Dale had not the spare capacity to meet all their requirements. It was at this time that the Coalbrookdale Company, in a letter to Boulton & Watt concerning a piston they had machined, expressed a dimension as 'nearly $6\frac{1}{2}$ inches or $6^{4,125}/_{10,000}$'. This evidence of extreme precision should not be taken too seriously, however. It is unlikely that the company could measure accurately to such fine limits, still less machine to them, and much more probable that they were concerned to impress an important new customer.

A number of other factors influenced the decision to build the new engine works. Thanks to the success of Watt's rotative engine, the problem of providing driving power for a large concentration of heavy machine tools existed no longer. Industry's age-old dependence on water power was over and this fact, combined with the new canal transport system, gave the manufacturer a new freedom in the choice of factory sites. In consequence there was a great and growing demand for the rotative steam engine which could not be met by the old system of construction. In any case, the development of design had made this system obsolete. Unlike the early non-rotative pumping engine which was built into its engine house, the house itself being a part of the engine structure, the rotative Watt engine was a self-contained unit. The first Watt double-acting rotative engine ever sold had been assembled complete and tested at Soho before being dismantled and dispatched to the customer. This made feasible the *manufacture* of steam engines in the modern sense of the term. Finally, rival engine builders were appearing on the scene in defiance of Watt's patent monopoly in response to a demand which Boulton & Watt could not alone fulfil. It had become clear to the partners that their pioneer business must be well equipped to meet the unfettered competition which would ensue as soon as the patent lapsed in 1800.

The building of the new Soho Foundry was begun in the summer of 1795 and in the spring of 1796 its completion was celebrated by a luncheon for 200 guests. Celebration was justified for this was an industrial concentration of an entirely new kind, including as it did the first heavy engineering machine shop the world had ever seen. We are told that the new works was divided into the following shops: Drilling Shop; Heavy Turning Shop; Nozzle Shop[1]; Fitting Shed; Parallel Motion and Working Gear Shop; Light Fitting Shop; Pattern Shop; Casters' Shop; Smiths' Shop.

Unfortunately no drawings or illustrations have survived to show what these historic shops were like or what machines they contained when first built, nor is there any description of them. When the Soho Foundry was finally dismantled in 1895, the heavy machine tools were described and illustrated in a series of articles in *The Engineer*, but although it is evident that by then the machines were of considerable antiquity and therefore of great interest, there was no record of the date of their installation. The heaviest tools were of massive proportions and, like the early beam pumping engines, were 'built in' to the buildings which housed them. This seems to have led the writer of *The Engineer* articles to assume too easily that they had been there ever since the foundry was first built. In fact they exhibit features which did not appear until the second and third decades of the nineteenth century, although in some cases these features may represent modifications of much earlier tools. Where machines of such a size were concerned it was easier to modify than to scrap and replace them.

The only tool specifically mentioned at the time the Foundry was building is a vertical cylinder-boring mill designed by Peter Ewart to work in a masonry pit. A drawing of this mill is preserved in the Boulton & Watt collection. Instead of the hollow bar with internal rack feed introduced by Wilkinson, Ewart's design shows a solid bar and two external rack feed bars connected to a loose ring on the cutting head. Pinions are shown engaging the racks but there is no further detail to show whether the method of feeding was manual or automatic. If Ewart's mill was ever built it was not installed at Soho. For some reason there was a change of policy and a horizontal mill was laid down instead. This started working in December 1796 but was not satisfactory because, it

[1] The 'nozzles' were the valve chest assemblies and the 'working gear' was the valve gear.

was judged, the boring bar was too light. In 1798 William Murdock, who had been the firm's right-hand man in Cornwall for many years, was recalled to Birmingham to take practical charge of the Foundry where he introduced many improvements. A new and much heavier boring mill was constructed and the boring bar for this was supplied by the Lowmoor Ironworks in May 1799. It weighed 3½ tons and may well have been the bar which was still lying in a disused state at Soho in 1895. If so, it was hollow, 17 feet 6 inches long, 16 inches in diameter and 4 inches thick. Presumably it was originally fitted with a form of rack feed to the cutting head because Murdock was not responsible for introducing lead-screw feed as has sometimes been stated.

A 64-inch cylinder was the first to be bored on this massive machine and a record of the operation has been preserved to show what a lengthy and laborious business it was. It reads as follows:

Getting on, ¾ day.
Centring and fixing, 1½ days.
Facing, ½ day.[1]
Setting Cutter, ½ day.
Boring, 11½ days.
Preparing to go through a second time, 1 day.
Boring, 8½ days.
Facing, 1¼ days.
Bell-mouthing, 1½ days.
Getting off, ½ day.
Total, 27½ working days.

Murdock equipped this machine with worm and wheel drive. The worm had a triple-start thread of two-inch pitch, while the wormwheel, mounted on the axis of the boring bar, had wooden morticed teeth. This form of drive proved very successful. It was silent and did not suffer from chatter or back-lash; consequently it was used to drive the horizontal and vertical

[1] The end faces of cylinders were machined in the following way by means of a special attachment to the boring bar. This consisted of an arm carrying a tool-holder which was free to slide along it. The tool-holder was traversed by a lead screw fitted, at its outer extremity, with a six-armed star wheel. By means of a striker attached to the bed of the machine this wheel turned the lead screw through one-sixth of a revolution for each revolution of the boring bar, thus providing automatic feed to the facing tool. A surviving example of such a facing attachment from Soho was described and illustrated in Vol. XXIII of the *Newcomen Society Transactions* ('Some workshop tools from Soho Foundry' by W. K. V. Gale). In this example the lead screw has 10 threads per inch so that the tool was advanced 1/60 inch at each revolution of the boring bar. The 'star-feed' slide, as it is now called, is still used today.

boring mills and the heavy-duty lathes which were subsequently installed and continued in use until 1895.

The horizontal boring mill still in use at Soho in 1895 and illustrated by *The Engineer* at that date may be conveniently described at this point because, although of later date, it is undoubtedly very similar to the first mill except in the method of automatic feed by lead screw. The picture shows the large morticed wormwheel, 4 feet 10 inches in diameter on the pitch circle, mounted between two bearings on a short driving shaft. The worm is invisible, being below floor level, but the top of the worm-shaft driving pulley can just be seen behind the standing figure. The driven end of the boring bar is carried in a third bearing and connected to the short driving shaft by a squared coupling. The two adjustable cradles for the cylinder are shown and likewise one of the two lashing bars by which it was secured. In order to run the cylinder onto the machine by means of the travelling pulley-block, the boring bar could be supported on a jack near its driven end and the set pins securing the tail bearing to its supporting block removed. The latter could then be run out sideways on the rollers provided. The roller ways are so designed that when restored to position the supporting block rests solid on the plate below, a spigot on the underside of the block dropping into a slot in the plate to provide positive location.

Although this boring bar was hollow, the lead screw is not arranged axially but runs in a slot in the side of the bar which also locates the sliding key of the cutter head. The lead screw is driven by a planetary gear train from a sun wheel on the axis of the bar which can be slid on its spindle to provide either a slow manual feed for facing work or rapid manual traverse when bringing the cutter head up to the work.

A large vertical boring mill having the same arrangement of worm drive and screw feed was later built at Soho and used for the heaviest work. It was used in 1854 to bore the four cylinders for the screw engine of Brunel's giant ship the *Great Eastern*. This engine, which was built entirely at Soho, was the most powerful in the world at that time, indicating nearly 2,000 horse-power. Each cylinder bore was seven feet in diameter.

Information about the other machine tools which were originally installed at the Soho Foundry is unfortunately very scanty. The earliest reference is a list compiled in December 1801 which includes some tantalisingly brief particulars. It was presumably made because William Murdock was either contemplating alterations to the pulley drive countershafts or the individual vacuum motors subsequently described by Nasmyth. Since few additions can have been made by this date, the list

32 *Horizontal cylinder-boring mill, Soho Foundry* (The Engineer)

does give us some idea how this pioneer machine shop was equipped. It reads as follows:

No. 1 Large drill; an upright one with convenience for putting in and out of gear and sliding socket. Present speed about 8 per minute. Proposed speed 8.
No. 2 Small drill; an upright one with same convenience as the preceding; present speed 50 per minute. Proposed speed 75.
No. 3 Large turning lathe with both centres and chock [chuck?]. Present speed 3⅛ per minute. Proposed speeds 2 per m. to 18 per m.
No. 4 Piston rod lathe, with spindle and dead centres. Present speeds 18, 38, 60. Proposed speeds 18, 30, 50, 80.
No. 5 Nozzle lathe, spindle and dead centre. Present speed about 65. Proposed do. 18, 50, 70.
Nos. 6 & 7 Parallel Motion lathe, spindle and dead centre. Present speed about 65. Proposed do. 18, 50, 70.
Nos. 8 & 9 Lathe in upper fitting shop; spindle lathe and dead centre in same cheeks. Present speed 88. Proposed do. 18, 50, 80, 120.
No. 10 Small lathe. Proposed speed 200, 300.
No. 11 Lapping Machine.
No. 12 Pattern-maker's lathe, speed from 220 to 300 p.m.
No. 13 Steam case drill.

This list begs many questions, but it is at least evident that four lathes were special-purpose tools designed and built to machine particular parts of Watt's steam engine, namely the piston rod, the nozzles (valve chests) and the links of Watt's famous parallel motion. We should dearly like to know more about the 'No. 3 Large turning lathe'. Its extremely low speed suggests that it may have been a very big face turning and boring lathe for machining large gearwheels and flywheels and yet this is seemingly contradicted by the reference to centres. There was at Soho in 1895 a massive facing and boring lathe which tradition asserted was older than the foundry, having been brought thither from the Soho Manufactury. This seems most unlikely and if there was any truth in the tradition, the lathe must have been completely reconstructed at a much later date with back-geared headstock and five slide rests with automatic feeds by lead screws. Another heavy facing lathe depicted in 1895 has the characteristic Murdock worm drive direct to the mandril, and although this has a compound slide rest with screw traverses driven by belt from a pulley on the mandril, it probably bears a much closer resemblance than its fellow to the No. 3 lathe of 1801.

Of the design of the smaller lathes we know nothing, yet it seems certain that in order to machine such parts as piston rods and valve chests with

33 *Heavy facing lathe with Murdock's worm drive, Soho Foundry* (The Engineer)

sufficient accuracy the cutting tools must have been held in a tool-holder on some form of slide rest. If this was the case, then, on the evidence of the boring mills, we should expect a longitudinal traverse by rack and possibly a small lead screw for manual cross feed. In this connection it must be emphasised that William Buckle, who was appointed manager at Soho in 1824 or 1825, is credited with the introduction of the first large screw-cutting lathe to the works. Hence when large lead screws were first adopted on the boring mills and other heavy machine tools they had to be produced by other means. A carefully marked paper pattern was stuck upon the shaft and the pattern lines of the screw thread pricked through onto the metal with a hand punch. The thread was then laboriously cut by hammer and chisel until it had attained sufficient depth to provide a lead. A type-metal nut was then cast upon the threads inside an iron box equipped with adjustable cutters. A large die nut was thus formed. With the shaft mounted vertically and the die nut held fast, the thread was cut to its finished depth by six men who rotated the screwed shaft by means of capstan bars.

Another illustration of 1895 shows two drilling machines housed in a massive framework of wooden beams supported on cast-iron columns. They were then said to be 100 years old and could well be the first and second machines on the list of 1801. The larger has the familiar worm and wheel drive and its design is similar to that of a boring mill, the drill socket sliding on a bar with rack feed. The smaller machine has a $2\frac{1}{4}$-inch-square spindle which slides within a hollow driving shaft rotated by mitre gears, the driver having wooden morticed teeth. As the illustration clearly shows, the spindle is raised, lowered or fed by means of rope tackle, overhead pulleys and a winch. If this machine was indeed one of the originals, then the stepped pulley drive was added later since the machine listed was single speed.

Boulton & Watt's first and most formidable rival in the engine-building business was Matthew Murray (1765–1826) the growth of whose engineering business in Leeds coincided with that of the Soho Foundry. With a partner named David Wood, Murray started his business at Mill Green, Holbeck, Leeds, in 1795. Its immediate success and the capital provided by a third partner, James Fenton, soon enabled Murray to build a large new engineering works at Camp Fields, Holbeck. This was the famous Round Foundry, the reputation of which soon rivalled that of Soho. The plant was planned upon an ambitious scale and although the first shops were in use by 1797 the round building which gave the works its name was not completed until 1802.

Murray was a consummate engineering craftsman and this practical gift was happily combined with a remarkable flair for invention. As a result of his talent and inspiration, the Round Foundry was soon producing work of a quality which his rivals at Soho could not equal. In 1799

34 *Two drilling machines, one with worm drive, Soho Foundry* (The Engineer)

William Murdock, accompanied by the Soho Foundry foreman (an ex-Bersham man named Abraham Storey), paid a visit to the Round Foundry. They were hospitably entertained and proudly shown the plant by the open-handed Murray who did not suspect that what was ostensibly a goodwill mission had in fact been planned to spy out his technical secrets. One of his employees was in fact suborned to act as a spy for the Soho firm. It was only when Murray attempted to pay a return visit to the Soho Foundry and was brusquely refused admission that he realised how he had been tricked. Thereafter the competition between the two pioneer undertakings became extremely bitter and no holds were barred.

Most unfortunately, a fire in 1872 destroyed the celebrated round building that had been Murray's machine shop and all Murray's records and drawings, which had been stored there, perished in the flames. Consequently the extent of Murray's contribution to machine-tool history is very difficult to assess. What is indisputable, however, is that Murray was one of the first, if not the very first, to manufacture engineering machine tools for sale. Whereas Boulton & Watt and their predecessors at Bersham and Coalbrookdale had designed and built such tools solely for their own use, Murray, having equipped his own works, went on to build machine tools for customers at home and abroad.

In his successful steam-engine designs Murray introduced the D slide valve and in order to machine the face of this valve he designed and built at the Round Foundry a planing machine. Samuel Smiles asked an old employee of Murray's about this machine and received the following reply:

> I recollect it very distinctly, and even the sort of framing on which it stood. The machine was not patented, and like many inventions in those days, it was kept as much a secret as possible, being locked up in a small room by itself, to which the ordinary workmen could not obtain access. The year in which I remember it being in use was, so far as I am aware, long before any planing-machine of a similar kind had been invented.

Murray evidently succeeded in keeping this machine secret; he does not appear to have manufactured it for others, neither did the Soho spies succeed in prising it out of him. Consequently no details of it are known.

Details and illustrations are available of two types of cylinder-boring machine, both with positive automatic feed, which Murray designed. The first has two rack bars which pass, teeth inwards, through slots in the sides of the bar to connect with a ring bearing on the boring head. These rack bars extend beyond the end of the bar to an extent equal to the travel of the boring head. Here they engage a short wormwheel fixed to an axial shaft. This shaft is carried in an outrigger bearing and also supports the ends of the rack bars by means of a sliding bearing. The wormwheel shaft is driven by gear trains from a pinion on the end of the boring bar to provide the automatic feed.

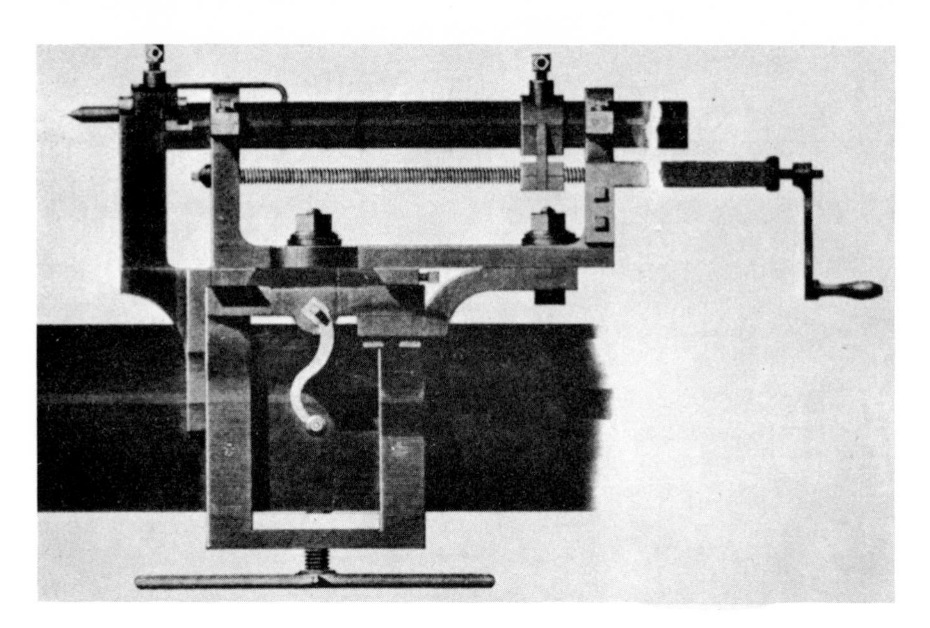

35 *Side view*

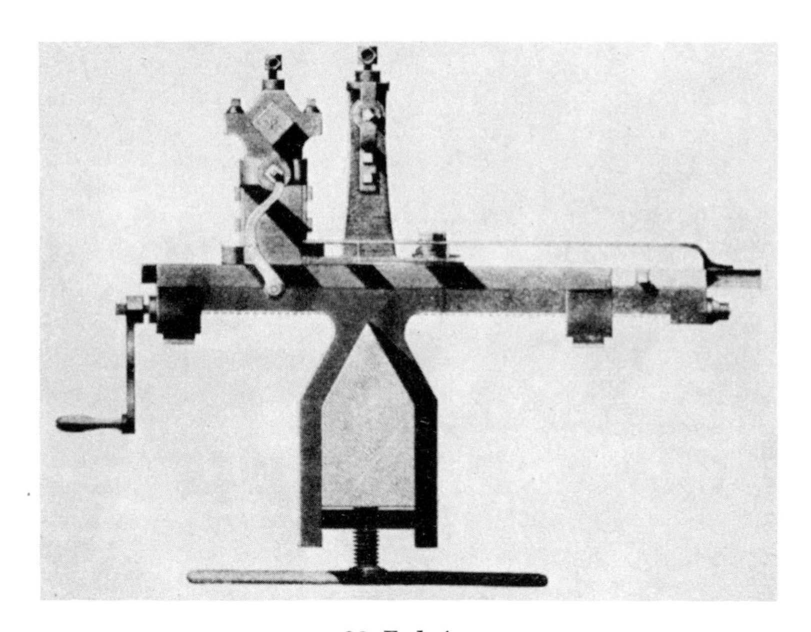

36 *End view*

BRAMAH'S PATENT SLIDE REST, 1794

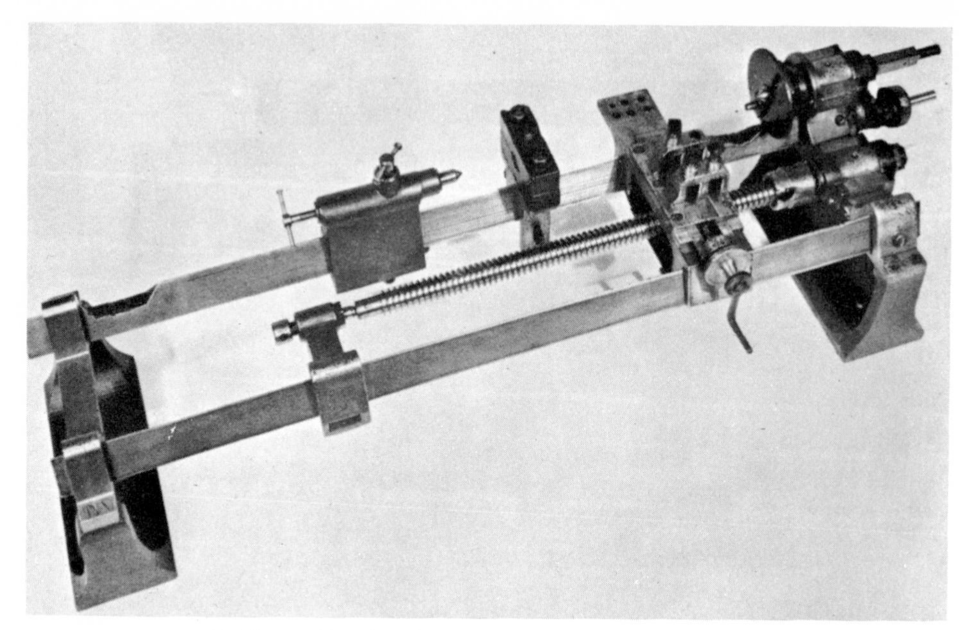

37 *Henry Maudslay's first screw-cutting lathe,* c. *1800*
(Crown Copyright. Science Museum, London)

38 *Maudslay's second screw-cutting lathe,* c. *1800*
(Crown Copyright. Science Museum, London)

The second Murray design substituted a single lead screw for the double racks. This lead screw is attached to the end of a solid bar upon which the boring head is fixed. A nut on the lead screw is driven by reduction gearing from the bar, the ratio of this feed gearing being so determined that the nut rotated relatively backwards at approximately one-eighth of the speed of the bar to provide a feed of 0·065 inch per revolution of the bar. With this arrangement the whole bar with its fixed boring head slid through its bearings and through its drive wheel when the feed was engaged.

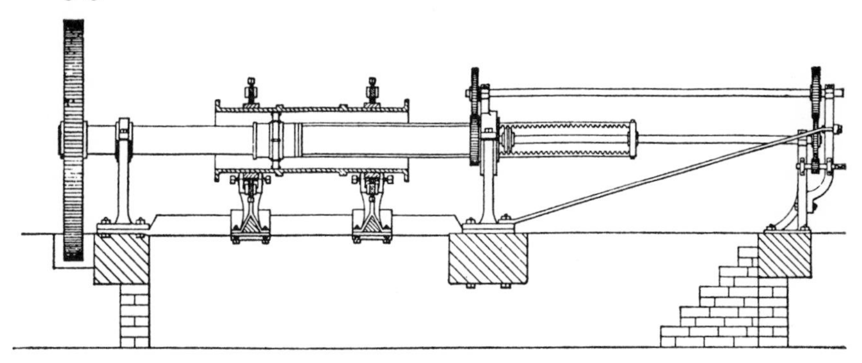

39 *Horizontal cylinder-boring machine by Matthew Murray at the Round Foundry* (The Engineer)

Both these designs worked well, their only disadvantage being their excessive length. Boring mills of this type were supplied by Murray to his friend Simon Goodrich at Portsmouth and to engineering works at Chaillot and St. Quentin in France where they were very highly esteemed, being the only machines of their kind in the country.

It is evident that at his own works Murray must have had yet a third type of boring mill of more compact design in which the lead screw was either within or beside the bar and advanced a sliding boring head. For James Watt Junior, in a letter to his partner Matthew Robinson Boulton written in 1802, says of this machine: 'The cutter head is pushed forward along the boring rod by an endless screw. We must adopt some similar contrivance.' This proves that in 1802 rack feed was still the rule at Soho and it would seem that credit for first introducing the lead screw on heavy-duty machine tools in England should go to Matthew Murray though, as we have seen, it may have been used by Andrew Schalch at Woolwich.

The effect and the influence of these two historic machine shops at Soho and Holbeck was immense. They set engineers a new standard which was widely and speedily emulated. Almost overnight, it seemed, they transformed the appearance of the steam engine. From a crude construction of heavy timber and 'black' ironwork it became a precise and ordered assembly of well-finished metal parts. Now that the engineers of the new iron age had won such command over their materials, the way was open for extraordinarily rapid technical development in every sphere of industrial activity. It was no accident that the first commercially successful steam locomotives in the world were products of the Round Foundry where Murray had the tools for the job and the power to drive them.

Both works became schools for engineers who disseminated their methods far and wide. When the firm of Fenton, Murray & Wood went out of business in 1843, the Round Foundry passed into the hands of Smith, Beacock & Tannett, the celebrated machine tool makers who trained the brothers Krupp (founders of the famous works at Essen) and perpetuated the Murray tradition until the historic shops finally closed down in 1894.

CHAPTER 4

Henry Maudslay–Metal Cutting becomes an Art

THE REASON WHY the question of priority of invention is so often the subject of heated debate is that an historic invention is never wholly original. The function of an inventive genius is to fuse together hitherto disparate elements of which he may have no knowledge in one classical and enduring combination. Where man's basic machine tool is concerned this was Henry Maudslay's role. As the previous chapters have shown, all the elements of the modern lathe existed long before Maudslay's day, but it was his genius and his exacting craftsmanship that refined, combined and ordered them in one beautiful tool whose polished precision set an example for posterity to follow.

Henry Maudslay (1771–1831) was born at Woolwich and from the age of 12 onwards he was employed at the Arsenal, first as a powder-monkey, then in the carpenter's shop and finally in the forge where his extraordinary aptitude as a metal worker soon brought him a reputation which spread abroad until it reached the ears of Joseph Bramah (1748–1814). This inventive Yorkshireman had a workshop in Denmark Street, St. Giles, London, where he was manufacturing his patent water-closet and at the time Maudslay came into his employ, at the age of 18, he was wrestling with the problems of manufacturing his patent lock.

H. W. Dickinson, in a paper[1] on the work of Joseph Bramah, describes the working principle of this ingenious lock as follows:

[1] 'Joseph Bramah and His Inventions,' in *Newcomen Society Transactions*, Vol. XXII, 1941–42.

As originally patented (A.D. 1784, Apr. 23, No. 1430) the end of the key, of the pipe kind, has a number of notches or slots; usually six, of varying depth and, by means of these, corresponding sliders arranged radially in slots in a barrel are depressed against the action of a spring so as to arrive at a predetermined surface; this allows the key to turn the barrel round and enables the latter to shoot the bolt by a crank pin. The bit on the key merely determines the depth to which the key is to be pushed in.

The result was a great advance upon any lock previously known, but it was a complex little assembly and its successful operation depended upon highly accurate workmanship. Satisfactory prototypes had been made by hand, but the labour involved was so great that it was obvious to Bramah that on this basis his lock could never become a commercial proposition. During the 12 months following Maudslay's engagement (1790) the production of the lock was completely mechanised. In the process the design of the lock was modified in detail to facilitate machine production but its working principle remained the same. John Farey, the engineer and author, was an intimate friend of Bramah's at this time and in 1849 he recorded[1] his recollections of the lock-making machines as follows:

The secret workshops . . . contained several curious machines for forming parts of the locks, with a systematic perfection of workmanship which was at that time unknown in similar mechanical arts. These machines had been constructed by the late Mr. Maudslay with his own hands, whilst he was Mr. Bramah's chief workman. . . . The machines before mentioned were adapted for cutting the grooves in the barrel and the notches in the steel plates. . . . The notches in the keys, and in the steel sliders, were cut by other machines which had micrometer screws so as to ensure that the notches in each key should tally with the unlocking notches of the sliders . . . the setting of these micrometer screws was regulated by a system, which ensured a constant permutation in the notches of succeeding keys, in order that no two should be made alike. Mr. Bramah attributed the success of his locks to the use of these machines, the invention of which had cost him more study than that of the locks.

In Chapter 2 we saw how the brothers Wyatt first applied mechanised production methods to the manufacture of a single component—the wood screw. Now, Bramah and Maudslay carried the same principle a stage further by applying it to the several components of an intricate assembly. Taking Farey's statement at its face value it would appear that Bramah supplied the ideas while Maudslay was responsible for their practical

[1] Quoted by Dickinson from *Proceedings of the Institution of Civil Engineers*, Vol. IX, 1849–50, pp. 331–2.

realisation, but in the light of Maudslay's subsequent achievements we are inclined to award him the major share of the credit for this historic installation. For it is not without significance that although Bramah had patented his lock in 1784, he made no headway with its commercial production until Maudslay joined him six years later. This suggests that although Bramah may have conceived the ideas, Maudslay alone possessed the practical ingenuity and the high craftsmanship required to translate Bramah's concepts into working machines.

Three of these historic tools have survived and are now preserved in the Science Museum in London. The first is a hack saw for cutting the slots in the lock barrel. The saw frame travels in adjustable vee slides and is operated manually by a two-handed lever. The barrel to be cut is mounted in a fixture which can be lifted against the saw by a long lever and is so indexed that 4, 5, 6, 7, 8, 10 or 12 slots may be cut. The second tool is a quick-grip vice resembling a pair of tongs with handles opened and closed by a slide. It is mounted on a gibbed cross slide, being intended for use in a lathe. The purpose of this fixture was to hold the cap of the lock while the bolt run was slotted out by a revolving cutter mounted on an arbor between the lathe centres. Revolving cutters had been used earlier by the Wyatts for slotting screw heads and by Vaucanson. Five of the Bramah/Maudslay cutters have survived to show that, like their predecessors, they are what we should call rotary files as distinct from a toothed milling cutter. It would therefore mislead the modern reader to describe such operations as milling although they do represent the germ of the idea of the milling machine.

The third surviving machine of this series was designed to wind the spiral steel lock springs and is therefore outside the terms of reference of this book. It must be mentioned, however, because it utilises the principle of the screw-cutting lathe and is therefore significant in the light of subsequent developments. The spool of spring steel wire is mounted on a carriage having vee slides and traversed by a lead screw driven from a headstock. This headstock carries between centres an arbor onto which the wire is wound under tension as the spool traverses. A single alternative gear for the lead-screw drive is provided to enable springs of two different coil pitches to be wound. The machine was worked by foot-treadle and flywheel.

The construction of these specialised lock-making machines was followed in 1794 by the invention of what has been called 'Bramah's original slide tool with slide rest & head in one'. The term 'head' in this description is misleading because the device in fact combined in one unit a slide rest and a tailstock with dead-centre. This was a true compound slide rest having longitudinal traverse and cross feed by manually operated lead screws, but because it was situated behind the tailstock the cross slide was lowermost. The longitudinal carriage above this was provided with quadrant and locking screw adjustment to permit taper turning. The upper part of the carriage could be advanced to a position beside the workpiece by the release of locking bolts. It supported a bar of square section mounted edge uppermost and upon this bar the tool-holder slid under the action of the lead screw.

Like its predecessors, this device is evidently an idea of Bramah's executed by Maudslay with a precision and finish unknown before. The idea of mounting a slide rest behind a lathe tailstock appears almost wilfully irrational, such an arrangement being inherently unstable since the tool-holder is always positioned far beyond its centre of support. But it is clear that the purpose of Bramah's invention was to produce a conversion unit which could be fitted onto the bed of existing hand-rest lathes in place of the old tailstock. As such it would be a great improvement on the hand-rest despite its evident defects and it probably enjoyed a good sale until lathes of basically improved design became available.

In 1797, having served Bramah faithfully for eight years and being now a married man with young children, Maudslay asked for a rise in wages and was curtly refused. Maudslay therefore left his employer and opened his own business at a small shop in Wells Street, off Oxford Street. The loss was Bramah's, but credit must be awarded him for having concentrated the outstanding ability of a great craftsman upon the problems of machine-tool development. As a result, Maudslay introduced to mechanical engineering those standards of precision which had hitherto been applied only upon a miniature scale by the scientific instrument-maker.

It was shortly after he left Bramah's employ that Maudslay produced the first of his classic screw-cutting lathes, a machine now preserved in the Science Museum in London. The bed consists of two triangular bars, revealing that its designer appreciated the advantages of the prismatic guideway first used by Vaucanson. An adjustable tailstock and a back-rest for opposing the thrust of the tool, as used by Senot, can be positioned as required on one of these guideways. This does not mean to say that Maudslay was acquainted with the work of these two French engineers; that he possessed such knowledge is in fact unlikely. The spindle of the lathe carries a small faceplate and drives the lead screw through change gears. The carriage traverses on both guideways and carries a gibbed cross slide. The manually operated screw controlling the latter is equipped with an index dial to enable the amount of cut to be accurately determined. A split nut and clamping device connects the slide rest to the lead screw when required. Thus far the machine is true prototype of the modern lathe; the only unusual and seemingly archaic feature is the way the lead screw itself is arranged. At its driven end the screw carries a cross pin and this fits into a socket on the end of the short driving shaft, the socket having a cross slot with which the pin engages. The opposite end of the lead screw is supported by a dead centre carried in a bracket mounted on one of the guideways. The reason for this curious arrangement, which Maudslay did not repeat, will be made clear presently.

Like Jesse Ramsden, Maudslay went to infinite pains to obtain accurate screw threads. He realised that an accurate screw was the bedrock of workshop precision whether used indirectly in a dividing engine to produce fine scales or directly in a measuring instrument. He tried all the known methods of generating screw threads and finally decided in favour of the inclined knife. He made a beautifully finished instrument for originating threads in this way. The knife is shaped to fit the cylinder to be cut and is mounted on a block sliding on a prismatic guide bar. The oblique incision made by the knife carried it along the cylinder as the latter revolved and in this way threads of any desired pitch could be generated by adjusting the angle of the knife. Having incised a thread in this way on a cylinder of wood or soft metal, Maudslay cut the thread by hand and then used the result in his screw-cutting lathe as a lead screw to reproduce its facsimile in iron or steel. Notwithstanding the provision of change gears, Maudslay undoubtedly designed his first lathe in such a way that different hand-cut lead screws could easily be fitted to it, and this accounts for the way in which the lead screw is mounted. The lead screw in the machine today was almost certainly produced by the machine itself using a hand-cut soft-metal prototype. It is one inch in diameter and carries a square thread of narrow section and of quarter-inch pitch.

Maudslay's second great contribution to machine-tool history was his appreciation of the fact that, in the quest for precision, true plane surfaces are of an importance second only to that of accurate screw threads. The only known method of producing a plane surface on metal at this date was by hand filing, an operation which requires considerable skill as any engineering apprentice should know. Yet although Maudslay was himself an acknowledged master of this art, no plane surface finished with a hand file could satisfy his exacting standards. He therefore introduced the method of finishing the plane surface by means of a surface plate, marking compound and hand scraper which is still widely used for precision work despite the advent of precision grinding machines. This raises an obvious question: how did Maudslay produce his original surface plate? The answer is that he produced three, or possibly four, plates simultaneously, checking one against the other to ensure that they were neither convex, concave nor 'out of wind'. Later, when Maudslay's business expanded into a large engineering concern, he saw to it that every one of his fitters was equipped with a surface plate.

Maudslay's screw-cutting lathe and his surface plates enabled him to construct his second, improved screw-cutting lathe of 1800 and his micrometer of 1805. A small hand-operated model of this second lathe in the Science Museum in London shows that it had flat plate guideways mounted on a substantial cast-iron bed and solid, well-splayed legs, showing that Maudslay appreciated the importance of rigidity. The carriage is equipped with a follower rest to resist the thrust of the cutting tool and, as on its predecessor, the cross feed is indexed. The use of the first lathe had obviated the need to employ hand-cut soft-metal lead screws so in this machine the lead screw is permanently mounted within the bed. The model lathe is equipped with a set of 28 change wheels having teeth varying in number from 15 to 50. The intermediate wheel has a wide face and is carried on an adjustable swinging arm to accommodate change wheels of differing diameters.

According to Holtzapffel, Maudslay next constructed a third machine in which he combined the prismatic bar bed of his first lathe with the flat bed used on his second. The head and tailstocks were mounted on a single triangular bar disposed midway between two large and flat guideways with chamfer bars. This anticipated the principle of modern machine-tool guideway design which makes use of both inclined and plane surfaces in order to combine accuracy with weight-carrying capacity. Maudslay also introduced a stepped vee pulley on the lathe spindle and a change-speed gear arrangement which anticipated the Norton gearbox. In this case, the lathe was driven from a swinging countershaft carrying a sliding pinion which could engage one of three gearwheels of differing ratios on the lathe spindle. In such heavy-duty machines Maudslay supported the front end of the lathe spindle in split brass bearing journals of ample length, while at the rear he employed tapered steel bushings to resist the thrust.

With these machines Maudslay was able to produce screw threads of ever-increasing accuracy as Jesse Ramsden had done before him, but upon a much heavier scale. He produced a brass screw seven feet long which was only one-sixteenth of an inch in error over its length. It was not practicable to correct so small an inaccuracy by means of change wheels, but the indefatigable Maudslay, never satisfied in his pursuit of perfection, devised an adjustable linkage, which doubtless operated on the principle used by Thiout (see Chapter 1) and by which the most minute error could be readily corrected. By these means Maudslay achieved his ultimate masterpiece of screw cutting—a screw of the utmost precision 5 feet long by 2 inches in diameter with 50 threads to the inch. The nut engaging this screw was 12 inches long and contained 600 threads. This superb piece of work far surpassed the standards of accuracy required in the industrial workshop. It was used for calibrating astronomical instruments at Greenwich where sub-divisions of the most minute accuracy were required and it won for Maudslay an award of £1,000 from the government.

The ultimate standard of precision in Maudslay's own workshops was his micrometer of 1805. Any dispute over accuracy of workmanship was referred to this instrument for judgement and it was for this reason that Maudslay christened it the 'Lord Chancellor'. Now preserved in the Science Museum in London, this historic instrument represents the fountainhead of mechanical engineering technique as we know it. It consists of a gun-metal bed carrying two saddles fitted with end-measuring faces, one of them extending downwards through a slot in the bed to terminate in a split nut. The saddles have bevel-edged windows through which the graduations on the bed may be read. The screw which engages the split nut has a pitch of 100 threads to the inch and carries an index wheel marked with 100 divisions on its periphery. Each division thus represents 0·0001 of an inch of movement between the measuring faces. The instrument is a characteristic example of Maudslay's superlative craftsmanship with delicate screw adjustments to the split nut and to eliminate end-play on the measuring screw. Tested by the National Physical Laboratory in 1918, its accuracy was found to be quite extraordinary considering its age.

Maudslay soon had an opportunity to demonstrate the capabilities of his new machine tools. In 1800 there came to his little shop in Wells Street Sir Marc Isambard Brunel who, while in America, had designed a series of machines for making ships' blocks and had been advised by a friend that Maudslay was the man to make them. The two men soon acquired a great respect for each other's ability and there began a fruitful technical collaboration similar to that earlier one between Bramah and Maudslay. Maudslay first constructed exquisite models of the block-making machines and these are now preserved in the National Maritime Museum at Greenwich. With these models Brunel was able to convince the Admiralty that his ideas were sound and a full-scale plant was ordered for Portsmouth Dockyard. Maudslay was to build the machines and Brunel was to superintend their installation.

There were 44 machines in all and their construction occupied Maudslay for six years. They were set running in 1809 and the Portsmouth block mill soon became a place of pilgrimage for illustrious and awe-struck visitors. It was a fully mechanised quantity production line such as the world had never seen before. Previously a labour force of 110 had been unable to satisfy the Navy's demand for blocks, but now a team of ten machine-hands could produce 160,000 blocks a year. Several of these historic machines may now be seen at the Science Museum in London; others are still at the Portsmouth block mill, some of them still in use to this day. Because they are wood-working machines, to describe them in detail here would be out of place; their significance in this context is that they were the product of Maudslay's workshop. Without the improved tools with which he had equipped that workshop their construction would have been impossible. Brunel had been well advised; at that date no other man in the world could have fashioned a series of machines so intricate, so precise and so beautifully finished.

Construction of the block machinery had not proceeded far before Maudslay moved to larger premises in Margaret Street, Cavendish Square, and in 1810 he moved again into a disused riding school in Westminster Road, Lambeth. There he founded the engineering works which, under the name of Maudslay, Sons & Field, speedily achieved a celebrity eclipsing that of Soho and Murray's Round Foundry. For many years the name of Maudslay signified the highest standard of craftsmanship in mechanical engineering.

Maudslay's story has one puzzling feature. The superiority of his machine tools was so great that we should expect to find him manufacturing them for others as Matthew Murray had done once he had equipped his own shops. For some reason this does not appear to have been the case. A small treadle-operated lathe selling at £200 was produced, but of the manufacture for sale of heavy industrial machine tools by the famous firm there is no record although it was a very versatile general engineering shop most celebrated for its marine steam engines. It was therefore left to Maudslay's contemporaries and immediate successors to equip the machine shops of a new industrialised Britain. With the exception of James Fox of Derby, the most celebrated of these great engineers and tool-makers, Nasmyth, Roberts, Clement and Whitworth, all worked for a time with Maudslay before going out into the world to found businesses of their own. The influence of Maudslay was therefore immense; indeed, among the hundreds of engineers who have played their parts in the story of machine-tool development he stands supreme. In the space of one lifetime mechanical engineering technique was completely revolutionised by his example. It was no coincidence that the same period saw the spectacular conquests of steam power on rails and on the sea and the complete transformation of many industries by the substitution of ingenious machines for hand methods. Such dramatic developments could never have come about had it not been for the 'behind-the-scenes' revolution in the engineer's workshop that was wrought by Henry Maudslay and his school.

In his Presidential address to the British Association at Manchester in 1861, William Fairbairn summed up this machine-tool revolution which he had himself witnessed in these words:

> When I first entered this city the whole of the machinery was executed by hand. There were neither planing, slotting nor shaping machines; and, with the exception of very imperfect lathes and a few drills, the preparatory operations of construction were effected entirely by the hands of the workmen. Now, everything is done by machine tools with a degree of accuracy which the unaided hand could never accomplish. The automaton or self-acting machine tool has within itself an almost creative power; in fact, so great are its powers of adaptation that there is no operation of the human hand that it does not imitate.

Such was the transformation that Maudslay began and which was carried to fruition by his near contemporaries and successors.

CHAPTER 5

Clement, Fox, Roberts, Nasmyth and Whitworth

THE SENIOR REPRESENTATIVE of the Maudslay school was Joseph Clement (1779–1844). The son of a Westmorland hand-loom weaver, he was but eight years younger than Maudslay and his career followed a somewhat similar pattern. Clement acquired little formal education, but a natural aptitude made him not only an expert practical mechanic, but also a fine engineering draughtsman. After spells of employment in several small workshops in Scotland, he saved enough money to come to London in 1813 and in 1814 he signed an agreement with Joseph Bramah to work for him as workshop superintendent and chief draughtsman for a term of five years. Before twelve months were out, however, Bramah died and as a result of a disagreement with the latter's sons, who then took charge of the business, Clement left and promptly joined Maudslay at Lambeth, where he became chief draughtsman, being responsible for the designs of some of the firm's first marine steam engines. By 1817 he had saved enough money to start a small workshop of his own in Prospect Place, Newington Butts, where he remained for the rest of his life. Whereas the engineers who will be mentioned later, founded large engineering concerns which made their names famous, Clement's business remained small. It was the equivalent of what we might now call a jobbing tool room. Precision hand-tools, improved instruments for draughtsmen of Clements' own design and 'one off' jobs calling for very accurate workmanship were the specialities of the Newington workshop. The construction of Babbage's intricate calculating machine was his most celebrated work. Nevertheless, Clement's skill and ingenuity has left an enduring mark on engineering practice.

Henry Maudslay standardised the screw threads used in his Lambeth works and to this end he produced standard sets of taps and dies for use there. This was a great advance because hitherto, when any piece of machinery was dismantled for repair, it had been essential to mark each nut and bolt individually for reassembly. At his Newington shop, Clement perpetuated this practice of his master's and at the same time improved the design of taps and dies. He designed a rotary cutter with a fixture adaptable to his lathe and this enabled him to produce fluted taps of the type with which we are familiar. Hitherto, the threads of taps had merely been notched or grooved by hand. Clement was also responsible for reducing the diameter of the shank of the tap and the size of its squared end so that it could fall through the hole it had tapped, thus saving the time previously spent in running the tap back and, particularly in the case of small taps, reducing the risk of breakage. Today we take such small but vital details of tool design for granted and never pause to wonder who first conceived them.

In 1827 Clement designed and constructed a facing lathe which, in its complexity, ingenuity and excellence of design and workmanship far surpassed any machine tool so far built. It won him a gold medal from the Society of Arts and is fully illustrated and described in the Society's proceedings. To enable workpieces of large diameter to be swung, the machine has virtually two beds, the headstock being mounted on one and the carriage and tailstock on the other.[1] The supporting columns are, however, braced together at a low level to ensure true alignment. The large faceplate has four jaws individually adjustable by radial screws. The belt pulley drive can either be taken directly to the lathe spindle, or to a layshaft carrying a pinion which engages a large gearwheel behind the faceplate. Clement paid particular attention to the spindle bearings which are tapered shells of hardened steel, the rear bearing embodying also a hardened-steel thrust plate with screw adjustment. The thrust plate is totally enclosed in an oil bath, the spindle being fitted with leather oil seal. Such a provision for adequate lubrication at this date is quite remarkable.

On the lathe spindle between the headstock bearings is a worm which engages a feed drive shaft passing beneath the spindle and at right angles to it. This in turn drives a longitudinal shaft through bevel gears and it can pivot about the axis of these gears through the limited range permitted by a quadrant mounted on the headstock. This is to allow the feed drive

[1] The machine could be used as a centre lathe though for this purpose its adaptability was limited and it had no automatic longitudinal feed to the carriage.

40 *Clement's constant-speed facing lathe, 1827 (based*

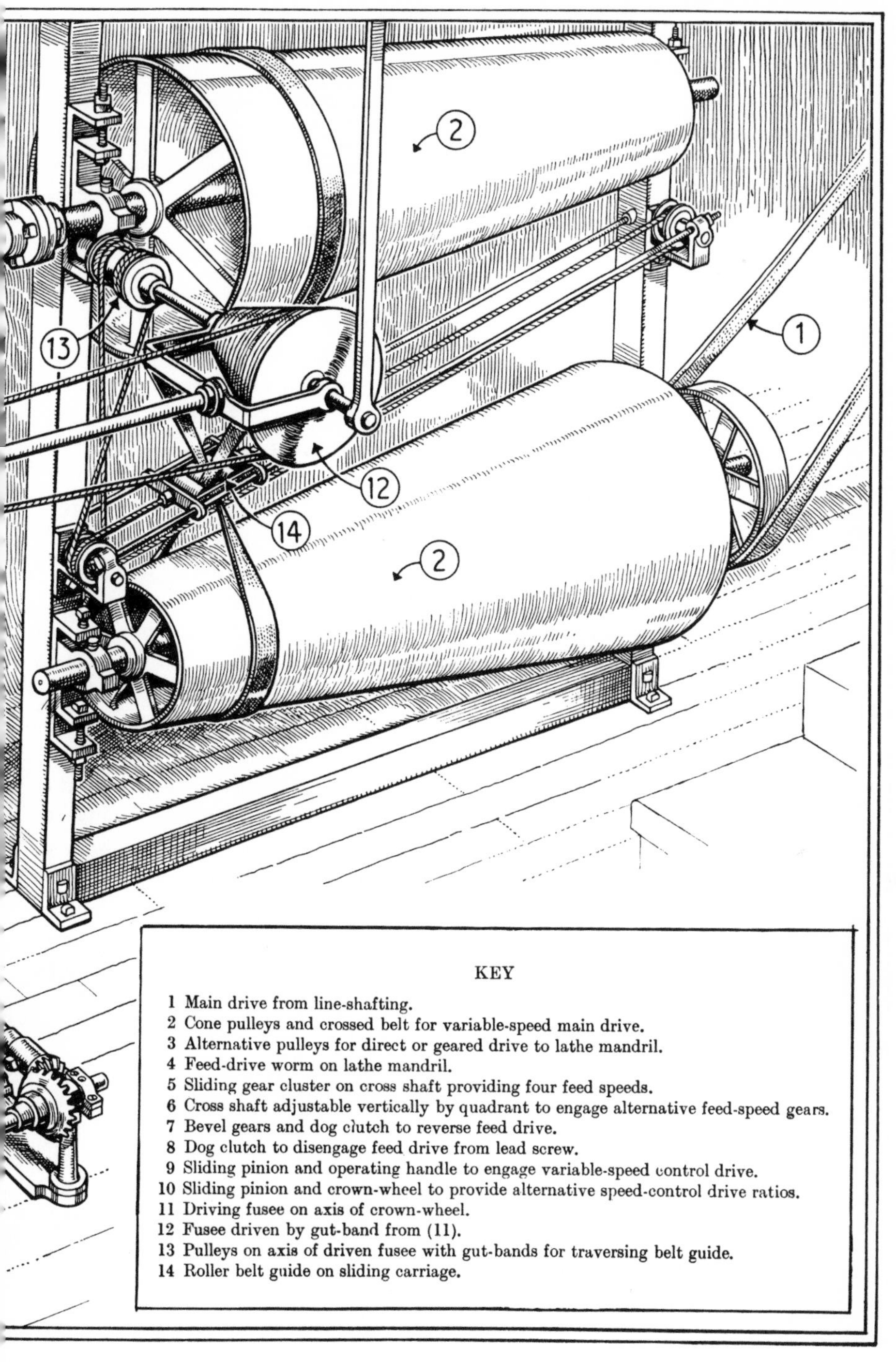

al drawings in the Journal of the Royal Society of Arts)

speed to be changed by engaging with the worm any one of the four alternative gears on the cross shaft. By means of a further set of bevel gears, the longitudinal shaft drives a third shaft which is on the same axis as the cross-slide lead screw and forms an extension to it. There are two free bevel wheels on this third shaft with a dog clutch sliding on a key between them so that the operator can reverse the feed. There is also a second clutch between the shaft and the end of the lead screw itself to disconnect the automatic feed.

The carriage with its gibbed slides is extremely well designed to provide maximum rigidity and good support for the tool even when the tool-holder slide is in the position of maximum advance. Above all, Clement was most concerned by the fact that in face-turning a workpiece of large diameter on a simple lathe, the cutting speed changes as the tool moves from the periphery to the centre or vice versa. If the speed is correct for the centre it will be much too fast at the periphery and blunt the tool. Alternatively, if the peripheral speed is determined correctly, tool speed will be much too low over the smaller diameters. Clement therefore set himself to devise a mechanism which would maintain a constant cutting speed by making the position of the tool in cross feed govern the speed of the lathe spindle proportionally. This was no easy problem and in his solution Clement adopted and applied the principle of the fusee which had long been used by the clock-makers.

By means of another bevel gear on the lead-screw extension shaft its motion is communicated to a vertical shaft and thence to a fusee mounted on a horizontal axis overhead. A change-speed adjustment is provided here, the gearwheel on the fusee axis having alternative rings of teeth and the small pinion on the top of the vertical shaft being made to slide so as to engage one or other of these ring gears. The fusee drives by gut band a second fusee, the largest diameter of one being opposite the smallest diameter of the other, so that the effect of the drive is to produce a progressive change of speed as the gut band follows the worm paths of the fusees from one end to the other of their tapering barrels. The two fusees are mounted in a swinging frame to maintain alignment and band tension.

The necessary change of speed to the lathe spindle is derived from two tapering conical drums mounted near the lathe on horizontal axes and opposed to each other in the same formation as the two fusees. One takes the drive from the line shafting and the other transmits it to the lathe spindle by means of normal flat belt pulleys on their respective axes. The two cone pulleys are linked by a short crossed belt passing through a roller guide at the crossing point. This guide is mounted on a sliding carriage having a travel equal to the length of the cone pulleys. A pulley on the

41 *Henry Maudslay*

42 *Richard Roberts (Photo. Science Museum, London)*

43 *Sir Joseph Whitworth (Crown Copyright. Science Museum, London)*

44 *James Nasmyth*

45 *Lathe by James Fox of Derby,* c. *1820, now in the Birmingham Museum of Science and Industry*

46 *Planing machine by Fox,* c. *1820, now in the Birmingham Museum*

axis of the driven fusee carries a gut band which, via suitable guide pulleys traverses the belt guide carriage with the effect that the cross belt is moved from one end to the other of the cone pulleys. The rate of this belt traverse is thus determined by the fusee motion and this in turn is derived from that of the cross-slide lead screw. In this way Clement achieved his difficult objective.

Samuel Smiles in his *Industrial Biography* briefly refers to this machine, but for some unaccountable reason it has been completely ignored by subsequent writers notwithstanding the existence of a full contemporary description and drawings. Whitworth is commonly credited with the first attempt to achieve a constant cutting speed in face turning, although his friction roller device did not appear until 1837—ten years after Clement. As late as 1893 the American, J. W. Boynton, patented a constant cutting speed device for facing lathes which was almost exactly the same as Clement's except that Boynton used a helical cam instead of the fusee motion to shift the belt along the cone pulleys. There was really no advance on Clement in this particular field until 1897, when E. Smith of America patented the first method of electrical speed regulation. No apology should therefore be necessary for a somewhat lengthy description of Clement's complex and beautiful lathe. Quite apart from its ingenious speed-control mechanism it represents an outstanding advance in machine-tool design and places Clement securely among the greatest of the early tool makers.

In 1828 Clement won a second award from the Society of Arts for what he called his 'two armed self-adjusting driver'. On the centre lathe at this time the practice of turning between two centres was practically universal, the alternative being a primitive form of chuck which was simply a socket with a clamping set-screw used for turning a standardised component from bar. For turning between centres a miniature faceplate called a driver was fitted on the end of the lathe spindle. This was simply a disc having a single projecting pin, which connected with the arm of a clamp or 'carrier' secured to the driven end of the workpiece by a set-screw. Of the defects of this primitive arrangement and of the unequal stresses it imposed on the lathe spindle and the live centre Clement was well aware. He therefore introduced a carrier having two arms and a two-armed driver. The two arms or pins of the driver were not secured to the faceplate itself but to a second plate superimposed upon it, the two plates being connected by countersunk pins working in concentric slotted holes. The relative movement permitted by these slots enabled the driver to adjust itself so that the power transmitted to the workpiece through the two arms was equalised.

In view of the ingenuity displayed by Clement and his contemporaries the reader may wonder why the self-centring chuck did not make its appearance at this time, especially when we remember that Leonardo da Vinci demonstrated the principle in his design for a pipe-boring machine in the sixteenth century. Holtzapffel and Deyerlein designed such a chuck in 1811, while L. E. Bergeron, in the 1816 edition of his *Manuel du tourneur*, illustrated a chuck in which three self-centring jaws were controlled by pivotting arms and spiral slots in the backplate. Henry Maudslay is credited with a chuck having two jaws controlled by a single screw with left- and right-hand threads, but according to Holtzapffel the orthodox design in which three jaws are controlled by a scroll on the backplate was first introduced in England by James Dundas in 1842. It was later widely exploited in America where Cushman in 1871 produced what is probably the best-known type. It is an essential requirement of the self-centring chuck that the cross section of the workpiece to be fixed in it shall be reasonably regular and dimensionally accurate. In the early nineteenth century this condition could rarely be met *before* the material had been machined, so that the use of the chuck could not obviate the time and labour which had to be spent in centring the workpiece accurately. Consequently, although they were no doubt familiar with its principle, the use of the self-centring chuck did not find favour with Clement and the other great tool-makers of his generation.

By 1820 Clement had in operation a planing machine, in which the workpiece was fixed upon a reciprocating table passing beneath a cutting tool clamped in a holder having vertical and horizontal feed motions. We do not know whether this first machine of Clement's was self-feeding. Credit for the introduction of the planing machine cannot be justly awarded to any one engineer. The machine made by Matthew Murray for machining his D slide valves (*c.* 1814) was mentioned in the last chapter and within the space of a few years several engineers, working quite independently, built planing machines differing only in size and detail. Such parallelism in invention is understandable because the planer employed the lathe principle in a different way and was an obvious answer to the pressing need for a mechanical means of producing large plane surfaces. To produce such surfaces by hand was infinitely laborious.

The self-propagating aspect of the planing machine was particularly important because every type of machine tool depends for its precision upon true plane surfaces. The first planers immediately made possible the construction of improved machines of like kind, while the ease with which the planer could machine lathe guideways greatly facilitated the production of large lathes of improved design and greater precision. Clement built his first planer for the specific purpose of machining lathe guideways.

Outside this closed circle of the machine-tool builders the effect of the introduction of the planing machine on mechanical engineering progress generally was immense, ranking only second to that of the lathe. It made possible the production of innumerable special-purpose machines, particularly in the textile trade—components for automatic looms soon became another job for Clement's planer—and it influenced the design of the steam engine profoundly. One reason why Watt had designed his beautiful parallel motion to link piston rod with beam was that a cross-head working between long guide bars, which seems to us so much the simpler solution, presented an insuperable production problem. With the introduction of the planer the problem of the long guide bar ceased to exist and the steam engine soon featured that classic, compact combination of guided cross-head, connecting rod and crank, which could be so readily adapted to locomotive and marine propulsion.

The success of Clement's first planer encouraged him to construct a second machine of very large size in 1825. The table moved over rollers mounted on a massive masonry foundation and these were bedded with such precision that Clement used to boast that a sheet of paper placed on one roller would be sufficient to take the weight off the next. On this machine Clement could plane a workpiece six feet square. For ten years thereafter no other machine of comparable size existed in England, or anywhere else in the world. A comfortable monopoly was thus the reward of Clement's ingenuity and although he charged his customers at the high rate of 18 shillings per square foot of machined surface, demand was such that the big machine frequently had to be kept running night and day. It is said to have supplied Clement with the major part of his income for the rest of his life.

Whereas other designers of planing machines in Clement's day and since favoured a single tool cutting in one direction and contented themselves with speeding up the carriage on its idle journey, Clement used two cutting tools mounted in a rocking tool-holder so that the machine cut when the carriage was travelling in either direction. He also adapted his machine to do the work of a heavy lathe, fitting head and tailstock units to the bed of the carriage for this purpose. He then mounted cylindrical workpieces between the centres and machined them longitudinally, the method of feed then being to rotate the workpiece against the cutting face of the planing tool. He also carried out orthodox turning on the same machine by applying power drive to the headstock, a slow feed to the planer carriage and adapting the cutter head as a fixed tool-holder.

The secret of Clement's success with this machine was the way he succeeded in making a travelling carriage capable of sustaining without

47 *Vertical planing machine, Soho Foundry* (The Engineer)

deflection extremely heavy weights. When designing planers of comparable capacity, Clement's immediate successors preferred to sidestep this problem by using a stationary work-table and a travelling tool carriage. A machine of this type may be seen today in the Birmingham Industrial Museum, being one of the two similar vertical planing machines originally installed at the Soho Foundry. Here the tool carriage runs on guideways designed to be securely braced to the wall of the building and is propelled by a long lead screw driven by belt from the line shafting. Before the introduction of high-pressure steam, larger cylinders were the engine builders' only answer to demands for greater power and such massive castings could only be handled effectively by machines such as this. A pair of oscillating cylinders for a channel packet steamer weighing 25 tons would have defeated even Clement's machine, but their port faces were successfully machined on this Soho planer.

A country parson's butler seems a highly unlikely character to feature in these pages, yet such was the calling of James Fox (1789–1859) before he turned engineer. Like Clement he obviously possessed a mechanical bent that was not to be denied and his spare time activities so impressed his master, the Reverend Thomas Gisborne of Foxhall Lodge, Staffordshire, that he not only gave Fox his blessing, but supplied the capital to enable him to found a business in Derby for the manufacture of improved textile machinery of his own designs. With the famous textile mills of Arkwright and Strutt on his doorstep and the Nottingham lace manufacturers not far away, Fox's business was well sited and it never looked back.

In those days when the manufacture of engineering machine tools for sale had scarcely begun, Fox, like many another pioneer engineer, had first to design and construct the machines to make his textile machines. Although he was never directly associated with Henry Maudslay, in the design of his lathes Fox undoubtedly followed where that master had led, but introduced significant improvements of his own. The most important of these was his use of both rack and lead-screw traverses for the slide rest, his object being to use the rack feed for plain turning and so preserve the precision of the lead screw for screw cutting. A worm on the carriage was connected by straight gearing to the rack teeth beside the guideways and was driven by a squared or keyed drive shaft extending the length of the bed. The worm was free to slide along this shaft. The operator could readily engage or disengage either form of feed and with only minor variations of detail this arrangement of Fox's eventually became standard practice on the British general-purpose lathe. Fox's spindle bearings, carriage tailstock and his design of guideways, which combined inverted vees and flatways, all reveal how clearly he appreciated the tool-maker's cardinal maxim that precision of the work can only be achieved by building still greater precision into the tool.

Fox is said to have built his first planing machine in 1814 and if this was so he was almost, if not quite, as early in his invention as Matthew Murray. No illustration of this machine has survived, but Samuel Hall, an old employee of Fox, gave Samuel Smiles a description of it. According to Hall the tool-holder was mounted on a compound slide rest having automatic feed by pawl and ratchet drive to both the vertical and the horizontal traverses. The table was power-driven, the motion of the table being automatically reversed by a combination of three bevel gears and a double-faced dog clutch sliding on a keyway between the two alternative driving gears. Adjustable strikers on the table tripped a weighted lever or 'tumbling bob' to actuate this clutch. If these features really were present in this machine of 1814, then Fox was undoubtedly the pioneer of the planing machine as we know it. The memories of old employees are fallible and in describing early machines they are apt to include features which were, in fact, modifications made subsequently. Yet there are good grounds for the belief that Fox built a planing machine having all these advanced features in 1817.

In the Birmingham Science Museum may be seen a remarkable planing machine and a lathe[1] from Milford Mill, Derbyshire, where they were used for the construction and maintenance of textile machinery. They were driven by waterwheel and as the date 1817 appears on the cast-iron beams and line-shafting brackets of the building that was evidently built to house them, it is reasonable to ascribe them to this year. The machines have been attributed to William Strutt, but while Strutt was a most ingenious engineer and was undoubtedly responsible for the Milford building, the advanced and masterly design of the tools clearly reveals the hand of Fox.

Both machines exhibit the combination of inverted vee and flat guideways pioneered by Fox, while the design of the planer agrees with the description given by Samuel Hall to Smiles so long ago except that open and crossed belts are used for the table motion. An additional feature of this machine worthy of remark is the ingenious way the weight of the main table has been reduced by the use of four sub-tables. These could be positioned as required when lengthy loom sections had to be machined.

The lathe is not equipped for screw cutting as were Fox's later machines,

[1] A small slotting machine from the same source is now in the Science Museum in London.

but it has the characteristic Fox arrangement of rack feed derived from a worm sliding on a square drive shaft. Stepped pulleys on a countershaft drive the lathe spindle through two alternative gear ratios, while a third gear-driven shaft on the headstock provides feed drive through stepped pulleys and a gut band. The tailstock is also characteristic of Fox and can be traversed manually by a cross-shaft and pinion engaging the rack. The saddle carrying the compound slide rest is extremely well designed, with wings carried well forward to provide extra stability under heaving boring cuts, and in this respect the machine is far superior to many lathes of much later date. Both machines bear eloquent testimony to the genius of James Fox.

Although Fox originally designed and built his machine tools solely as a means to a different end—the improvement of textile machinery—their success was such that he began to manufacture them for sale both at home and abroad. He exported his machine tools to France, Germany, Poland, Russia and Mauritius. One Fox lathe is now preserved in the Sielpia Wielka Museum in Poland and another, in reduced model form, is in the Conservatoire des Arts et Métiers in Paris. The latter, built in 1830, is clearly a developed version of the Milford lathe. The original was a large machine with a bed 22 feet long and a swing of 27 inches.

Another pioneer of the planing machine was Richard Roberts (1789–1864) whose planer of 1817 is now in the Science Museum in London. This is a very crude tool compared with the Fox machine of the same date. Its most significant feature is the evidence of chisel and file marks on the flat guideways to prove that they were not themselves planed. It is evident, therefore, that this is the first planer to be built by Roberts, even though similar machines may have existed earlier in the workshops of Murray and Fox.

The slide rest has manual vertical and horizontal feeds, angular adjustment and a separate feed for the head which has a hinged clamp to permit the tool to lift on the return of the table. The latter is 52 inches long by 11 inches wide and is designed to be worked to and fro manually by means of a hand-capstan and chains.

Richard Roberts' birthplace was a toll house at Carreghofa, near Llanymynech, on the borders of Shropshire and Montgomeryshire. It is strange that so many of the leaders of Britain's industrial revolution were drawn to the new workshops from remote rural areas, not by the pressure of necessity or by the influence of their surroundings or parental example, but by a mysterious aptitude for and love of mechanics. But is this, after all, any stranger than the inexplicable flowering of poetic or artistic genius? For the truth is, surely, that these pioneer engineers were the artists of their profession whose careers were determined by the artist's compulsive need to fulfil his creative endowment. Roberts was no exception. His father was a shoemaker and until he was 20 he worked as a quarryman, but his bent for mechanics would not be denied. It drove him from the Welsh border to the Black Country, where he was employed for a time at the Bradley and Horseley Ironworks, and finally, on foot, to London where he was engaged by Henry Maudslay as a turner and fitter in 1814.

The artistry of that great mechanic had a profound influence upon all who became associated with him and it inspired Roberts to set up in business on his own account in Deansgate, Manchester, in 1816. He began with a single lathe and drilling machine and, according to legend, his wife used to turn a crank and flywheel in the basement which drove the lathe by a belt carried up through the floor of the little workshop above. By 1821 he had equipped a larger workshop with machine tools of his own design and construction and was employing from 12 to 14 mechanics. But his machines were still hand-driven and he employed three men at the rate of 11 shillings per week for this monotonous labour.

In addition to the planing machine already mentioned, Roberts also built improved lathes, a gear-cutting machine, which will be mentioned in the next chapter, a special screw-cutting machine and a slotting machine. According to James Nasmyth this last was developed from the mortising machine in the series of block-making machines designed by Marc Brunel. Against this it has been argued that Roberts could not have seen or worked upon this machine because the Portsmouth Dock contract had been completed long before he went to work for Maudslay. This objection, however, overlooks the fact that similar sets of block-making machinery were subsequently built at Lambeth for Chatham and for export to Spain. It seems likely, too, that Roberts was the originator of the radial drilling machine in the industrial workshop. Hitherto drilling machines were of the fixed head type described in the last chapter, but Holtzapffel wrote: 'Probably no individual has originated so many useful varieties of drilling machines as Mr. Richard Roberts.'

Preserved with his planer in the Science Museum in London, is Roberts' industrial lathe of the same date. Surprisingly modern in appearance and of substantial size, six feet long and with a swing of 19 inches, it illustrates the improvements in lathe design for which he was responsible. It has the form of back gearing which was to become orthodox on the industrial lathe. The stepped drive pulley and the small pinion driving the layshaft float upon the lathe spindle, while the large gearwheel immediately behind the headstock is fixed. A double reduction gear is thus provided for heavy turning. For lighter work the layshaft can be moved out of engagement and the pulley locked to the large gear to provide direct drive. Roberts introduced a similar form of back gearing on his heavy drilling machines.

The carriage is propelled by a lead screw carried outside the bed of the lathe and the method of driving this screw is unique. Instead of the orthodox change gears, Roberts has used a crown wheel having six concentric sets of pin teeth arranged upon it. A small pinion on the tail of the lathe spindle can be slid to and fro to engage whichever ratio is desired. The drive from the crown wheel to the lead screw is the same as that used by Fox on his planing machine—three bevels and a double-faced dog clutch engaging one or other of the driven gears. In this case, the clutch lever linkage is connected to a convenient control rod passing along the bed of the lathe. The automatic feed can thus be easily started, stopped or reversed by the operator, or it can be stopped automatically by adjustable strikers on the carriage. Although this particular lathe remained in constant use until 1909, the crown wheel drive to the lead screw was not perpetuated. The principle of disengaging the feed automatically at the end of the cut was, however, a significant development.

Roberts is also said to have been the first man to introduce plug and collar gauges in the industrial workshop and he also made extensive use of templets to ensure uniformity of parts. As in the case of Fox, Roberts' machine tools and workshop methods were evolved in the first place to enable him to build improved machines for the textile trade. The Manchester cotton mill owners were his first customers and he became celebrated for his invention of the automatic spinning mule. Later, when he became associated with the brothers Sharp in the famous firm of Sharp, Roberts & Co., he applied the same workshop methods to the manufacture of steam locomotives with the effect that, to a limited extent, standardisation of component parts was achieved for the first time in the history of locomotive building. At the same period Roberts designed a steam road carriage with differential drive to the wheels. Although the principle of the differential gear had already been applied in textile machinery, this is believed to have been its first appearance in a road vehicle.

In 1847 Roberts patented his 'jacquard' multiple punching machine, so called because the method of actuating the punches by means of a revolving prism was derived from the working principle of the jacquard loom. Earlier machines could only punch a single hole at a time and Roberts' machine was designed to meet the need of the contractor responsible for building Robert Stephenson's great tubular iron bridges at Conway and over the Menai Straits. By its aid the rivet holes of the thousands of wrought-iron plates used in the bridges were punched much more expeditiously and at precisely equal spacing.

Roberts has been called the greatest mechanical inventor of the nineteenth century and there is no doubt that his engineering machine tools acted as a potent inventive stimulus to him by making practicable ideas which would have appeared fanciful a generation earlier. Nevertheless, like many another mechanical genius, invention eventually became almost an obsession with Roberts greatly to the detriment of his business affairs. Many of his ideas were never followed through to practical success and as a result of his lack of commercial acumen he died in poverty.

The youngest of Henry Maudslay's disciples was James Nasmyth (1808–1890), famous as the inventor of the steam hammer which revolutionised the production of heavy forgings. He was the son of Alexander Nasmyth of Edinburgh, the celebrated Scottish portrait painter who was also a gifted amateur engineer. James Nasmyth was endowed with both his father's gifts but made engineering his profession. Maudslay's fame as a mechanical engineer was such that it spread to Scotland and inspired in young Nasmyth a consuming ambition to work for this master mechanic. In 1829, accompanied by his father, he set sail from Leith to London, taking with him a model steam engine he had constructed as evidence of his ability. Maudslay was suitably impressed and to Nasmyth's great joy he was appointed personal assistant in the master's private workshop. Thanks to this intimate association, Nasmyth was later able to write a delightful account of Maudslay, his workshop and his methods, in his autobiography.

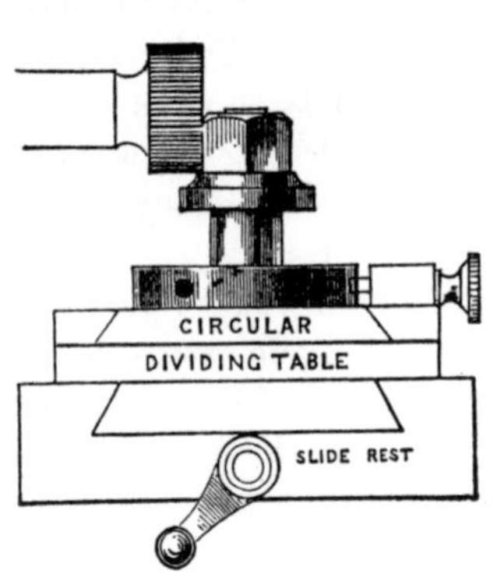

48 *James Nasmyth's nut-milling fixture, 1830 (Nasmyth)*

At this time the Lambeth firm were building a very large marine engine for H.M.S. *Dee* and Nasmyth helped his master to make the magnificent model of this engine which is now in the Science Museum in London. A great number of small hexagon nuts were required for this, many of them with circular collars below the hexagon, and Nasmyth devised a method of producing these with speed and precision on Maudslay's bench lathe. He made a small indexing plate for attachment to the slide rest and this had a vertical arbor to which the nut blank could be secured. A milling cutter, or 'circular file' as Nasmyth called it, was then mounted in the lathe chuck for the purpose of machining the six flats. A spring-loaded plunger accurately located the index plate in each of the required positions and so ensured that the flats were perfectly true.

Another device of Nasmyth's that arose out of these model-making activities was a flexible shaft of coiled spring steel designed for drilling holes in inaccessible places. The flexible drive shaft has since become commonplace, not only in the engineer's workshop but in countless other applications, but Nasmyth did not patent his idea and its origin was forgotten within his own lifetime. He tells in his autobiography how, on going to have a tooth filled, the dentist proudly showed him his new flexible shaft drill as the very latest American invention.

For a short while after Maudslay's death in 1831, Nasmyth remained at the Lambeth works but at the end of August in that year he decided to return to Edinburgh and set up business on his own account. With the blessing of Maudslay's partner, Joshua Field, he was allowed to take with him by sea to Leith a set of castings for a replica of the best large lathe then at Lambeth. He acquired a temporary workshop close to his old home in Edinburgh and here he installed an old treadle lathe of his father's which he modified with slide rest and 'slow motion', as he called it, so that he could use it to machine parts for his great 'Maudslay lathe'. When completed, the latter in turn was the progenitor of a small planing machine and of drilling and boring machines. This is an excellent example of the way a mechanical engineer equipped himself in those days, using one machine tool to beget others. As Nasmyth himself put it: 'I soon had a progeny of legitimate descendants crowded about my little workshop, so that I often did not know which way to turn.'

Having thus equipped himself, Nasmyth, like Roberts before him, decided that Manchester offered the best prospects and he installed himself and his machine tools in part of an old mill building in Dale Street where power was available. Here he prospered until the success of the Liverpool & Manchester Railway brought about so great a demand for machine tools and their products that the Dale Street premises became no longer adequate. With admirable foresight Nasmyth bought land at Patricroft, between Manchester and Liverpool. At this point the new railway crossed the Bridgewater Canal so that the site was served by both forms of transport. Here was built the celebrated Bridgewater Foundry which started production in 1836. The firm of Nasmyth & Gaskell, later Nasmyth, Wilson & Co., became noted as general engineers and locomotive builders, but the manufacture of machine tools both for home and export formed a substantial part of their business. Many of these tools went to St. Petersburg where Czar Nicholas had decided to equip a locomotive works rather than import engines from England for the new Russian railways. A model of a Nasmyth vertical cylinder-boring machine, the original of which was erected at Woolwich Dockyard in 1838, is to be seen in the Science Museum in London.

The fame of Nasmyth's steam hammer and the fact that he did not patent his inventions has tended to overshadow his contribution to the history of metal-cutting tools. He introduced a novel type of slotting machine for cutting the internal keyways in the hubs of wheels. The diameter of wheel which could be so machined on Clement's keyway slotting machine was limited by the gap or jaw of the machine because the reciprocating cutter operated above the worktable. Nasmyth arranged the cutter and its mechanism below the worktable so that wheels of any diameter could be accommodated. Nasmyth also produced a slot-drilling machine on a different principle using a rotary tool. The spur to this invention was the labour involved in cutting the slot for the cross-head cotter in locomotive piston rods. No type of reciprocating slotting machine could be used effectively for such a purpose and the method used was to drill the rod and then produce the slot from the drill holes by hand with chisel and file. Nasmyth's solution to this production problem was to take one of the spear-point drills then universally used (the twist drill was many years away) and, by removing its centre point, to convert it into a crude form of two-bladed end-milling cutter. The machine in which this cutter was used had a vertical spindle for the tool and a worktable with automatic reversible traverse to move the workpiece to and fro under the cutter as it formed the slot. The worktable was also moveable vertically in order to feed the tool and this feed was applied automatically to a vertical lead screw by means of strikers actuating a ratchet and pawl each time the table reached the end of its horizontal traverse in either direction. In addition to the purpose for which it was designed, the machine could be used for forming feather keyways in shafts, another job unsuited to any reciprocating type of slotting machine.

In the similar slot-drilling machines subsequently produced by Whitworth and other makers, the automatic horizontal and vertical motions were transferred from the worktable to the tool carriage. This was an obvious improvement because such a machine might be required to carry out a comparatively small operation on a heavy or unwieldy workpiece.

From a commercial point of view, Nasmyth's small shaping machine was probably his best seller. Finding that the planing machine with its reciprocating table was needlessly slow and cumbersome in action when used for machining plane surfaces on small components, Nasmyth decided to transfer the motion from the table to the tool and designed a simple machine which, with its crankshaft and flywheel, connecting rod, cross-head and slide-bars, closely resembled a small horizontal steam engine with a tool-holder fitted in place of piston and cylinder. It was by virtue of this resemblance that mechanics of the day nicknamed the machine 'Nasmyth's Steam Arm'. The tool-holder was mounted in a vertical slide with manual adjustment, but ratchets and pawls provided either vertical

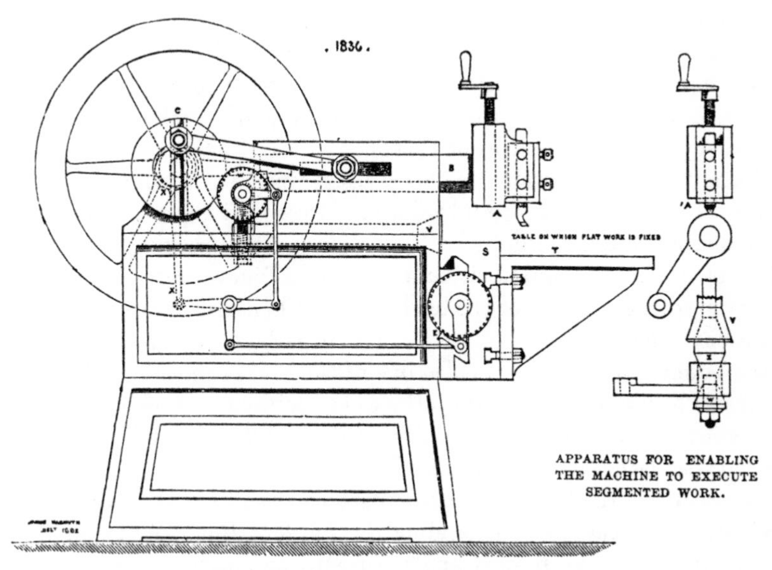

49 *James Nasmyth's 'Steam Arm' shaping machine, 1836 (Nasmyth)*

or horizontal automatic feeds to the worktable. By substituting a suitable fixture for the work table, the machine could be used for segmental work as well as for plane facing. This was a simple, unspecialised tool of the greatest value. Nasmyth constructed this original shaping machine in 1836 and from that day to this its descendants, unchanged in principle, have remained an essential item of equipment in the general engineer's workshop.

For his large planing machines Nasmyth used a rack motion to actuate the table, but the small Nasmyth planer in the Science Museum in London uses a different principle. Like the earlier Roberts machine, the table is worked to and fro by chains passing via pulleys to a chain wheel, but in this case, instead of manual operation, semi-rotary motion is imparted to the chain wheel by gearing. On the axis of the chain wheel is a large-diameter disc fitted with pin teeth on a segment of its circumference only.

The small driving pinion engaging these teeth is mounted on a shaft whose bearing housing at the pinion end is allowed a limited lateral movement in the frame. Consequently the pinion is able to gear alternately with the outside and the inside of the pin teeth, thus reversing the motion. The pin teeth are secured to the wheel by nuts so that the length of travel of the table can be varied by adding to or reducing their number. The cross feed of the tool box is actuated by ratchet and pawl, the latter receiving its motion from the lateral movement of the pinion shaft. Nasmyth also applied this 'mangle wheel gear', as he called it, to a lathe where it enabled him to machine the external periphery of locomotive eccentric straps or similar parts in which a circular or semi-circular form is interrupted by projecting flanges or bosses.

Nasmyth's contributions to lathe design included a simple reversible drive to the lead screw. He introduced between driving and driven gears two identical meshing idler wheels on a lever with a rocking pivot. Movement of the lever produced either a three- or a four-gear driving train and so reversed the rotation of the lead screw while it also provided a neutral position.[1] This arrangement, introduced in 1837, was widely adopted by lathe builders. Nasmyth was also one of the first engineers to attempt to increase the productivity of the lathe when required to machine a quantity of uniform components. He constructed what he called his 'double or ambidexter lathe' for this purpose. This had a siamese headstock mounted in the centre of the bed, tailstocks at each end and two carriages traversed by a common lead screw extending the full length of the machine. This screw was driven by ratchet and pawl with automatic control so that a single operator could plain-turn or screw-cut two identical workpieces simultaneously. Nasmyth used this machine chiefly to turn large bolts and he also designed a simple bench fixture consisting of vee blocks and an adjustable poppet head by means of which such components could be more speedily and accurately centred before turning.

Finally, a small but important contribution to workshop practice made by Nasmyth was his introduction of the principle of the guided tap. He lengthened the shanks of his taps and issued his fitters with right-angled jigs and bushes to ensure that holes would be tapped truly. From this simple innovation sprang all the elaborate jigs and fixtures which we use today to ensure accuracy and uniformity.

Above all, James Nasmyth was an eloquent and untiring publicist of the value and virtues of machine tools. Whatever may be said in their defence, workmen in the Manchester of his day were not distinguished

[1] Unaccountably, this device is wrongly described and illustrated in Nasmyth's *Autobiography* (p. 417).

for their sobriety and reliability and their shortcomings exasperated an engineer who had been trained in the perfectionist school of Maudslay. His ingenuity in workshop contrivance was his method of defence against the fallibility of his workmen and he would boast of his machine tools that they 'never got drunk; their hands never shook from excess; they were never absent from work; they did not strike for wages; they were unfailing in their accuracy and regularity. . .'.

Of all the engineers who were influenced directly or indirectly by the example of Henry Maudslay, Joseph Whitworth is the best-known. This is because he was responsible for determining the first standard range of screw threads, with the result that his name became part of the daily vocabulary of succeeding generations of engineers. In fact, Whitworth's fame rests on far more than this. Notwithstanding the inventive achievements of Clement, Fox, Roberts and Nasmyth, there can be no doubt that it was Whitworth who succeeded Maudslay as the dominant figure in the history of machine tools. Moreover, the firm which he founded became the most celebrated manufacturers of machine tools in the world.

Joseph Whitworth (1803–1887) was born in Stockport, the son of a minister and schoolmaster. His uncle owned a cotton-spinning mill in Derbyshire and thither he was sent at the age of 14 to learn the commercial side of the business. But, like the other characters in this chapter, Whitworth's mechanical bent proved irresistible. He could not tolerate the prospect of a monotonous white-collar job. Whenever he could escape from his clerk's desk he studied the mill machinery, and, having learnt all he could in this way, he ran away to Manchester where he worked as a mechanic. Eventually, however, the magic of the Maudslay name drew him to London and he obtained employment at the Lambeth works in 1825. He soon demonstrated an aptitude which must have delighted his master and according to some writers it was Whitworth and not Maudslay himself who first demonstrated the art of finishing a surface plate with a hand scraper.

Whitworth later left Maudslay and worked for a time under both Holtzapffel and Clement before he returned to Manchester in 1833 to start his own business. Like Nasmyth he rented a small part of a mill building where power was available and there he proudly displayed a sign which read: 'Joseph Whitworth, Tool Maker from London'. The wording of this sign is significant. It reveals that the reputation for superlative workmanship which the great London instrument-makers acquired in the eighteenth century had been extended to the engineering tool trade through the agency of Bramah, Maudslay and Clement. In the new standards of precision they set, these three men were undoubtedly influenced by the instrument-makers. But in this new field the London mystique did not endure, indeed it could not. Roberts, Nasmyth and Whitworth showed foresight when they migrated to Manchester. As a great centre of mechanical engineering, London could not hope to survive, being too far away from the new industrial concentrations based on coal and iron and textiles that were expanding so rapidly in the Midlands and the North. Only marine engineering survived stubbornly in London, thanks to the strength of the ship-building tradition of the Thames, but even this was eventually doomed when hulls of iron and steel replaced wood. For the general engineers and machine makers it was essential that they establish themselves nearer the sources of fuel and raw material and close to the mill owners who were, at the outset, their best customers. The man who proudly boasted of his London training when he first came to Manchester soon became the dominant figure in an industrial success story which, by 1850, had made that northern city the machine-tool-making centre of the world.

Whitworth was responsible for a number of detail improvements in machine tools. Where the lathe was concerned he was the first to drive both longitudinal and cross feeds automatically on one machine using a single lead screw. This design appeared in 1835. For the longitudinal

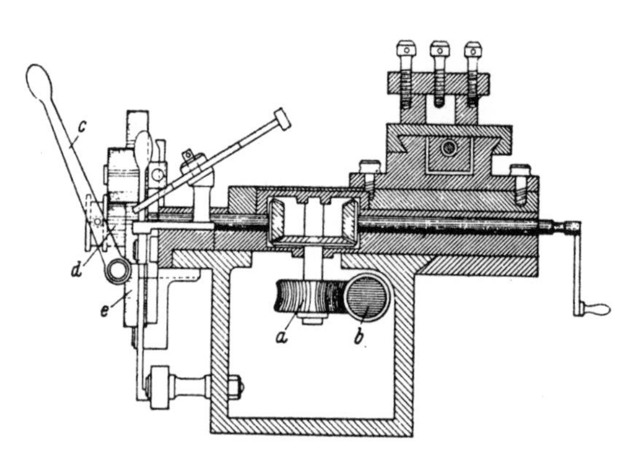

50 *Joseph Whitworth's automatic cross feed for lathes, 1835* (*Wittmann*)

traverse a half nut engages the lead screw. To operate the cross feed a worm gear on a short vertical shaft is in permanent engagement with the lead screw but turns only when the carriage is stationary. The drive is taken through bevel gears from the top of the vertical shaft to two half shafts lying parallel to the axis of the cross-feed lead screw in the carriage.

51 *Back-geared lathe by Richard Roberts,* c. *1817, showing the feed-drive change-speed gearing (Crown Copyright. Science Museum, London)*

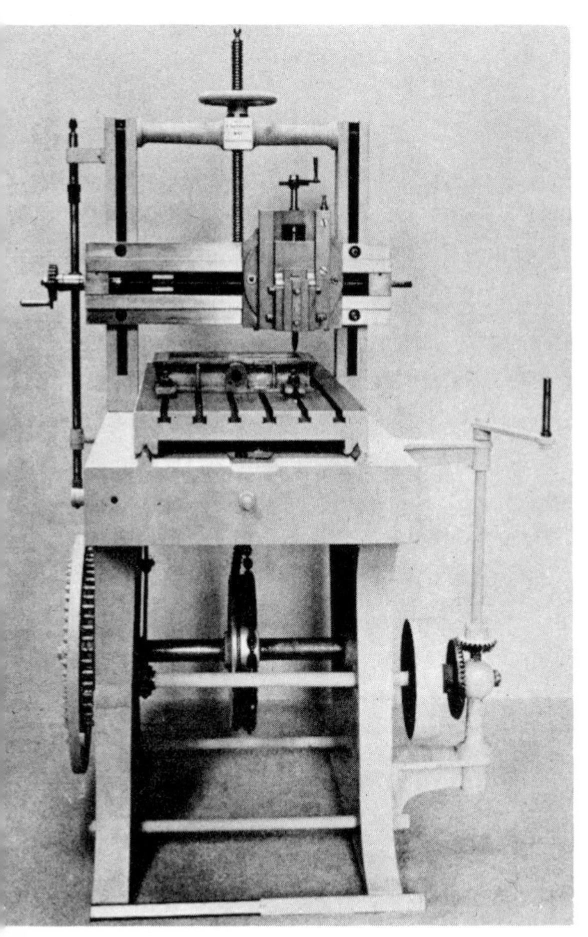

52 *Small planing machine by James Nasmyth, 1857 (Crown Copyright. Science Museum, London)*

53 *Lathe by Joseph Whitworth with automatic cross feed, 1843*
(Crown Copyright. Science Museum, London)

54 *J. G. Bodmer's worm gear cutters, 1839*
(Lent to Science Museum, London, by R. Bodmer, Esq.)

One of these half shafts terminates in a hand crank; the other drives the lead screw through a pair of straight gears, one of which can be drawn out of mesh by a lever to disconnect the feed. With the machine stopped and both feeds disengaged the operator can use the hand crank as a quick longitudinal traverse to bring the carriage up to the work, the main lead screw acting as a rack for this purpose.

Whitworth's first planing machines were designed to cut in both directions of the table, but instead of using a rocking tool-holder and two tools like Clement, he used a single tool in a holder nicknamed a 'Jim Crow' which was turned automatically through 180° at the end of each motion of the table. Later he reverted to the unidirectional cut combined with a quick return motion of the carriage. He also applied a quick return motion to the shaping machine. To reverse his planer carriage, Whitworth used the method of twin drive belts, one open and the other crossed, which would be widely used for many years. With this arrangement the carriage drive shaft of the machine carries two identical drive pulleys separated only by a loose pulley of the same diameter. A belt shifter actuated by the carriage moves the two belts to and fro so that when one belt is driving the other is on the loose pulley. The addition of a second loose pulley provided a neutral position. For such purposes this form of reversible drive proved more satisfactory and smoother in action than the bevel wheels and sliding dog clutch used by Fox and others.

It is not upon such innovations, however, that the fame of Joseph Whitworth chiefly rests. The general principles of the basic machine tools had been laid down by other engineers before he rose to fame. Instead, Whitworth's machine tools reflect that meticulous attention to every detail of design which was the secret of his success. In machine-tool history Whitworth occupies the same position as Henry Royce in the history of automobile engineering. Neither man was an inventive genius but both possessed standards so exacting that even the best was never good enough. With unerring judgement they sought out the best features of contemporary design, improved upon them and combined them in one masterly synthesis. This is a conscious and deliberate process not to be confused with the kind of unconscious synthesis Henry Maudslay achieved when he built his first screw-cutting lathe. Works of the latter kind require inventive genius because the fact that they are combinations of preconceived ideas only becomes evident to the historian. Yet the role of men like Royce and Whitworth is equally important in the history of technology. Royce's car made his name a synonym for excellence and for the same reasons the name of Whitworth on a machine tool guaranteed superlative workmanship and performance.

The lesson Whitworth had learnt from his master Maudslay with his 'Lord Chancellor' micrometer was that accurate end measurement was the bed-rock of workshop precision. He applied and extended this basic principle to such effect that in 1856 he exhibited a machine capable of detecting differences of one millionth part of an inch. Further than this it was impossible to go by direct mechanical means. 'We have', said Whitworth, 'in this mode of measurement all the accuracy we can desire; and we find in practice in the workshop that it is easier to work to the ten-thousandth of an inch from standards of end measurements, than to one-hundredth of an inch from lines on a two-foot rule. In all cases of fitting, end measure of length should be used, instead of lines.'

55 *Whitworth's millionth-measuring machine, 1856*

Although optical methods of measurement were subsequently developed in America (see Chapter 8), time has vindicated Whitworth's dictum. Forty years later the Swede, C. E. Johannson, developed and improved the end-measuring method so much that it remains the basic system of all workshop measurement.

In his work on screw threads, Whitworth was again following where Maudslay had led. The influence of the work of Maudslay and Clement was such that by 1840 all the larger engineering firms in Britain had adopted standardised ranges of screw threads, but these standards differed between firm and firm and Whitworth realised that the process had not yet been carried far enough. Nothing less than a national standard would do, a standard which would ensure that, size for size, threads would be identical, not only in pitch, but in depth and form also. He obtained and measured samples of screw threads from all the leading manufacturers, finding that the mean of the angles made by the two sides of these threads was 55°. He decided to standardise this angle irrespective of size, with the effect that a constant proportion between pitch and depth was established throughout his proposed range. He announced his findings and proposals to the Institution of Civil Engineers in 1841 and by 1860 the Whitworth thread had been generally adopted throughout Britain. Later, the age of steel would demand threads of finer pitch and for this reason it is sometimes thought that Whitworth lacked foresight. Such a criticism is unjust. No engineer can ignore the present in his concern for the future and in determining his standards Whitworth had to bear in mind the fact that a great deal of use was then made of cast-iron threaded components. A fine-pitched, shallow thread in so brittle a material was not practicable and would never have been accepted by industry. Whitworth himself made this quite clear when he announced his recommendations in 1841. He said: 'It will be remembered that the threads, of which the preceding table [i.e. his standards] shows the average, are used in cast iron as well as wrought; and this circumstance has had its effect in rendering them coarser than they would have been if restricted to wrought iron.'

The proportions of the modern machine tool, massive, austere, strictly functional, owe more to Joseph Whitworth than to any other man. The great London instrument-makers of the eighteenth century frequently endowed their products with a baroque or classical elegance unrelated to their function. The same could be said of those who made ornamental lathes for the amusement of wealthy amateurs. Most of these craftsmen were also clock-makers so it seemed natural to them and to their clients that other examples of precision mechanism should be graced, like the case of a clock, with ornamentation or classical proportions. Through the agency of Bramah, Maudslay, Clement and their London contemporaries this tradition passed into the mechanical engineer's workshop. Its influence is at once evident in the design of the framing of the Brunel/Maudslay block machinery. In forms becoming ever more debased and meaningless it lingered on into the present century; in the framing of some printing machinery, for example, or in the convoluted cast-iron supports of the domestic treadle sewing machine. Whitworth was responsible for sweeping away the last traces of this tradition from his machine-tool designs. He realised that conventions which might be harmless when applied to machines for wood-working, printing or sewing could not be tolerated in the design of heavily loaded metal-cutting tools whose precision depended upon their absolute rigidity.

Elegance is not necessarily the product of artistic convention. When applied to engineering such conventions generally appear false, whereas in this sphere a true elegance springs from the designer's concern to save weight and so to proportion each member precisely to fulfil its function. This functional elegance was likewise cast aside by Whitworth in his single-minded pursuit of precision. He appreciated that machine tool making was almost the only branch of engineering to which considerations of weight saving did not apply. The reverse was true. It was a case of the heavier the better and consequently Whitworth's machine tools, in sheer weight of metal, were far more massive for the work they had to perform than were those of his contemporaries. Not that Whitworth used metal needlessly. In the Conway and Menai tubular bridges the civil engineers of his day had demonstrated the strength of the box section and Whitworth adopted it extensively in his machine-tool designs, the effect being to exaggerate their uncompromising, rectilinear appearance. Box-section supports replaced the splayed, columnar or curved legs used by other makers. The typical Whitworth lathe also had a very deep bed of box section with a minimal opening between the guideways for the vertical shaft which took the drive for the automatic cross feed from the lead screw. The lead screw was positioned inside the bed beneath one of the guideways, for Whitworth always took care so to position the lead screws of his machines that they were protected from dirt and swarf.

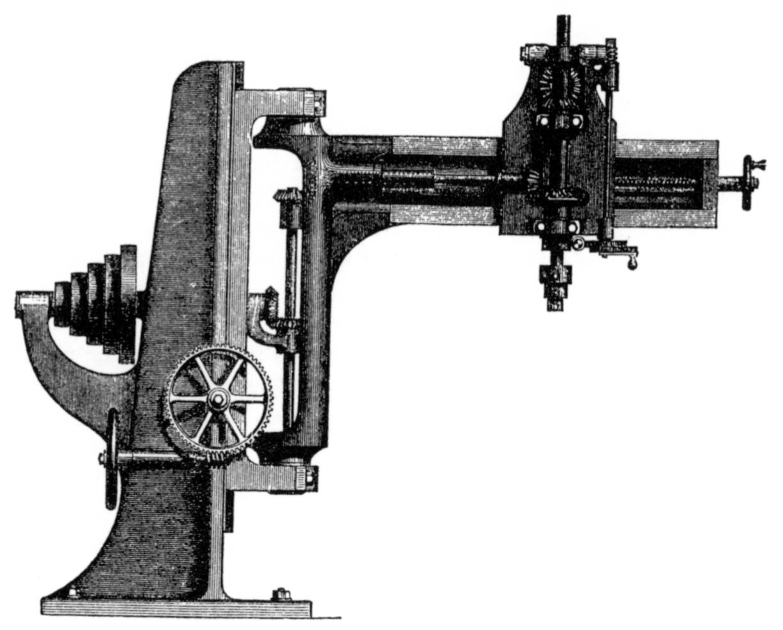

56 *Whitworth's radial drilling machine, 1862* (*Whitworth*)

Whitworth, like Nasmyth, was concerned to increase the productivity of the lathe and his solution took the form of a machine with two cross-slide rests enabling two cutting tools to be brought into action simultaneously. He argued that the opposing tools would act like a carrier rest, damping out chatter and relieving the lathe centres of pressure under heavy cutting loads. He introduced the hollow spindle for bar lathes and patented a collet chuck on the expanding cone principle. Both would later be essential features of automatic screw machines or 'bar automatics'.

In later life Whitworth became deeply concerned in the improvement of armaments, first on his own account and later in association with William Armstrong, but during the period with which we are here concerned machine tools were his chief preoccupation. Despite the design improvements he made and the meticulous standards he applied, the greatest significance of Whitworth in this history is that he became the first great manufacturer of engineering machine tools. In this he differed from all the other engineers so far described. Their careers followed a strikingly similar pattern. All began business with little or no capital in small workshops where any engineering job that offered was welcome. As they prospered the small workshop became a large factory like Nasmyth's Bridgewater Foundry where work upon a far larger scale could be undertaken, but the pattern of the business did not alter; the workshop tradition of versatility was perpetuated. Such firms prided themselves on their ability to solve any technical problem that was put to them, by designing and building the right answer. The astonishing speed of technological advance during the first half of the nineteenth century was largely the product of such brilliantly flexible general engineers. Yet the very pace of this advance, with the increasing demand for engineering products which it caused, brought about a more specialised form of engineering undertaking. Whether Joseph Whitworth consciously anticipated this trend, judging that the time was ripe for such a change, there can be no knowing, but the fact is that at his Manchester works he specialised in the production of engineering machine tools to an extent that was quite unprecedented. His venture was immensely successful. For the first time the manufacturer could obtain a machine tool of the highest quality promptly and at reasonable cost. Owing to their multifarious activities the less-specialised tool builders could not compete with him in rapid delivery or price. Consequently Whitworth built a reputation that was second to none and by 1850 his machine tools had dominated the workshops of the world.

CHAPTER 6

Drives, Gears and Gear-cutting Machines

THE WIDESPREAD INTRODUCTION of steam power and of new machines revolutionised the traditional craft of the millwright during the first half of the nineteenth century. The old builders of wind and water mills worked almost exclusively in wood and it was men such as John Smeaton and John Rennie who pioneered the great change-over from wood to iron in the construction of power-transmission systems during the last decades of the eighteenth century.

It was John Smeaton who began this revolution at the Carron ironworks. At the time of William Murdock's death in 1839 there stood upon a pedestal on the lawn before his house at Handsworth an iron-toothed pinion which the old man claimed to be the first ever used in millwork. It had been cast for his father at Carron and bore the inscription: 'This Pinion was cast at Carron Ironworks for John Murdock, of Bellow Mill, Ayrshire, A.D. 1760, being the first tooth-gearing ever used in millwork in Great Britain.'[1]

The next step forward was taken by John Rennie when he designed and erected the millwork for the celebrated but short-lived Albion Mill at Blackfriars between 1784 and 1788. This was the first large steam flour mill in the world and the first in which iron was used almost exclusively for transmitting the power of the two Boulton & Watt engines to the

[1] This inscription is quoted in Smiles' *Lives of Boulton and Watt*, but elsewhere, in his *Life of John Rennie*, he states that Smeaton introduced the first iron gearwheel at Carron in 1754.

machinery. Smiles, in his life of Rennie, describes the installation as follows:

> The whole of the wheels and shafts of the Albion Mills were of these materials [cast and wrought iron], with the exception of the cogs in some cases, which were of hard wood, working into others of cast iron; and where the pinions were very small, they were of wrought iron. The teeth, both wooden and iron, were accurately formed by chipping and filing to the form of epicycloids. The shafts and axles were of iron and the bearings of brass, all accurately fitted and adjusted, so that the power employed worked to the greatest advantage and at the least possible loss by friction.

The Albion Mill was a remarkable technical *tour-de-force* and it would be a mistake to use it as a measure of the general level of competence in this field either at that date or for many years after. Before the lessons it had to teach could be widely assimilated the great mill was totally destroyed by fire in 1791, and the fact that this fire was caused by an overheated bearing suggests that the new techniques had not been fully mastered. Until well into the nineteenth century the majority of millwrights continued to work empirically, adopting iron but using it on traditional lines to construct ponderous combinations of pulleys or gearwheels slowly revolving on massive square shafts of cast iron.

When the great nineteenth-century tool-makers produced their machine tools and used them to create a variety of new and complex special-purpose machines such as Roberts' self-acting spinning mule, it speedily became obvious that the old system of power transmission was totally inadequate to the demands which the new machines made upon it. The best method of transmitting power to machines became the subject of great debate among engineers. The respective merits of ropes, flat leather belts or gut bands were argued at length, but all were agreed that it was essential to reduce the weight of the power transmission system by increasing its rotational speed. One engineer, William Murdock of the Soho Foundry whose worm gear drive to heavy machines we noticed in an earlier chapter, attempted to do away with long transmission line shafts altogether. James Nasmyth paid a visit to the famous foundry in 1830 and described the machine shop as follows:

> I went through the workshops, where I was specially interested by seeing the action of the machine tools. There I observed Murdoch's admirable system of transmitting power from one central engine to other small *vacuum* or atmospheric engines attached to the individual machines they were set to work. The power was communicated by pipes led from the central air or exhaust pump to small *vacuum* or atmospheric engines

devoted to the driving of each separate machine, thus doing away with all shafting and leather belts, the required speed being kept up or modified at pleasure without in any way interfering with the other machines. This vacuum method of transmitting power dates from the time of Papin; but until it received the masterly touch of Murdoch it remained a dead contrivance for more than a century.

Fired by this example, Nasmyth later used small steam engines to power individual machine tools at his Bridgewater Foundry.

First hydraulic and later compressed-air power transmission systems would presently appear but their use in engineering workshops would be confined to forge and boiler shop. The goal which the far-seeing Murdock sought to attain would be achieved only with the advent of the electric motor. In the textile trade, where a smooth, reliable constant-speed transmission was required, rope drive won the day and rope-driven mills have survived down to our own day. The gut band was the ancestor of the vee rubber belt drive of today. Henry Maudslay at first used it as main drive for his machine tools, but it was soon relegated to subsidiary drives as on the change-speed motion of Clement's face-turning lathe. In the engineer's machine shop the flat leather belt soon became universal because of its obvious advantages. It greatly simplified speed changes by means of stepped pulleys and it made possible smooth reversible motions such as that used by Whitworth on his planing machine.

Many of those who pioneered machine tools also improved the means of driving them. For example, James Nasmyth introduced a self-aligning bearing for line shafting. In long runs of line shafting it was practically impossible to maintain perfect bearing alignment and Nasmyth's bearing with its spherical brass shells and housing greatly reduced bearing failures and the costly stoppages of machines so caused. But undoubtedly the greatest of a new generation of millwrights was William Fairbairn (1789–1874) whose book *Mills and Millwork* superseded the earlier work on the subject by Buchanan and remained for many years the standard one.

William Fairbairn became famous in the fields of civil engineering and iron shipbuilding while his younger brother, Peter, founded a celebrated engineering machine shop at the Wellington Foundry, Leeds, in 1828. In this context, however, we are concerned solely with the former's work as a millwright. Of Scottish birth, William Fairbairn became a working mechanic who, after many vicissitudes, succeeded in 1817 in starting a small general millwrighting business in Manchester with a partner named James Lillie. The partners soon realised that the power transmission arrangements in the neighbouring textile mills left plenty of room for improvement.

They found [writes Smiles] the machinery driven by large, square cast-iron shafts on which huge wooden drums, some of them as much as four feet in diameter, revolved at the rate of about forty revolutions a minute; and the couplings were so badly fitted that they might be heard creaking and groaning a long way off. The speeds of the driving-shafts were mostly got up by a series of straps and counter drums, which not only crowded the rooms, but seriously obstructed the light where most required for conducting the delicate operations of the different machines. Another serious defect lay in the construction of the shafts and in the mode of fixing the couplings, which were constantly giving way, so that a week seldom passed without one or more breakdowns.

Apart from defective design and workmanship, Fairbairn appreciated that the principle of using a low-speed main drive and then having to speed it up by means of countershafts in order to transmit it to the fast-running textile machines was totally wrong. For the transmission of a given amount of power the weight and strength of shafts and wheels can be reduced in direct proportion to the increase in the speed of their rotation. Fairbairn determined to effect a substantial increase in the speed of line-shafting so that it could drive the textile machines directly or, if need be, through reduction countershafts. So successful were Fairbairn's first essays in this direction, that in 1818 the partners were ordered to equip a new mill for the firm of MacConnel & Kennedy who were at that time the largest cotton spinners in Britain. Here Fairbairn introduced the type of line-shafting which has only been superseded in recent time by the electric motor, and the improvement was so overwhelming that other manufacturers were forced to follow suit.

In the course of a few years [Smiles tells us] an entire revolution was effected in the gearing. Ponderous masses of timber and cast iron, with their enormous bearings and couplings, gave place to slender rods of wrought iron and light frames or hooks by which they were suspended. In like manner, lighter yet stronger wheels and pulleys were introduced, the whole arrangements were improved, and, the workmanship being greatly more accurate, friction was avoided, while the speed was increased from about 40 to upwards of 300 revolutions a minute.

Naturally the engineers responsible for this revolution in the textile mills speedily applied the lessons learned to their own machine shops. In the first engineering shops machines had appeared haphazard among the fitters' benches or, as was the case at the Soho Foundry, they were built into the fabric of the workshop. Now, the multiplication of compact, self-contained machine tools, the introduction of the new light line-shafting and a recognition of the need to simplify the transfer of work from one machine to another all combined to produce an orderly and carefully planned disposition of machine tools in a shop exclusively devoted to their use. In this process the brilliant Swiss engineer, John George Bodmer (1786–1864), played a notable part.

Bodmer was born in Zürich and the most significant of his continental activities will be mentioned in a subsequent chapter. He paid his first visit to England in 1816, when he made it his business to visit all the most important iron works, engineering shops and textile mills. On his second visit in 1824, he equipped a small factory for making textile machinery at Bolton. This venture was not a success and Bodmer returned to the continent, but it is notable because the shop featured what is believed to have been the world's first overhead travelling crane. He returned to England for the third and last time in 1833 and stayed for a number of years. Sharp, Roberts & Co. of Manchester now undertook to manufacture his improved textile machinery, but this arrangement proved unsatisfactory so Bodmer decided to make the machinery himself. He proceeded to build a machine shop in Manchester and to equip it with machine tools which were all of his own design and construction. With the exception of his gear-cutting machines, these tools did not embody any very remarkable developments,[1] but the installation as a whole was a model of its kind. It was described as follows in the lengthy memoir of Bodmer which appeared in the *Transactions of the Institution of Civil Engineers* in 1868.

> Gradually, nearly the whole of these tools were actually constructed and set to work. The small lathes, the large lathes, and the planing, drilling and slotting machines were systematically arranged in rows, according to a carefully-prepared plan; the large lathes being provided, overhead, with small travelling cranes, fitted with pulley blocks, for the purpose of enabling the workmen more economically and conveniently to set the articles to be operated upon in the lathes, and to remove them after being finished. Small cranes were also erected in sufficient numbers within easy reach of the planing machines, etc., besides which several lines of rails traversed the shop from end to end for the easy conveyance on trucks of the parts of machinery to be operated upon.

[1] It is worth noting, however, that in 1839 Bodmer patented a vertical facing lathe, the first of its kind, though it is said that he never completed an actual machine of this type. Bodmer's invention did not make headway in conservative Britain, but became popular in America, where it was considerably developed, notably by E. P. Bullard and Conrad Conradson, both of whom designed multi-spindle fully automatic forms.

There were also, we are told:

> A large radial boring machine and a wheel-cutting machine capable of taking in wheels of 15 ft in diameter, and of splendid workmanship, especially in regard to the dividing wheel, and a number of useful break or gap-lathes, were also constructed and used with advantage. It is especially necessary to mention a number of small, 6-inch, screwing lathes, which, by means of a treadle acting upon the driving gear overhead, and a double slide rest—one of the tools moving into cut as the other was withdrawn—screw cutting could uninterruptedly proceed both in the forward and in the backward motion of the toolslide, and therefore a given amount of work accomplished in half the time which it would occupy by the use of the ordinary means. Some of the slide-lathes were also arranged for taking simultaneously a roughing and finishing cut.

The process of increasing rotational speed in order to obtain greater power without increasing the size and weight of the parts required for its generation and transmission has been going on continuously throughout the whole course of the industrial revolution, from the Watt engine running at a stately 20 r.p.m. to the gas turbine running at 50,000 r.p.m. The rate of this progress is a reliable guide to the progress of technology generally, since increased rotational speeds are only made practicable by more accurate workmanship, better metals, better bearings, better lubrication and, above all, improved transmission systems. The effect of Fairbairn's particular contribution to this speeding-up process was to highlight the one department in which the techniques of the great early nineteenth-century engineers and tool-makers were still sadly deficient—the design and production of gears.

Nowadays, highly stressed gears—in the gear-box of a car for example—are made from hardened high-duty alloy steels. Yet the toughest materials would rapidly fail if such gears were not designed and machined in such a way that, irrespective of their differing diameters, the teeth of a train of wheels will mesh sweetly with one another without friction or interference. The profiles of the teeth must be so curved that they will maintain continuous contact with each other with the minimum of friction and at the same time they must be strong enough to transmit the required amount of power without failure. This is a result which the most ingenious practical mechanic cannot achieve empirically; it involves the solution of quite complex mathematical and geometrical problems.

Two forms of curve, the cycloid and the involute, have been found to give the best results in the design of tooth profiles and the simple definition of these given by W. O. Davies in his *Gears for Small Mechanisms* cannot be bettered:

> A cycloid is the curve traced by a point on the circumference of a circle when the circle rolls without slipping along a straight line. Two variants of this curve are used in gearing, the epicycloid, in which the circle rolls on the outside of another circle, and the hypocycloid, in which the circle rolls on the inside of another circle. . . . An involute is the curve traced by the end of a string when it is held taut, as it is unwound from a drum.

How these curves are used in the design of modern gears is a matter for the engineering textbook. Suffice it to say here that cycloidal or involute curves may be used either singly or in combination with each other or with straight or radial flanks depending upon the duty the gears have to perform, whether they be the tiny wheels in the movement of a wrist watch or a massive pair of marine turbine gears. As we shall now see, the reduction of gear design to so exact a science is a comparatively recent achievement, for when the making of gears first began to emerge from pure empiricism the epicycloidal curve alone was employed, often incorrectly. Moreover, even when the epicycloid was correctly used it was only suitable for a pair of gears and not for a gear train of differing diameters. It was the introduction of the involute form that first solved this problem and marked the first important step on the road to modern gear design.

While mathematicians and practical designers argued over tooth forms, the machine-tool makers faced the difficult task of producing machine tools capable of accurately reproducing these forms, right or wrong, upon the gear blank. They had to take into account the type of gear to be cut, spur, bevel, spiral or worm, the type of cutting tool available and, finally, whether their machine would be required to produce a variety of 'one-off' gears or a large number of uniform components. Small wonder, then, that their solutions took a bewildering variety of forms.

For 'one-off' or very large gears, the templet or odontographic methods were preferred because both could be applied to the motion of the shaping machine using a single-point tool. In the first method a master templet ensures that the tool shall follow the correct curvature as the feed is advanced. In the second method a fixture on the tool head applies a radial motion to the tool and so produces the same result as a templet by mechanical means. The alternative to these methods was to use a tool whose cutting faces are accurately formed to the profile of the teeth required. In its simplest form, using a single-point cutter, this technique, too, can be applied to the shaping machine. Alternatively a similarly formed multipoint rotating tool, in other words a formed milling cutter, can be used in the same way.

By 1850 all these methods were in use. The machines concerned really form one family, being variants upon the theme of the planing or shaping machine. In every case the gear blank was mounted on an arbor having an accurate index which was at first moved manually after each excavation was completed and later mechanically. There is, however, a third way of gear cutting which also has its variants. This is the generating method. Instead of an indexed arbor on the work table, the rotation of the gear blank is continuous and the motion of the cutter is synchronised. Either in effect or in fact, the cutter becomes a master gear progressively reproducing its fellow on the blank when the two are engaged. Although such a method of gear cutting was proposed well before 1850, it was not widely used on production machines until much later.

This very brief summary of the problems of gear design and production may enable the layman to appreciate why it was that in this particular department of mechanical engineering the marriage between theory and practice was for so long unconsummated. There was no lack of practical ingenuity. The great British tool-makers succeeded in producing effective and reasonably accurate gear-cutting machines using the templet, odontographic and formed cutter methods, but the results they achieved were deficient because they were either ignorant of, or misunderstood, the essential geometrical and mathematical principles governing tooth form. This was a circumstance of the greatest significance in the history of technology, because, until those principles had been successfully translated from the mathematician's study to the engineer's workshop the efficient transmission of power through gearing was not possible. The marine steam turbine and the motor car are but two examples of many major inventions the practical success of which was dependent on the engineer's ability to produce efficient and accurate gears.

The mathematical theory of gear design has a very long history. Nicholas of Cusa studied the cycloidal curve in 1451, while the epicycloids were discovered by Albrecht Dürer in 1525. In France, Philippe de la Hire produced the first mathematical treatise on the design of gears in 1694. De la Hire came to the conclusion that of all possible curves the involute was the best, but such was the depth and breadth of the gulf between theory and practice that 150 years had to pass before the involute form was adopted. That such theories failed to filter through to the horny-handed builders of wind and water mills is not surprising, but we might expect to find the clock-makers sitting up and taking notice when we remember that they were using small gear-cutting machines from the sixteenth century onwards. This was not the case, however. The clock-makers went to great pains to obtain accurate indexing on their machines, because the utmost regularity and uniformity of gear teeth was essential to their purpose, but the *form* of the teeth was of less account, the power the gears were required to transmit being so small. It is true that in a large clock the gears of the striking train are subjected to considerable stress when the train is stopped, but the requirements of this intermittent motion could be met by brute strength and not by attention to tooth form.[1]

In the wooden gearing of mills, inefficiency was mitigated by the extremely slow rate of rotation and was not made apparent to the ear because of the nature of the material. When iron gearing was first introduced in mills, the problem was side-stepped by using wooden mortice teeth in the larger wheels. These were easily renewable and had a similar silencing effect. It was when iron was meshed into iron in millwork that the trouble began. Kipling, in his poem *MacAndrew's Hymn*, speaks of the main eccentrics of a steam engine 'starting their quarrel on the sheaves' but this was nothing to the row that broke out when a pair of early iron gears began to revolve. Practical millwrights of the time accepted the conflict philosophically and would remark that if they were left to run themselves in they would settle their quarrel in time. More often than not, however, instead of running themselves in, the gears wore them selves out.

It was at this juncture that the engineer began to court the mathematician, but this was only the prelude to a long engagement, fraught with misunderstanding on both sides, before the eventual happy marriage was achieved. It was unfortunate that the British engineers' first teachers were those who dealt only with the epicycloid. The works of de la Hire and his successor Leonhard Euler, the great Swiss mathematician, who had worked out the mathematics of the involute curve and its advantageous application to gear teeth, remained a closed book to them. Even cycloidal theory was improperly understood and frequently misapplied. Engineers formulated their own pet rules for generating epicycloidal teeth and more often than not they were rules of thumb. The Albion Mill was the scene of one of the earliest attempts to translate theory into practice for there, as Smiles has told us, patient craftsmen laboriously chipped and filed the gear teeth to an epicycloidal form—or rather the form which Rennie conceived to be correct. Rennie and his men merit admiration as pioneers. The result they achieved may have been woefully inaccurate and inefficient by

[1] This paragraph should not be taken as meaning that scientific tooth forms are unnecessary in horological work, but simply that, for the reasons given, eighteenth-century craftsmen were able to produce remarkably accurate movements by empirical means. Nowadays highly specialised epicycloidal and involute tooth forms are used in the movements of clocks and watches for the 'going trains' and the winding or minute-to-hour reduction trains respectively.

our standards but it could not fail to be a great improvement on what had gone before.

From this point onwards the production of epicycloidal gears advanced in three stages. First, the fashioning of the patterns for cast gears by hand; second, the machining of such patterns; and third, the machining of cast or wrought gears from the rough or from the blank respectively. Industrial gear-cutting machines evolved from the small 'dividing engines' used by the clock-makers and, like the latter, using a formed fly-cutter, were at work in England by 1820, if not earlier. On 5 May 1821, Richard Roberts published in the *Manchester Guardian* an advertisement which is probably the first of its kind. In it he

> Respectfully informs Cotton-Spinners, Iron-Founders, Machine-Makers and Mechanics that he has CUTTING-ENGINES at work on his new and improved principle, which are so constructed as to be capable of producing any number of Teeth required: they will cut Bevil, Spur or Worm Geer, of any size and pitch, not exceeding 30 inches diameter, in Wood, Brass, Cast-Iron, Wrought-Iron or Steel, and the Teeth will not require fileing-up.

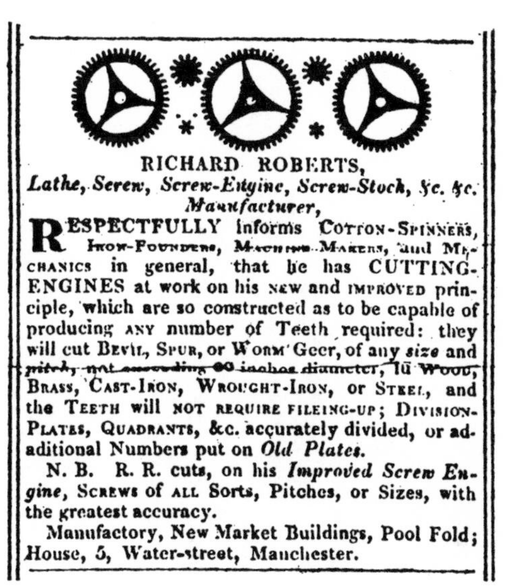

RICHARD ROBERTS,
Lathe, Screw, Screw-Engine, Screw-Stock, &c. &c. Manufacturer,

RESPECTFULLY informs COTTON-SPINNERS, IRON-FOUNDERS, MACHINE-MAKERS, and MECHANICS in general, that he has CUTTING-ENGINES at work on his NEW and IMPROVED principle, which are so constructed as to be capable of producing ANY number of Teeth required: they will cut BEVIL, SPUR, or WORM Geer, of any *size* and [illegible] diameter, in WOOD, BRASS, CAST-IRON, WROUGHT-IRON, or STEEL, and the TEETH will NOT REQUIRE FILEING-UP; DIVISION-PLATES, QUADRANTS, &c. accurately divided, or additional Numbers put on *Old Plates.*

N. B. R. R. cuts, on his *Improved Screw Engine*, SCREWS of ALL Sorts, Pitches, or Sizes, with the greatest accuracy.

Manufactory, New Market Buildings, Pool Fold; House, 5, Water-street, Manchester.

57 *Richard Roberts' gear-cutting advertisement, 1821* (Manchester Guardian)

Roberts' machine was a clock-maker's engine up-ended so that the arbor carrying the index wheel (at the back of the frame) and the gear blank is horizontal. The index wheel is rotated by a worm through change gears so that the number of teeth can be readily varied. The cord-driven fly-cutter is fed in horizontally by hand, but the cutter head can be angled for bevel gear cutting.

Other early machines using fly-cutters were produced in Manchester by Lewis and by Bodmer, but these had vertical arbors with index wheels under the machine table. Bodmer used the clock-maker's type of fly-cutter for cutting wooden pattern gears only and was the first engineer to use a true formed milling cutter on metal gears. To produce these cutters

Bodmer used a gear-cutting machine equipped with a milling cutter and this operated on the templet principle.

Bodmer was also a pioneer of gear cutting on the moulding generating principle.[1] Preserved in the Science Museum in London is a specimen of one of the special cutters covered by his patent of 1839. Designed to cut wormwheels, it consists of a steel worm identical with that into which the wormwheel to be cut was intended to mesh, except that it was provided with cutting teeth. If the cutter and the gear blank were rotated at the correct relative speeds and the two fed together, the former would excavate teeth of the correct pitch, form and depth in the blank. This process would later become known as hobbing.

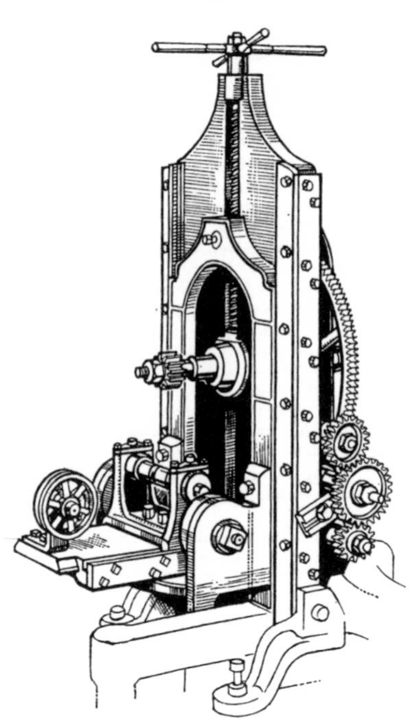

58 *Richard Roberts' gear-cutting machine,* c. *1821*

John Hawkins, who translated the work of the eminent French mathematician Charles Etienne Louis Camus in 1806, Robertson Buchanan, who included an essay on the teeth of wheels in his work on mills and millwork in 1808 and, finally, the Cambridge mathematician Robert Willis, who published his work in 1837 and 1841, all helped to translate the language of the mathematician into terms understandable in the work-shop. Unfortunately Camus's work, completed in 1766, only dealt with the epicycloid curve, while Willis, though his work was brilliant, made it quite clear that he had not concerned himself with the dynamics of gears, by which he meant the effect of loads and speeds. Consequently, although Willis dealt with both epicycloidal and involute gears he did not resolve the practical argument as to their respective merits. Hawkins confused the issue by wrongly interpreting the method of generating epicycloidal teeth. As for the involute, mechanics objected to the fact that teeth so formed tend to force the meshing gears apart. The truth was that so long

[1] Joseph Whitworth patented a spiral gear-cutting machine on the same principle in 1835, but if such a machine was built no cutters have survived.

as rotational speeds were slow and prime movers even slower, involving 'speed-up' gears to drive machines, the cycloidal type of gear was adequate. There was little incentive to develop the involute form until rotational speeds had increased so greatly that it became necessary to 'speed-down' machine drives. Consequently the epicycloid form—rightly or wrongly interpreted by the mechanics—persisted. That is why, when we look today at an early machine tool by Roberts, Fox or Whitworth it is the gearing which, above all else, strikes us as archaic. We may know nothing whatever about gear design, but we have grown so familiar with modern tooth forms in thousands of applications that the deep, coarse pitched teeth of these early epicycloidal gears appear to us as primitive as the crude cast gears of an old mangle or an early agricultural machine.

In the 1830s John Hawkins, the translator of Camus, carried out an exhaustive inquiry into current workshop methods of generating gear teeth. This covered all the most celebrated engineering shops, including Maudslay & Field, the Rennie Brothers, Bramah, Clement and Sharp, Roberts & Co., as well as the leading clock- and instrument-makers. Hawkins summarised the results of this inquiry in an appendix to a new edition of Camus which he published in 1837 and it gives such a clear and graphic picture of the position at this date that it deserves quotation at length.

> A painful task now presents itself [wrote Hawkins] which the editor would gladly avoid, if he could do so without a dereliction of duty; namely, to declare that there is a lamentable deficiency of the knowledge of principles, and of correct practice, in a majority of those most respectable houses in forming the teeth of their wheel-work.
>
> Some of the engineers and millwrights said that they followed Camus, and formed their teeth from the epicycloid derived from the *diameter* of the *opposite wheel*. . . . [1]
>
> One said, 'We have no method but the rule of thumb'; another, 'We thumb out the figure'; by both which expressions may be understood that they left their workmen to take their own course.
>
> Some set one point of a pair of compasses in the centre of a tooth, at the primitive circle [i.e. pitch-circle], and with the other point describe a segment of a circle for the off side of the next tooth. . . . Others set the point of the compasses at different distances from the centre of the tooth, nearer or farther off; also within or without the line of centres, each according to

[1] This criticism is ironical because the error stemmed from Hawkins himself. To his first edition of Camus, Hawkins added as an appendix parts of a work by John Imison which wrongly stated that the proper generating circle of the epicycloid should be one with its diameter equal to the *diameter* of the opposite wheel, instead of equal to the *radius*. See R. S. Woodbury, *History of the Gear-cutting Machine*, p. 18.

some inexplicable notion received from his grandfather or picked up by chance. It is said inexplicable, because no tooth bounded at the sides by segments of circles can work together without such friction as will cause an unnecessary wearing away. . . .

Among the Mathematical Instrument Makers, Chronometer, Clock and Watch Makers, the answers to the inquiries were, by some, 'We have no rule but the eye in the formation of the teeth of our wheels'; by others, 'We draw the tooth correctly to a large scale to assist the eye in judging of the figure of the small teeth'; by another, 'In Lancashire, they make the teeth of watch wheels of what is called the bay leaf pattern; they are formed altogether by the eye of the workman; and they would stare at you for a simpleton to hear you talk about the epicycloidal curve.' The astronomical instrument makers hold the bay leaf pattern to be too pointed a form for smooth action; they make the end of the tooth more rounded than the figure of the bay leaf.

Small wonder that early nineteenth-century gears look strange to us, but out of this chaos order was soon to come. J. G. Bodmer was a pioneer in the use of the diametral pitch system, which was so widely adopted in the north-west that it became known as 'Manchester Pitch'. Robert Willis laid down the rule that 'the diameter of the constant describing circle in a given set of wheels shall be made equal to the least radius of the set', and this became the standard for cycloidal gearing to this day. At the same time the involute began to make progress at last and in this belated revolution Hawkins played no small part. In association with Joseph Clement, he carried out a series of experiments with cycloidal and involute gear forms which had the effect of changing all his preconceived ideas on the subject. As a result, he added to his 1837 edition of Camus, a paragraph which virtually contradicted the rest of the book. It reads as follows:

Since M. Camus has treated of no other curve than the epicycloid, it would appear that he considered it to supersede all others for the figure of the teeth of wheels and pinions. And the editor must candidly acknowledge that he entertained the same opinion until after the greater part of the foregoing sheets were printed off; but on critically examining the proportions of the involute with a view to the better explaining of its application to the formation of the teeth of wheels and pinions, the editor has discovered advantages which had before escaped his notice, owing, perhaps, to his prejudice in favour of the epicycloid, from having, during a long life, heard it extolled above all other curves; a prejudice strengthened too by the supremacy given to it by de la Hire,[1] Doctor Robison, Sir David

[1] Hawkins cannot have studied de la Hire thoroughly.

Brewster, Dr. Thomas Young, Mr. Thomas Reid, Mr. Buchanan and many others, who have indeed, described the involute as a curve by which equable motion *might* be communicated from wheel to wheel, but scarce any of whom have held it up as equally eligible with the epicycloid; and owing also to his perfect conviction, resulting from strict research, that a wheel and pinion, or two wheels, accurately formed according to the epicycloidal curve, would work with the least possible degree of friction, and with the greatest durability.

But the editor had not sufficiently adverted to the case where one wheel or pinion drives, at the same time, two or more wheels or pinions of different diameters, for which purpose the epicycloid is not perfectly applicable, because the form of the tooth of the driving wheel cannot be generated by a circle equal to the *radius* of more than one of the driven wheels or pinions. In considering this case, he found that the involute satisfies all the conditions of perfect figure, for wheels of any sizes, to work smoothly in wheels of any other sizes; although, perhaps, not equal to the epicycloid for pinions of few leaves.

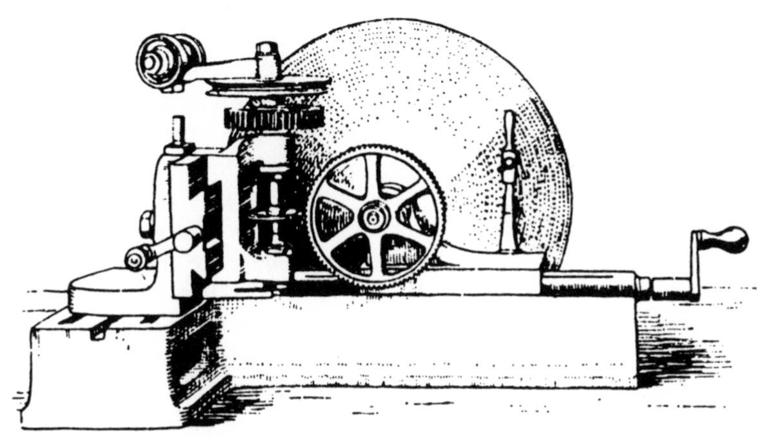

59 *Joseph Whitworth's machine with formed cutter for involute gears, 1844–51*

Hawkins goes on to explain that he had merely sketched the advantages of the involute and that a great deal of research and experiment on the subject was still required. This was so. In fact, the last round in the battle over the form of gear teeth was not fought until the last decade of the century in America. Yet Hawkins had, as we should say, 'started something'. The progress of technology was rapidly gathering momentum; gears were being called upon to run at ever greater speeds and to transmit ever greater powers with the result that hit-or-miss methods of forming gear teeth were everywhere found wanting. In such a situation no engineer could afford to ignore Hawkins's words and many acute minds were soon following the path which he had sign-posted.

By 1844 Joseph Whitworth had perfected a characteristically massive machine for cutting involute gears by means of a formed milling cutter. This had geared indexing for the blank arbor and power drive to the cutter by flat belt through worm and wheel. In 1851 the machine was fitted with power feed to the cutter head.

Another portentous development was Hawkins's description, in his book, of a new type of gear-cutting machine which had been designed by 'Mr. Saxton, of Philadelphia, now in London, who is justly celebrated for his excessively acute feeling of the nature and value of accuracy in mechanism'. Joseph Saxton's design was upon a small scale, being intended for the clock trade, but it is highly significant. Like those of the English tool-builders, the machine used a milling cutter, but it worked on the describing generating principle. The face of the cutter lay in a plane which passed through the axis of a describing circle. This was rolled round a pitch circle on the axis of the blank to be cut. In the machine, the two circles were represented by two gearwheels with milled teeth of very fine pitch. Now whereas the gear-cutting machines with indexing arbors developed by the English tool-makers could be designed empirically and used—or misused—to reproduce any individual notion of tooth form and pitch, a machine such as this, working on the describing generating principle, could only be designed by an engineer who had mastered the theory of gears.

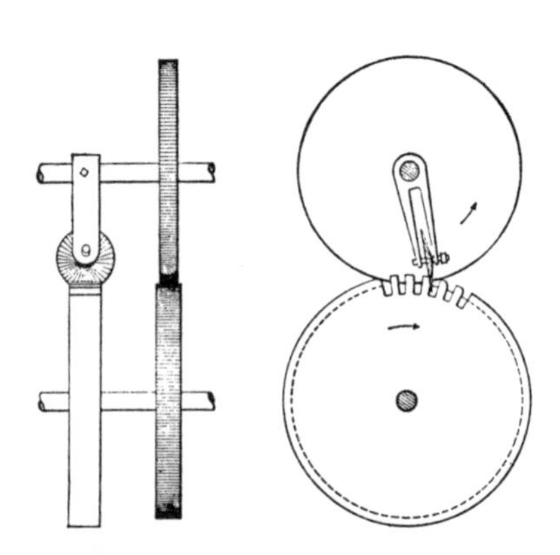

60 *Joseph Saxton's gear-cutting machine,* c. *1842*

In a much wider context Saxton's machine was a portent of change. Its designer was an American, the first to be mentioned in these pages. While the work of the great British machine tool builders was rapidly raising their country to a position of engineering supremacy seemingly invincible, events had been taking place across the Atlantic that would very soon enable America to wrest that proud leadership away.

CHAPTER 7

The Rise of America–Interchangeable Manufacture

In 1851, when the Great Exhibition was staged in Hyde Park, Britain's claim to be the workshop of the world was unchallenged. Britain's scientists and engineers had given her a commanding lead in all the techniques which had brought about the industrial revolution and there was no evidence to suggest that this leadership could ever be disputed. True, the revolution had swept through the continent of Europe, but Europe's railways had been built by British engineers, her new factories had been equipped with British machines and there appeared to be no serious threat from that quarter. In fact, the very magnitude of the industrial advantage the pioneers had won for Britain was a danger. It encouraged that complacency and conservatism which was all too commonly manifest in British engineering during the second half of the nineteenth century. This tendency to rely too long on the fruits of past achievements became particularly evident in that birthplace of new ideas and new techniques—the engineer's workshop. The great tool-builders, notably Joseph Whitworth, had provided the British engineer with machine tools so good that they fostered his belief that they could not be bettered. This was an illusion soon to be shattered.

In 1853 a group of British engineers toured America and, as a result of their visit and the recommendations they made in 1855, a new Government rifle-making plant at Enfield was equipped with no less than 157 American machine tools including 74 milling machines. This amounted to an acknowledgement of the fact that the Americans had already grasped the initiative in machine-tool design. That a one-time British colony, which had only won its independence in 1783, should have reached such a position of technological supremacy so rapidly was due to a variety of closely associated causes, not the least of them being the ineptitude and folly of the British Government. Here it must be said, however, that the true authors of most of these political blunders were the British industrialists who succeeded in making their Government the instrument of their singularly short-sighted policies.

The trouble began when the first imports of American iron reached Britain in 1718. These imports were very small, but they were enough to alarm the British iron-masters. They looked upon the American colonies as an assured export market and feared that if the colonists were permitted freely to exploit their ample resources of ore, wood fuel and water power this colonial export trade would soon be lost. As a result of their lobbying the production of bar, pig or manufactured iron in the colonies was prohibited. Such an arbitrary measure could not be enforced. Furnaces and forges continued to multiply in America though their output was very low and could not satisfy more than a small part of the colonial demand.

By 1737 it was being argued in England that if, instead of buying from Sweden and—to a much smaller extent—from Russia, pig iron was imported from America a great saving would result because such imports could be paid for by exports of manufactured goods to the colony. This scheme was bitterly opposed by the Midlands iron-masters, but in 1750 the Government sanctioned the importation of pig iron—and, under certain restrictions, bar iron—from America, but maintained the embargo on colonial manufacture by forbidding the erection of slitting or rolling mills, plating forges or steel furnaces within the colony.

Such attempts by business interests 3,000 miles away to restrict and distort the economy of a new country of vast size and enormous potential wealth could not hope to succeed and led inevitably to the War of Independence. After it, the British Government's crowning act of folly was to pass in 1785 a law which forbade, under threat of dire penalties, the export to America of any tool, machine or engine and the emigration of any individual in any way connected with the iron industry or the manufacturing trades associated with it. Nothing could have supplied a more stimulating challenge to the ambitious mechanics of the new world than this embargo on machines; as for the attempt to prevent skilled men from emigrating, the promise of the new world proved too strong for it. William Crompton and Samuel Slater, who had worked under Arkwright and the Strutts, were only two of the many skilled British craftsmen who successfully evaded the ban. Both made important contributions to the rapid growth of America's textile industry. In 1822, Slater was one of the founders of a small textile mill at Goffstown on the Merrimac river. Goffstown grew into the city of Manchester, N.H., while the little business became the greatest textile mill in the world. That the owners of this giant mill, the Amoskeag Manufacturing Company, also became general engineers and machine tool makers emphasises the fact that, in America as in Britain, the development of engineering machine tools was intimately linked with the manufacture of special machinery for an expanding textile trade.

The armaments industry supplied the second great incentive for the development of machine tools in America. Here again European history was being repeated in the new world, but in this case the end was very different. Instead of the ponderous cannon which had led to the appearance of the boring machine in Europe at so early a date, the need here was for the supply of lighter, more reliable and more rapid firing small arms in greater quantities than had ever been known before. The white man's conquest of a great continent depended on this. The first tentative advances towards the Middle West had shown that the settler armed with a heavy flint-lock musket was no match for the North American Indian with his expert bowmanship and his fleet horses. Moreover, if the white man's weapon was damaged it became so much scrap metal since it could only be repaired by the nearest gunsmith who might be hundreds of miles away. The need was not only for better firearms and more of them, but for weapons whose parts were interchangeable. Interchangeability would mean that by carrying stocks of spares or by 'cannibalising' damaged weapons, adequate stands of arms could be maintained in the frontier forts and compounds of the Middle West.

Like many another new development from this time forward, the idea of interchangeable manufacture originated in Europe but was first fully and successfully exploited in America. It was latent in the Brunel/Maudslay block machinery, but the ship's block was a simple assembly of pulley and sheave and the object of the machines was simply to produce more of them; if a degree of interchangeability was achieved in the process it was coincidental and was not turned to account. On the other hand, in the case of the military firearm all the conditions favouring interchangeability were present. It was a relatively complex assembly of precision components and it was required in large numbers of uniform design. Three attempts to produce interchangeable firearms were made in France, the first, about which nothing is known, in 1717, the second by the gunsmith Le Blanc in 1785 and the third in 1806 by J. G. Bodmer at a small factory at St. Blaise in the Black Forest.

Thomas Jefferson, who was American minister to France in 1785, made it his business to visit Le Blanc's workshop and reported to his government on what he saw there. Le Blanc handed him a box containing the parts of fifty musket locks arranged in compartments.

> I put several of them together myself [wrote Jefferson] taking pieces at hazard, as they came to hand, and they fitted in the most perfect manner. The advantages of this, when arms need repair, are evident. He effects it by tools of his own contrivance, which at the same time abridge the work, so that he thinks he shall be able to furnish the musket two livres cheaper than the common price. But it will be two or three years before he will be able to furnish any quantity.[1]

Of Bodmer's attempt at St. Blaise this was said:

> Instead of confining himself to the ordinary process of gun-making by manual labour, Mr. Bodmer invented and successfully applied a series of special machines by which the various parts—more especially those of the lock—were shaped and prepared for immediate use, so as to insure perfect uniformity and to economise labour.[2]

The fact that in 1811 the British government had on hand no less than 200,000 musket barrels which were useless because of the lack of skilled men to repair the locks, is evidence of the potential value of the methods Le Blanc and Bodmer tried to introduce. Yet for some reason their efforts came to nothing. This may have been due merely to the prejudices and conservatism of officialdom, but it has been suggested that the reason why the American engineers would succeed where Le Blanc and Bodmer failed may have been that the latter did not use limit gauges to size their components. The principle of establishing the margins of error, plus or minus, which are tolerable for critical dimensions and then enforcing them in the workshop by means of suitable gauges is essential to the success of the interchangeable system. The American engineers appear to have grasped this fact from the outset.

Recalling his visit to Le Blanc many years afterwards, Jefferson wrote: 'I endeavoured to get the U.S. to bring him over, which he was ready for on moderate terms. I failed and I do not know what became of him.' Whether, through Jefferson, Le Blanc had any influence on the course of events in America it is impossible to say. It seems unlikely, for 13 years passed before, in January 1798, Eli Whitney accepted from the U.S. government his first contract for muskets produced by his interchangeable

[1] *The Writings of Thomas Jefferson*, ed. H. A. Washington, Vol. I, p. 411, New York, 1853

[2] Memoir in *Proceedings of the Institution of Civil Engineers*, Vol. XXVIII, p. 573, London, 1868.

system. It is possible, however, that Whitney knew something of the work of Le Blanc at the time he planned his production methods.

The development of industry and technology in America in colonial days could be likened to the steam in a closed boiler, and in this analogy the British government represented a very heavy weight on the arm of the safety valve. The activities of the pioneer ironmasters and mechanics of New England were the first small leaks from the seams of this great boiler, betraying the mounting pressure of an immense latent energy. When that pressure blew the weight off the safety valve in the war of independence a great store of energy was suddenly released with the effect that henceforth the pace of material progress was far more rapid than it ever was in Europe. Within 60 years the European advantage had been overtaken and the new world took the lead. The pace was such that developments in technology, which would have taken generations to effect in Europe, were accomplished within the span of a single lifetime and consequently the work of a few pioneers could produce results that were astounding by European standards. Outstanding among the first generation of these 'go-getting' pioneers was Eli Whitney (1765–1825). The first of the great American inventors, it is doubtful whether any other engineer has lived to see developments so far-reaching follow so swiftly the application of his ideas. His ingenuity influenced both the textile and the armament industries in America and because the development of machine tools at first depended on these trades he is therefore a key figure in this history.

Whitney was a farmer's son, born at Westborough, Massachusetts, and his first great invention was made while he was staying in Georgia in 1792. This was the cotton gin which successfully removed the seeds from short staple cotton. The task of removing the seeds by hand was so great that the plant was considered almost valueless and the only species of cotton grown commercially at this time was the long staple variety. This only flourished in the Sea Islands and would not grow inland. The success of Whitney's machine was so spectacular and the demand for it so insatiable that it was widely pirated and Whitney was quite unable to uphold his patent. The world's greatest textile industry grew rapidly from the cotton gin. When it appeared, America's output was less than 2 million pounds a year; by 1800, production had risen to 35 million and by 1845, the United States was producing seven-eighths of the world's total annual output of 1,169,600,000 pounds. After a long and bitter struggle Whitney succeeded in proving the validity of his patent, but it brought him little profit and it was this disappointment which turned his attention towards the new field of armament production.

Whitney had no previous experience of gun-making and when he secured his first contract for 12,000 muskets in 1798—4,000 to be delivered in the first year—he had not even laid down a plant to make them. Yet such was the confidence which Whitney inspired that ten of the foremost men in New Haven, Connecticut, agreed to stand surety for him. 'I am persuaded', wrote Whitney, in his letter applying for the contract, 'that machinery moved by water, adapted to this business would greatly diminish the labor and greatly facilitate the manufacture of this article. Machines for forging, rolling, floating, boring, grinding, polishing etc., may all be made use of to advantage.' Furthermore, his aim from the outset was—to quote his own words—'to make the same parts of different guns, as the locks, for example, as much like each other as the successive impressions of a copper-plate engraving'.

The design and construction of the machines for his new mill at New Haven was an immense task and Whitney must have realised that to complete this and produce 4,000 muskets in the first year was not possible. Only 500 muskets were completed by September 1801, and it took him eight years instead of two to finish the contract. Nevertheless the government never lost confidence in his ability and advanced so much money towards the development of his machinery that when the contract was completed very little remained to be paid. But by this time Whitney's methods were a proved success and in 1812 he was awarded contracts for a further 30,000 muskets. After 1842, when Whitney's son had succeeded to the management, the first percussion-lock rifle, known as the 'Harper's Ferry' was made at the mill and in 1888 the historic plant was sold to the Winchester Repeating Arms Company who used it for the production of their famous ·22-calibre repeating rifle.

A visitor to the Whitney Armoury in its early days described it as follows:

> The several parts of the muskets were, under this system, carried along through the various processes of manufacture, in lots of some hundreds or thousands of each. In their various stages of progress, they were made to undergo successive operations by machinery, which not only vastly abridged the labor, but at the same time so fixed and determined their form and dimensions, as to make comparatively little skill necessary in the manual operations. Such were the construction and arrangement of this machinery, that it could be worked by persons of little or no experience, and yet it performed the work with so much precision, that when, in the later stages of the process, the several parts of the musket came to be put together, they were as readily adapted to each other, as if each had been made for its respective fellow . . . It will be readily seen that under such an arrangement

> any person of ordinary capacity would soon acquire sufficient dexterity to perform a branch of the work. Indeed, so easy did Mr. Whitney find it to instruct new and inexperienced workmen, that he uniformly prefered to do so, rather than to attempt to combat the prejudices of those who had learned the business under a different system.

On the strength of Whitney's own claims and such contemporary accounts as the above, subsequent writers have encouraged the belief that Whitney was alone responsible for the introduction and perfection of the interchangeable system in America. Recent research[1] has shown, however, that Whitney's claims, and those made for him, were exaggerated. He may well have done more than any other man to popularise the *idea*, but that he alone should have been responsible for its execution is indeed improbable. The whole history of technology proves that major technical revolutions of this order are never brought about by one individual.

The indisputable evidence of surviving arms proves that though Whitney's methods may have expedited manufacture, he did not in fact achieve interchangeability in the fulfilment of his first contract. Again, it has been said that Whitney lent skilled mechanics to the Government armouries at Springfield and Harper's Ferry and in this way introduced his methods there, whereas, so early as the summer of 1799, Whitney wrote in a letter: 'I might bribe workmen from Springfield to come to make me such tools as they have there.' It is clear that, in fact, the perfection of the interchangeable system was the product of a fruitful flow of ideas between the Government armouries and private armouries such as Whitney's and those at Berlin and Middletown, Connecticut, founded by Colonel Simeon North.

In this process the contribution made by Government employed engineers, especially by Captain John H. Hall, has been unjustly overshadowed by the claims made for Whitney. Hall's rifle, and the machinery to manufacture it on the interchangeable system, was the subject of his patent of 1811 and by 1817 he was introducing his methods and machines at Harper's Ferry. As a result of a claim for compensation made by Hall, an investigating committee inspected his machines and reported that they 'differ materially from any other machines we have ever seen in any other establishment . . . By no other process known to us (and we have seen most, if not all, that are in use in the United States) could arms be made so exactly alike as to interchange . . .'

This was in 1827. Much later, in 1840, Hall explained the crucial

[1] See R. S. Woodbury, 'The Legend of Eli Whitney', *Technology and Culture*, Vol. I, No. 3, 1960.

distinction of his method in a letter to Congress. He wrote: 'In manufacturing a limb of a gun so as to conform to a model, by shifting the points, as convenience requires, from which the work is gauged and executed, the slight variations are added to each other in the progress of the work so as to prevent uniformity. The course which I have adopted to avoid this difficulty was, to perform and gauge every operation on a limb from one point, called a bearing, so that the variation in any operation could only be the single one from that point.'

From 1815 onwards, government arms contracts specified that the parts of the firearms should not only be interchangeable with all others in the contract lots but also with weapons of the same design made at the national armouries. Master weapons were distributed to the various armouries with instructions that no deviations from them should be made. The success of this extension to the system was decisively proved in 1824 when 100 rifles from different armouries were brought together, completely dismantled and reassembled at random. Hall's methods undoubtedly contributed greatly to this result.

To the student of the 'Wild West' in fact or fiction, a gun means only one thing—a revolver. Armed with this light, deadly, quick-firing weapon there was no longer any holding the white man in his westward advance. The precision production methods of the new system were essential to the success of this new arm and they were adopted by the makers of both the best-known types. Horace Smith was a workman at Whitney's New Haven armoury before he founded the Smith & Wesson Company at Norwich, Connecticut and later at Springfield, Massachusetts. Colonel Samuel Colt (1814–1862), the inventor of the first successful revolver, could make no headway with his invention until he placed the first government contract he secured with the Whitney Arms Company in 1847. So impressed was Colt with the system that he determined to apply it in a more highly developed form at the new plant he planned to build at Hartford, Connecticut.

Notwithstanding the success of his revolver, Colt was neither an inventive genius nor a great engineer, but he was an enterprising and daring business man with a flair for picking the best men and the best methods. In 1848, when his new armoury was still only an idea, he outbid several rivals for the services of Elisha K. Root (1808–1865), a Massachusetts farmer's son who was then considered the best mechanic in New England. Colt appointed Root superintendent of the small temporary workshop which he rented in Hartford and made him entirely responsible for the machinery and equipment of his new armoury. This was begun in 1853 and completed in 1855. Colt and Root determined to carry the new principles of manufacture much further by eliminating even the smallest manual operation such as the removal of burrs from machined parts. To this end no less than 1,400 machines were installed, many of them designed by Root. Not all these were metal-cutting tools; Root was responsible for the design of die-stamping machines or drop hammers for the rapid production of small forgings of great accuracy. This very important develop- lies outside the scope of this book, but it was only made possible by the metal-cutting techniques used to produce accurate dies for the drop hammers.

Lavish though this expenditure on machines was, it was exceeded by the cost of the special jigs, fixtures and gauges with which Root equipped the new plant. This fact was quite unprecedented and rival arms manufacturers who watched progress with keen interest considered that Colt and Root had lost their senses and that the whole project was doomed to spectacular failure. Instead, the new Colt armoury proved a brilliant success, so much so that in 1861 the plant was doubled. When Colt died in the following year, Root succeeded him as President of the Company until his own death in 1865.

Like Maudslay's famous works at Lambeth, the Colt Armoury spread its influence far and wide through the agency of the men who worked there. Among these men were A. F. Cushman, founder of the Cushman Chuck Company, Francis Pratt and Amos Whitney. The last-named was not directly related to Eli Whitney but descended from the same stock. On leaving the Colt Armoury, Pratt and Whitney worked together for ten years as foremen at the Phoenix Ironworks in Hartford, a plant owned by the George S. Lincoln Company, makers of many of the machines for Colt and Root. It was during this period that the two men started as a spare-time venture the business which would eventually make the names of Pratt and Whitney as familiar in America as are those of Rolls and Royce in England. A great expansion of the arms industry following the outbreak of the Civil War enabled Pratt and Whitney to leave the Lincoln Company and concentrate entirely on their own business. After that war was over they began manufacturing machine tools for the gun trade and their re-equipment of overseas armouries made them one of the first great exporters of American machine tools. They also introduced a standard range of pipe threads and sponsored the research which determined the American standards of linear measurement.

The spread of the principle of interchangeable manufacture soon made essential the acceptance of the same standards of measurement throughout America. The Pratt & Whitney Company commissioned Professor William Rogers of Harvard and George Bond to establish such standards.

In determining a standard foot and its derivatives and in using these absolute standards to check the accuracy of precision gauges and measuring instruments, Rogers and Bond rejected Joseph Whitworth's principle of end measurement, returning to a method of linear measurement using a microscope with micrometer adjustment of the eyepiece. With this 'comparator', as they called it, they were able to check any gauge or instrument against the master standards without touching the latter. The one defect of the end measurement system—risk of inaccuracy due to wear of the measuring faces—was thus eliminated.

There was one other New England armoury where the introduction of interchangeable manufacture by machines of novel design owed much more to the presence there of three gifted mechanics than to any outside influences. This was the Robbins & Lawrence shop at Windsor, Vermont, and the three men concerned were Richard S. Lawrence, Frederick W. Howe and Henry D. Stone. The history of the company began in 1838 and its success was such that the construction of a new and larger plant was begun in Hartford in 1853. Shortly after this, however, an unrewarding contract for guns, undertaken in anticipation of a much larger order which failed to materialise, brought the whole venture to an untimely end. Nevertheless, as we shall see in the next chapter, this short-lived enterprise and the men associated with it profoundly influenced the design and development of machine tools in America. Moreover, in 1851 Robbins & Lawrence sent a set of rifles built on their interchangeable system to the Great Exhibition in London where they were awarded a medal. The interest they created was directly responsible for the subsequent visit of the English engineers to America, and it was Robbins & Lawrence who supplied the machines for the Enfield armoury to the order of the British government on the recommendation of this visiting commission. With the machines went several skilled men from the Springfield Armoury whom the United States government had agreed to release. They were the first of many. Did the parties to this amicable arrangement appreciate its irony? It was only a single lifetime ago that the British Government had fruitlessly endeavoured to stem the flow of skilled men and new ideas from the old world to the new, yet already the current was beginning to flow in the opposite direction.

The commission included the doyen of the British machine-tool industry, Joseph Whitworth, and in his summing up of the impressions he had formed on his American visit he said:

> The labouring classes are comparatively few in number, but this is counterbalanced by, and indeed, may be regarded as one of the chief causes of, the

eagerness with which they call in the aid of machinery in almost every department of industry. Wherever it can be introduced as a substitute for manual labour, it is universally and willingly resorted to.... It is this condition of the labour market, and this eager resort to machinery wherever it can be applied, to which, under the guidance of superior education and intelligence, the remarkable prosperity of the United States is mainly due.

Whitworth also praised the American trend towards standardisation and commended it to the attention of British manufacturers.

The production methods pioneered in the armouries have now been universally adopted with the effect that their advantages appear to us self-evident. Consequently we might expect to find enterprising manufacturers in Europe speedily adopting the new technique. This was not the case. Although the 'American System', as it was called, could be seen in action in England at Enfield and at the branch factory established by Samuel Colt in Pimlico[1] as well as in German and other European armouries, these examples had little or no general effect on European production methods for 50 years or more. In America, on the other hand, the new technique was eagerly and speedily applied and extended, notably to the manufacture of clocks and watches, sewing machines, typewriters, agricultural machinery and bicycles. The reasons for this divergence, which had social, economic and political consequences of the greatest significance, were many and complex.

Whitworth's report on his American visit gave rise to the widely held and long-cherished belief that the 'American System' originated solely because of a shortage of labour and the high wage rates consequent upon such a shortage. The implication of this was that where, as in England, labour was plentiful and cheap there was little to be gained by the adoption of the system. Yet, as we have seen, the spur which drove Eli Whitney to introduce the new system was not a labour shortage but the particular need for interchangeable firearms in quantity. Even if an unlimited supply of cheap labour had been available to him, Whitney could not have met this demand except in the way he did. This is proved by the subsequent introduction of the system to armouries in England and Europe where labour was plentiful and cheap. Moreover, the purpose of saving labour is to reduce the cost of the product, but this was not Whitney's aim and it was not achieved. An official of the Springfield Armoury told the visiting British engineers that the new system had not reduced the cost of a musket as compared with the old method. The aim, like that of

[1] This enterprise was unsuccessful due to the fact that the British workmen of the day would not tolerate the 'American System'.

contemporary British engineers, was greater precision in manufacture and it only differed from them in carrying the process of 'building the skill into the machine' much further than they had done, or would do, for many years to come.

Armament production has ever been a special case to which normal economic considerations do not apply. Hence it is not the inception of the interchangeable system in America but its rapid application to industry generally that requires explanation. Here the higher cost of labour as compared with Europe was undoubtedly an important factor, but to say that there was a labour shortage as Whitworth maintained is a dangerous half truth. A visitor to one of the great new American textile mills, where immigrant labour worked under conditions worse than those in Lancashire mills, would have disagreed vehemently with Whitworth on this point. It would be nearer the truth to say that there was a shortage of skilled labour and that the American manufacturer experienced a far more rapid turnover of labour than was the case in Europe.

To the enterprising emigrant from the old world, America was a land of limitless opportunity. A skilled tradesman could rapidly become a master man, while for the able-bodied and hardworking family there was land to the west, fertile virgin land free from tithes and the exactions of landlords where, with very little capital, a man who in England would have been condemned to a lifetime of ill-paid labouring could earn a good living as a farmer thanks to the combination of low outgoings and high soil fertility. The American manufacturer had to compete against these attractions and they therefore determined the high level of wages. Successive and ever greater waves of immigrants disprove the notion of a chronic general labour shortage, but the rich promise of an independent life in farming or trade repeatedly skimmed the cream off this incoming labour force. A highly skilled craftsman could command his own price and was likely to pack up his tools at the slightest provocation. Also, the craftsman is never easily won over to new methods, short of initiating them himself. Hence, on his own admission, Whitney preferred to use unskilled labour which had no prejudices and, because it was less intelligent and less enterprising, tended to be more stable.

Even so there were many who moved on. A high proportion of workmen were attracted by the high wages only as a means of saving enough capital to enable them to 'go west' and launch out on their own. There were two ways, one short-term and the other long-term, by which the American manufacturer ensured continuity of production with his floating labour force. The first was the widely used contract system. If, for example, a gun-maker obtained a contract for 10,000 muskets he would make a

61 *Eli Whitney*

62 *Samuel Colt*

63 *Pioneer plant: the Colt Armoury, Hartford, Connecticut, 1855 (from J. W. Roe,* English and American Tool Builders, *1916, by permission of the McGraw-Hill Book Company)*

64 *Pioneer plant: the Robbins & Lawrence Armoury, Windsor, Vermont,* c. *1840* (*from Roe,* English and American Tool Builders)

65 *A forest of belting: a typical American machine shop of the 1860s*

sub-contract with his employees, he to supply all materials and tools and pay wages, whilst they in return bound themselves to complete the work. On the completion of such a contract, many of the men engaged would leave so that the long-term solution was to build the skill into the machinery and equipment to such an extent that new hands were able to take over the work with the absolute minimum of training time.

As Whitworth had remarked, there was not, under these conditions, any opposition to the introduction of new machines. Whereas in England the Chartists inveighed against machines for taking the bread out of the mouths of the poor, in America they were welcomed as the means whereby unskilled men could earn high wages and so save the capital which would give them at least a small stake in the growing prosperity of the new world. Because wages were directly related to the productive efficiency of machine methods, the more backward American industries were speedily compelled to adopt such methods in order to attract labour. Immigrant labour was not firmly rooted and could be drawn to the highest bidder as irresistibly as iron filings to a magnet.

Whitworth also referred to the 'guidance of superior education and intelligence' in the new American industry, and this was true. In England, class distinctions were such that all who were engaged in trade, whether business men or technicians, were held inferior to those who followed the learned professions or who held commissions in the fighting services. Consequently the latter continually siphoned off a great deal of talent. In America such distinctions did not exist; material success was the only yardstick and ambitious youth everywhere strove to emulate the wealthy business man or the brilliant technician who were the supreme symbols of that success.

In such a climate it is no wonder that the progress of technology in America in the second half of the nineteenth century far outstripped Europe. There, new ideas encountered none of the prejudices which so frequently blocked them in Europe.[1] They were eagerly sought and speedily exploited. Consequently we find that although many inventions were originally conceived in Europe they were first successfully developed on a large scale in America.

The idea that the 'American System', which we now call mass production, was introduced for the purpose of saving labour is therefore fallacious.

[1] For example, Pierre Frédéric Ingold (1787–1878), whose watch-making machines were decisively rejected by the Swiss who declared that they represented 'the degradation of a valuable art'. Ingold then took his ideas to England (1839) but fared no better. Georges Auguste Leschot (1800–84) succeeded in 1845 where Ingold had failed, but only by keeping his machines secret from rival Swiss craftsmen.

It is true that it increased the productivity of labour, but the motive for its introduction was not to save labour but to attract it. The widely held European belief that the end product of the new system was necessarily cheap and of inferior quality was equally fallacious. It was not true of American firearms and it was not true of most of the first commercial products of the system. The sewing machine, the typewriter, the bicycle and new agricultural machines such as the reaper and binder were all new and intricate mechanisms whose successful commercial production by any other means would have been quite impossible.

It is only when we consider American machine tools and other engineering products directly comparable with those being produced in England that the case for American inferiority becomes arguable. Although the visiting British engineers praised the ingenious design of the new American machine tools, they considered them inferior to British tools in workmanship and durability. Judging by the standards Joseph Whitworth had set, this criticism was justified. Many other American products, particularly in the heavy engineering field, met the same criticism from England. As late as 1914 an English locomotive-builder could write: 'American competition, owing to her entirely different, one might say indifferent, standards will never threaten this country's locomotive exports until she can build with something like accuracy and finish.'

The man on the shop floor in England held the same view as his master. Writing of the American tools introduced at Swindon Works before the first world war, Alfred Williams had this to say: 'The chief features of American machinery are—smartness of detail, the maximum usefulness of parts, capacity for high speed and flimsiness, styled "economy", of structure; everything of theirs is made to "go the pace". English machinery, on the other hand, is at the same time more primitive and cumbersome, more conservative in design and slower in operation, though it is trustworthy and durable; it usually proves to be the cheaper investment in the long run. One often sees American tackle broken all to pieces after several years' use, while the British-made machine runs almost *ad infinitum*.'[1]

This deep-rooted and enduring contempt with which so many British engineers regarded 'Yankee' standards of workmanship was not due solely to a conservative tradition of craftsmanship but also to a failure to understand the American philosophy. In England the bright hopes which had been such a powerful dynamic in the early years of the industrial revolution became tarnished. The belief that the new technology

[1] Alfred Williams, *Life in a Railway Factory,* Duckworth, 1915.

would lead man to a new utopia of material prosperity was no longer unquestioned and there was a tendency to consolidate past gains rather than to seek fresh conquests. In America, however, faith in the wonders the new technology could perform was unbounded; it was the difference between youthful optimism and staid middle age. In a country where the pace of technological advance was so rapid and where its possibilities appeared limitless, it seemed folly to build a machine to last for 50 years when it might be outmoded in ten. When, in 1832, the French writer, Alexis de Tocqueville was gathering material for his famous book *La démocratie en Amérique*, an American friend said to him:

> There is a feeling among us about everything which prevents us aiming at permanence; there reigns in America a popular and universal belief in the progress of the human spirit. We are always expecting an improvement to be found in everything. . . . I asked our steamboat-builders on the North Bank a few years ago, why they made their vessels so weak. They answered that perhaps they might even last too long, because the art of steam navigation was making daily progress. In fact, these boats which made 8 or 9 knots could not, a little time afterwards, compete with others whose construction allowed them to make 12 or 15 knots.

If, therefore, the typical American product appeared deficient by European standards, this was often the reflection of a deliberate policy and was not, as so many British engineers supposed, due to defects inherent in American production methods. This misunderstanding is of great historical importance because it undoubtedly raised a barrier of prejudice which delayed the widespread adoption of American techniques in Europe for many years. From the end of the 1860s onwards, American machine tools, either imported or built under licence, began to appear in European machine shops in increasing numbers, but it was not until the present century that the 'American System' was widely applied to commercial manufacture by European industrialists. By that time the great New England mechanics who had pioneered that system were generally forgotten. Yet, as though to disprove the criticism by British engineers, when Joseph Roe wrote his book on the great tool-builders in 1916 he found that some of the original machine tools built by Elisha Root and Robbins & Lawrence were not only still in existence but still in use.

CHAPTER 8

American Machine Tools and their Makers

IT HAS BEEN SAID that when Eli Whitney first introduced the system of interchangeable manufacture in 1798 'the work was done mostly by hand'.[1] There may be truth in this, but Whitney would undoubtedly have adapted the miniature machine tools then current in the workshops of the clock-makers for producing the small parts of the lock and it is likely that the barrels of the muskets were externally ground from the outset because this technique was in use in Europe in 1780, if not earlier. A very large power-driven sandstone grinding wheel was used for this purpose, the face of the wheel being so wide that it exceeded the length of the gun barrel. The barrel was forced against the face of the wheel by a block on the worktable attached to a pivoting lever against which the operator pressed with his back. At the same time he rotated the gun barrel by means of a rod and hand-crank attachment.

One of the greatest problems would have been to produce on small components, plane faces sufficiently accurate in themselves and in their angular relationship to each other to ensure interchangeability. Planing and shaping machines had not then been developed on either side of the Atlantic, and in any case they would not have been suitable for this purpose. It is clear that such components must have been produced by hand filing, but that a series of jigs were devised to ensure the necessary accuracy and uniformity.

[1] *A Century of Machine Tools*, Connecticut Tercentenary Publication, Hartford, Conn., The Taylor & Fenn Co., 1935.

The exact date when a machine tool using a rotary cutter was substituted for the hand file at the new armouries is unfortunately not known. As the previous chapters have shown the principle of the fly-cutter and, later, the rotary file, had been applied before for gear-cutting by clockmakers and others and by Bramah in the production of his lock, but there is no evidence to show that it was used to machine a plane surface before the nineteenth century. In view of his subsequent record Bodmer may have used rotary cutters for this purpose at St. Blaise in 1806, but in England the first recorded application was Nasmyth's little device of 1829 for machining the flats on small nuts. The Americans were certainly earlier in the field than this.

66 *Grinding musket barrels, Springfield Armoury,* c. *1818* (American Machinist)

It will be recalled that Nasmyth adapted one of Maudslay's small bench lathes for his purpose, mounting his cutter on the lathe spindle and the small indexing arbor for the workpiece on the cross slide. Later, about 1830, Nasmyth produced a special-purpose machine which was simply a scaled-up version of his original device with the addition of power feed to the cross slide by ratchet and pawl. The machine could be used for plain milling by substituting a work vice for the indexing head and changing the cutters. For the first time coolant was piped to the cutter from a small tank. To a greater or lesser degree, the early American milling machines show a similar derivation from the lathe.

The earliest recorded American milling machine is said to have been installed in 1818 in a small arms factory at Middletown, Connecticut, by the English gun-maker Robert Johnson. Details of the machine were set down in 1900 by one who had seen it and had been told its origin by Johnson in 1851. It was similar to Nasmyth's later machine in that it consisted of the headstock unit of a lathe, with stepped pulleys on the spindle, mounted on a substantial block. This block also carried a cross slide worked by a hand-crank through rack and pinion gearing. There was no indexing head, the machine being used for plain surface milling only. If there is any substance in the belief that Colonel Simeon North used a milling machine as early as 1808, it was probably of this type.

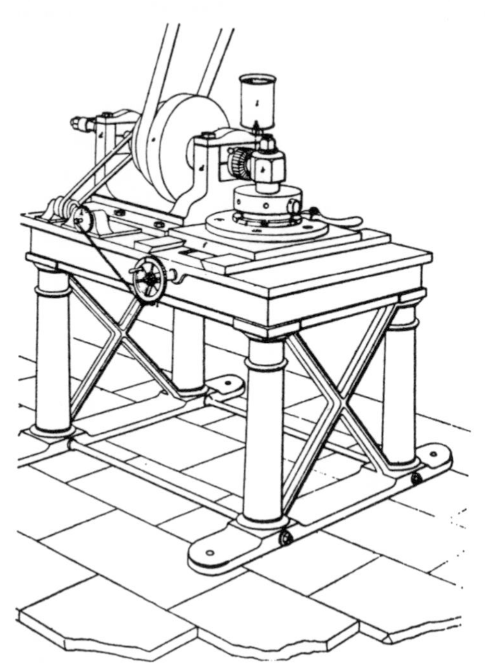

67 *James Nasmyth's milling machine,* c. *1830* (*Nasmyth*)

The oldest surviving milling machine was used at the Whitney armoury and is believed to date from about 1820. Most probably Whitney, like Johnson, and perhaps North, used a lathe adaptation at an earlier date, but this machine represents an advance on these. The cross slide is unfortunately missing, but it was carried on a gibbed bracket cantilevered from the substantial box frame and cast integral with it. In this respect it anticipates the knee and column type of horizontal milling machine. The spindle and its two bearings still resemble a lathe headstock unit, but in this case the pulley drive is taken to the projecting rear end of the spindle (the pulley is missing) and the stepped vee pulleys between the bearings are used as a feed drive for the cross slide. This was effected by a lead screw rotated by worm and wheel from the pulley-driven layshaft. The rear bearing of the layshaft is carried in trunnions and the front bearing is mounted on a vertical slide controlled by a spring latch so that the worm can be disengaged from the wheel. The slide could then be traversed by a hand-crank. Though earlier in date, this automatic feed drive by lead screw is superior to Nasmyth's ratchet and pawl because the latter would give an intermittent motion to the slide. It is also superior to the rack and pinion feed motion used on many later milling machines.

68 *Eli Whitney's milling machine,* c. *1820*

All these early machines shared two defects. First, there was no provision for vertical adjustment between the rotating cutter and the worktable. Consequently, if a second cut was required the workpiece would have to be packed up with shims of equivalent thickness. In the manufacture of interchangeable arms, the machines were doubtless used to perform a single operation in one cut on a standard component, but vertical adjustment was obviously necessary before the milling machine could become a useful general-purpose tool. Secondly, the support for the cutter spindle was inadequate. So long as the cutters remained virtually rotary files capable of only a very light cut the need for improvement was not apparent. But the trend in tool design was towards coarser cutters until the bladed milling cutter capable of cutting a substantial chip soon appeared. Such a cutter, with its heavy and intermittent cutting action, imposed an intolerable load on the front headstock bearing and it became essential to support the cutter between bearings.

In solving the problem of vertical adjustment the early American tool-designers suffered from one of those 'blind spots' that sometimes occur in the history of technology and appear so inexplicable in restrospect. In this case it arose from the way in which the milling machines had evolved from the lathe. Designers seem to have taken for granted the lathe type of bed and cross slide; consequently their efforts to provide vertical adjustment were concentrated upon the cutter spindle and not upon the worktable. This was doing the job the hard way. When the need to support the cutter between bearings was recognised the problem became even more complicated and the solutions more cumbersome.

The oldest known machine to combine vertical adjustment with adequate support for the cutter spindle was a small miller made at the shops of Gay, Silver & Co., of North Chelmsford, Massachusetts. It is believed to date from about 1835 and it was photographed while still at work there in 1908. This was a brave attempt to break away from the lathe convention but it had no immediate successors. The headstock unit is, in effect, turned upside down, the spindle bearings being underneath the main body of the casting. Moreover, the casting is extended in the form of an overarm to support the outer end of the cutter spindle. The whole assembly is carried on a pillar with a vertical slide adjustable by screw and hand crank. A jockey pulley is provided on the belt drive to the spindle in order to keep the belt in tension. When photographed in 1908 the machine had a power feed to the cross slide almost identical in design to that fitted by Whitney to his miller of 1820, but an earlier illustration proves that the machine originally had manual feed only and that it was not 'modernised' in this way until after 1896!

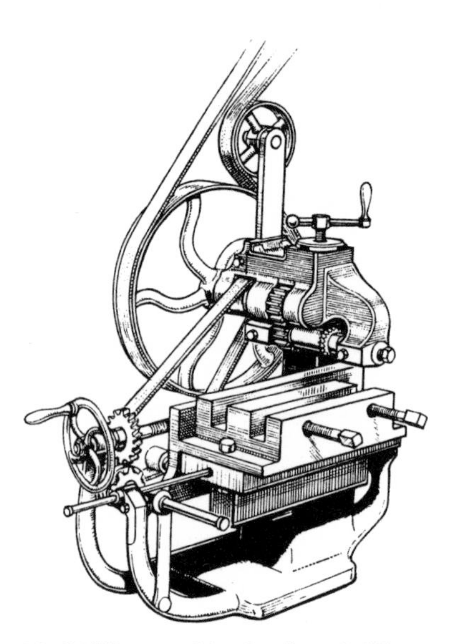

69 *Milling machine by Gay & Silver,* c. *1835*

The brothers Ira and Zeba Gay were associated with Pawtucket, one of the birthplaces of mechanical engineering in New England, and with the Amoskeag Company before they started the Gay & Silver shop at North Chelmsford in the late 1820s. The main purpose of the venture was to build machinery for the textile trade, but they were among the earliest manufacturers of planing machines in America, *c.* 1831. Of more significance in this history, however, is the fact that Frederick Howe (1822–1891) was trained by the Gay brothers before he joined Robbins & Lawrence at Windsor, Vermont.

At Robbins & Lawrence, Howe, with the possible collaboration of Richard Lawrence, produced in 1848 a milling machine capable of much heavier duty than any of its predecessors although it represented a retrograde step, diverting the machine away from its true evolutionary path. In this machine the affinity with the lathe was very marked. It had a long, lathe-like bed and a tailstock unit with poppet head for supporting the end of the cutter spindle. The belt drive was taken to a layshaft on the headstock so that it drove the cutter spindle through a single pair of reduction gears. Both the headstock bearings and the tailstock unit were carried in vertical guideways, their movement being governed manually by three screws. The two headstock screws were interconnected by gears beneath the bed so that vertical adjustment of the headstock was coordinated, but the tailstock had to be adjusted separately. A tortuous arrangement of shafts and gearing driven by belt from the cutter spindle provided power feed for the cross slide by rack and pinion. This chattered badly under load. The cross-slide table was given a limited amount of longitudinal adjustment and the pinion which engaged the rack was elongated to allow for this. Both the main and feed drive belts had jockey pulleys to allow for the vertical adjustment of the spindle.

Two years later, in 1850, Robbins & Lawrence produced an index milling machine. This represented a radical departure in design and is said to have been the first miller to be manufactured for sale. Here again we have what is virtually a lathe bed with guideways, but in this case the headstock unit, carrying a cutter spindle with a single drive pulley between its bearings, is mounted on a sliding carriage with its axis at right angles to the guideways. Power feed is applied to this carriage instead of to the worktable and, in addition, the cutter spindle could be advanced through its bearings and through its drive pulley by means of a lever and stop. The worktable is supported on a vertical column carried in bearings on a bracket cantilevered from the side of the bed. The column carries an index plate so that the worktable can be accurately adjusted to any angle in the horizontal plane and it can also be adjusted vertically by means of a lead screw. This lead screw is rotated through gearing and a vertical shaft by a conveniently placed hand-wheel so that it could be used, not merely to adjust the height of the table, but to apply vertical feed if required. This was a notable attempt to make the milling machine more versatile. It was also the first to escape from the lathe convention by applying vertical adjustment to the table instead of to the spindle. But there was no support for the end of the cutter spindle and the worktable lacked rigidity.

In his last milling-machine design for Robbins & Lawrence in 1852, Frederick Howe evidently had these defects in mind, while he may also have had in mind the little machine he had seen many years before in the Gay & Silver shop. As in this much earlier machine he now inverted a geared headstock unit, provided overarm support for the cutter spindle,

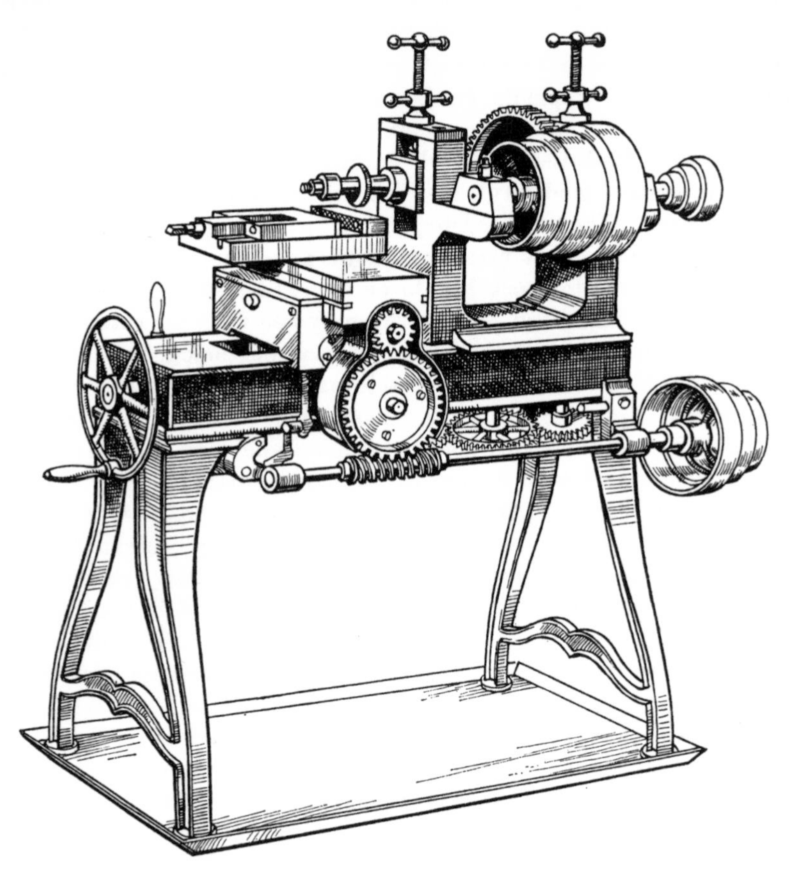

70 *The Lincoln Miller: Frederick Howe's design of 1848 with modifications by Elisha Root*

and mounted the whole assembly in vertical guideways. For the rectangular worktable used on all previous designs Howe substituted a circular chuck. As on his previous design, this is supported on a vertical column and fitted with an index plate, but the method of support is at once more rigid and more versatile. Designed on the knee and column principle, it incorporates vertical and horizontal slides and means of inclining the knee carrying the chuck column. The work-holding chuck could thus be rotated under index control, inclined and traversed either horizontally or vertically with power feed in both planes if required. This machine was called a 'universal' miller, but although it was remarkably versatile it was not universal in the sense that we understand the term. It was also needlessly complex. The first truly universal milling machine which, like Maudslay's lathe, would be an inspired synthesis of all the best design features, was still nine years away in the future.

These were the milling machines supplied by Robbins & Lawrence on the British Government's order for the new Enfield armoury. Howe's designs were also adopted by Elisha Root for the new Colt armoury at Hartford, but owing to the difficulties which brought the promising career of Robbins & Lawrence to so speedy an end, the Colt machines were built at the George S. Lincoln Company's Phoenix Ironworks in Hartford. In the process, Elisha Root and his assistant, Francis Pratt, introduced certtain improvements to Howe's design of 1848. The machine was made more compact and robust and a feed drive by worm and wheel and lead screw was substituted for the chattering rack and pinion. Howe's tailstock with its separate vertical adjustment by screw was dropped. For the Colt machines Root adopted a cylindrical overarm carrying an adjustable bracket with dead centre, but contemporary illustrations show that in other examples, the end of the cutter spindle was either left unsupported or carried in a bearing on a simple angle bracket secured to the bed and adjustable horizontally or vertically.

In these forms the machine became famous under the name of the Lincoln Miller. One hundred of them were supplied to the Colt Armoury alone when the capacity of that plant was doubled in 1861. Great numbers were built for home use during the American civil war and subsequently for export to Europe by the Lincoln Company and by Pratt & Whitney. The 65 machines supplied to the Prussian Government Armoury in June 1872 represents a typical export order. The gun factories at Spandau, Erfurt and Danzig were completely equipped by Pratt & Whitney. Production continued for many years and Joseph Roe estimated that the total number of Lincoln Millers built must have exceeded 150,000. Some worked continuously for more than 70 years. Index millers were also built but in smaller numbers. An early illustration of a Lincoln index miller shows a machine almost identical with Howe's design of 1850 except that it is without power feed.

No other tool contributed more than the milling machine to the early history of the 'American System'. It was created by that system, but the

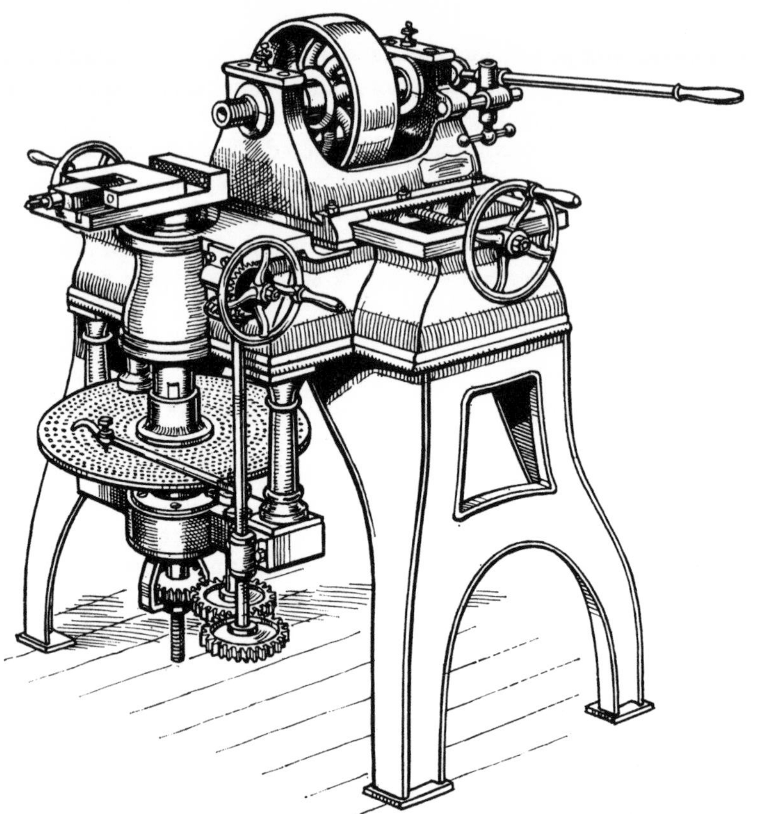

71 *Lincoln index milling machine following Frederick Howe's design of 1850*

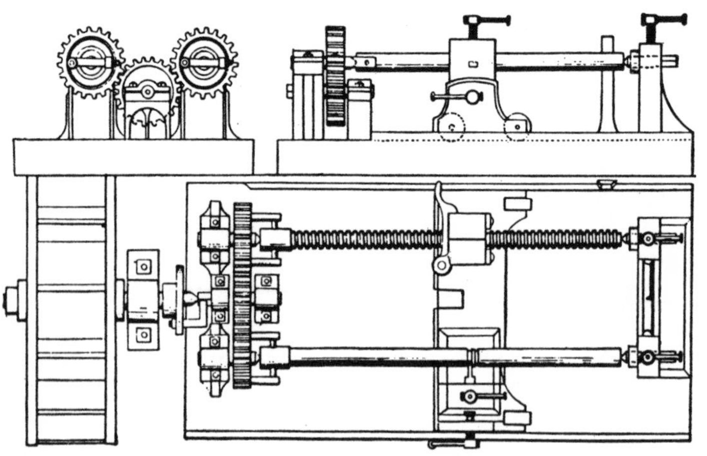

72 *David Wilkinson's screw machine of 1798* (American Machinist)

lathe and the drilling machine played their parts also and it is desirable at this point to see how the American tool-builders developed these older machines to the requirements of their system before following the evolution of the milling machine any further.

As early as 1798 David Wilkinson of Pawtucket patented what has been described as a screw-cutting slide-rest lathe and on the strength of this his name has been bracketed with that of Henry Maudslay. It would be fairer, however, to call Wilkinson's invention a screwing machine. Duplex head and tailstock units were fixed at either end of a table to carry a lead screw and the workpiece side by side. At the headstock end the two were geared to a central driving shaft. A carriage moving along the table on rollers carried the tool-holder and a nut which engaged the lead screw. If we look back to Leonardo da Vinci's screw-cutting machine of 1500 the similarity is remarkable, but whereas Leonardo provided change gears, Wilkinson did not, so that his machine could only be used to reproduce its own lead screw. Yet Wilkinson's machine was practically successful for its limited purpose and shows the efforts the early American mechanics were making to overhaul the commanding British lead.

Nevertheless, for many years the general purpose American lathe remained very markedly inferior to the British product. In the 1840s, when Joseph Whitworth reigned supreme in England, the average American lathe still had a wooden bed with iron-plated guideways. It was in the design of special-purpose machines for interchangeable arms manufacture that American engineers made their first significant contributions to the story of the lathe. In 1818 Thomas Blanchard (1788–1864) built the first of his patent lathes for turning gun stocks in a small workshop at his home town of Worcester, Mass. It was installed at the Springfield Armoury where it was used for over 50 years. This strange contrivance looks at first glance less like a lathe than some primitive piece of agricultural machinery, but we should not smile for it introduced an important new principle to the industrial workshop. Methods of turning irregular forms had been used by ornamental turners in Europe since the seventeenth century, but to ensure uniformity Blanchard's machine operated on the pantograph principle, using a master gunstock, and it is therefore the parent of all subsequent copying or profile turning lathes.

The precision of Blanchard's wood-working machines was such that for a time they outstripped the accuracy of the metal-working machines used in the armouries. To ensure that the lockplates fitted the stock snugly, therefore, Blanchard devised a stock-mortising machine using the actual lock-plates as formers. Hundreds of Blanchard's gun-stocking lathes were built by the Ames Manufacturing Company of Chicopee, Mass., for the armouries of America and Europe and the inventor lived comfortably on his royalties for the rest of his life.

The next important lathe development arose from the need in the armouries for many small uniform components which required turning in a chucking lathe. This need was intensified in the 1840s when the first percussion locks began to replace the old flintlocks in muskets and pistols. We have seen how, at this time, Whitworth, Nasmyth and other English tool-builders were seeking to increase the productivity of the centre lathe

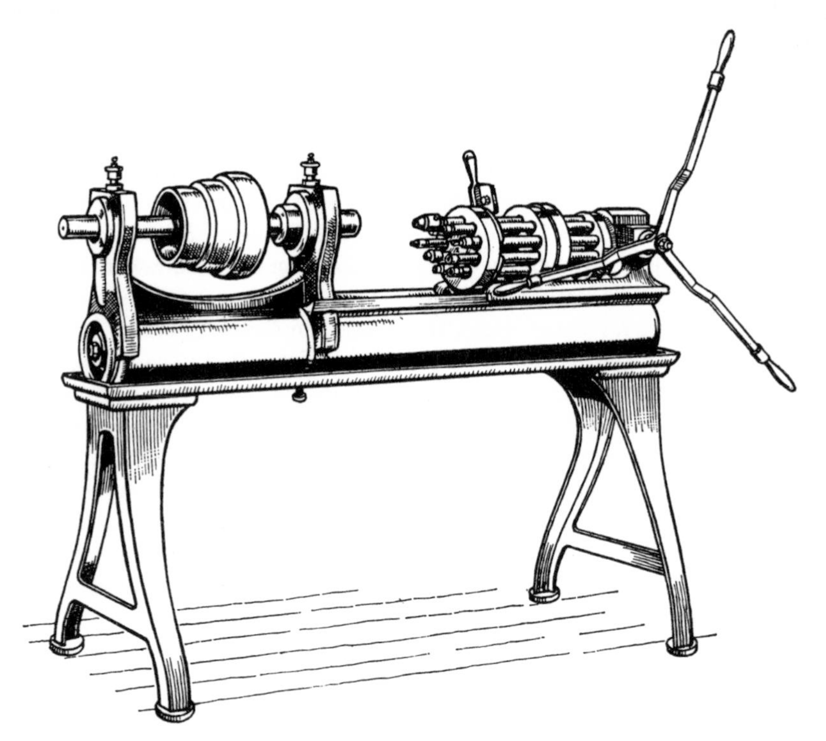

73 *The first turret lathe: built by Stephen Fitch, 1848*

by using more than one tool in the tool-holder, by using two opposing cross slides, or by using two carriages as in Nasmyth's 'ambidexter' lathe. These devices have their refined counterparts in the modern centre lathe, but the American need for higher output from a chucking lathe called for a different solution.

To produce the vast number of screws required for the percussion locks of a government contract for 30,000 pistols, Stephen Fitch of Middlefield,

Connecticut, designed and built in 1845 the world's first turret lathe.[1] Fitch's long cylindrical turret revolved on a horizontal axis and carried eight tools mounted on spindles each of which could be advanced as required, the operative one being the uppermost. A three-armed capstan advanced the turret carriage and applied the feed. In this way eight successive operations could be rapidly performed without stopping the machine to change tools. This was the most fundamentally important development in the lathe to appear since the days of Maudslay. In 1900, the American E. G. Parkhurst wrote: 'One only does justice to the memory of Stephen Fitch when one recognises in him the creator of one of the most time-saving machines ever invented.'

As was the case with the milling machine, the Gay & Silver shop at North Chelmsford appears to have had a seminal influence on the development of the turret lathe through the agency of Frederick Howe. When he was being schooled there before 1850 there were already two turret lathes in the shop. One of these was of the Fitch type, but the other had a turret rotating on a vertical axis, the earliest recorded example of its kind. The advantages of the turret were so great that it was speedily taken up by others after 1850. Elisha Root and J. D. Alvord of Hartford introduced horizontal-axis turret lathes at the Colt and Sharpe armouries respectively, but Robbins & Lawrence, with greater foresight, plumped for the vertical turret. While it is said that both Henry Stone and Richard Lawrence contributed to the design of the first Robbins & Lawrence turret lathe, the presiding genius was Howe and the choice of a vertical turret was probably based on his practical experience of the two machines at Gay & Silver.

For both screw machines[2] and chucking lathes designed to perform successive operations on a single workpiece, the vertical-axis turret championed by Howe became universal. Many of the devices associated with the screw machine such as the box tool and the hollow mill, originated at Robbins & Lawrence, and after that historic firm closed down development was continued elsewhere by both Howe and Stone. Windsor, too,

[1] English engineers distinguish between a turret lathe, in which the turret is mounted directly on the main carriage of the machine, and a capstan lathe, in which the turret is fitted to a separate longitudinal slide upon the carriage. Americans do not use the term capstan but refer to the latter type of machine as a ram-type turret lathe. Because the English distinction is apt to be confusing, the term turret lathe is used exclusively in this book.

[2] A 'screw machine' is really a form of lathe and can be used to produce many small components besides screws. To this day the term is used to describe automatic lathes of both single and multi-spindle types, so it is employed throughout this chapter in this wide sense.

again became a centre of turret lathe development when the historic Robbins & Lawrence shops were acquired by the Jones & Lamson Machine Company which specialised in the production of lever-operated high turret lathes with power feed and back gearing. In 1889, James Hartness joined this company and was responsible for many improvements, most notably a series of flat turret lathes. He was astonished to discover a series of drawings and sketches anticipating many of his ideas. These had been made by Frederick Howe nearly forty years before and clearly showed that Howe's ideas on machine tool design were a generation ahead of their time. Indeed, in 1900 when the celebrated machine tool engineer Edward G. Parkhurst reviewed a lifetime's experience of the industry, he expressed the opinion that no man in America had contributed more to the development of the metal-cutting lathe than Frederick Howe. Bearing in mind the contribution Howe also made to the evolution of the milling machine, it would scarcely be an exaggeration to describe him as the Henry Maudslay of America.

Before turning to other American machine tool developments of the mid nineteenth century it will be convenient to follow the story of the turret lathe through to its logical conclusion—the fully automatic screw machine in its single and multi-spindle forms. In August 1871, Edward G. Parkhurst patented a collet chuck and closing mechanism to enable bar stock to be fed through a hollow lathe spindle and then gripped by the chuck without stopping the machine. Whether or not Parkhurst's device was based on the earlier collet chuck produced in England by Joseph Whitworth, it was certainly decisive in its influence, for the first automatic screw machines speedily followed.

The pioneer in this field was Christopher Miner Spencer (1833–1922) who was born in Manchester, Connecticut. A versatile inventor, Spencer built himself a steam carriage in 1862, made many improvements in textile machinery and invented a seven-shooter repeating rifle. Made in great quantity for the Northern forces, this Spencer rifle played a decisive part in the Civil War. His patent automatic silk-winding machine was manufactured by Pratt & Whitney and first set their business on the road to fame. They began making it in their spare time in their first small rented shop in Hartford.

After the civil war, Spencer joined forces with C. E. Billings, an old Robbins & Lawrence mechanic whom he had met while working at the Colt Armoury, and together they formed the Billings & Spencer Company at Amherst, Massachusetts. Here Spencer built a special automatic lathe for turning sewing-machine spools and it was this machine which gave him the idea of making a completely automatic turret lathe for turning metal

74 *The birth of automation: Christopher Spencer's first automatic machine with 'brain wheels'*, c. *1873*

75 *An early Lincoln treadle-operated four-spindle drilling machine*

76 *Joseph Brown*

77 *Frederick Howe* (*from Roe,* English and American Tool Builders)

78 *William Sellers*

79 *Charles Churchill*

screws. The prototype machine was built in a rented workshop above the Cushman Chuck Company's plant. It consisted of a standard Pratt & Whitney manual turret lathe converted by Spencer to automatic operation. The key feature of the conversion was the 'brain wheel' as Spencer called it. This was, in fact, a cam wheel, being a large-diameter drum having strip steel cams bolted to its periphery. As this wheel revolved, the cams engaged followers which actuated the collet chuck, the turret and the slide by means of levers and segmental gears. By altering the positions and angularity of the strip cams, the motions of the machine could be readily adjusted to suit different jobs.

In this first experimental adaptation a single 'brain wheel' was mounted behind the turret and driven by a long shaft from the headstock. Spencer evidently realised that this was a clumsy expedient, for in his first production screw machine patented in 1873, he introduced two 'brain wheels' for the collet and turret motions respectively and mounted them and their driving shaft under the lathe bed.

Like many another inventor, Spencer had no head for business. Wrongly, he decided that it would be more lucrative to exploit the high productive capacity of his machine himself than to manufacture it for others. He therefore joined George A. Fairfield, another Colt employee, in founding the Hartford Machine Screw Company. Meanwhile he licensed Pratt & Whitney to manufacture his machines, but this brought him little profit. By an inexplicable blunder, Spencer's patent attorney had failed to protect the 'brain wheel' which was the key feature of the invention with the inevitable result that it was widely and speedily copied.

Having multiplied the lathe tools and made their successive action automatic, the next step was to multiply the spindles so that the tools might be brought to bear simultaneously instead of successively. This, of course, involved the radial arrangement of tools as used by Fitch on his first turret lathe. Here again it was Spencer who took the first step by designing a three-spindled automatic for making small screws from coiled wire. An ex-Pratt & Whitney apprentice resident in Hartford named Reinhold Hakewessel purchased several of these machines and used them to compete against the Hartford Machine Screw Company, much to the latter's annoyance. Hakewessel used the profits of this undertaking and the experience gained to develop a four-spindle bar automatic screw machine which he christened the Acme. After various commercial manœuvres and business vicissitudes, Hakewessel's machine found its home in the National-Acme Screw Manufacturing Company of Cleveland, Ohio. As its name indicates, this concern at first followed Spencer's example at Hartford by exploiting the high production capacity of the new machine themselves, but in this case they later yielded to demand by manufacturing the National-Acme screw machine for the open market.

Meanwhile, George O. Gridley, a protégé of James Hartness, had developed his own improved design of a four-spindle automatic screw machine at Windsor, Vermont in 1906. By the sale of rights the two designs were eventually merged in the Acme-Gridley machine. Later, Gridley became chief engineer of the New Britain Machine Company for whom he designed the New Britain-Gridley automatic. Next, Gridley's foreman at Windsor, Frank L. Cone, evolved a further refinement of the four-spindle automatic and formed the Cone Automatic Machine Company to exploit his invention. The distinguishing feature of Cone's machine was that instead of mounting the camshaft with its drums below the bed, the shaft was supported overhead by a top-bed extending the full length of the machine. This arrangement had many advantages and resulted in a very precise and versatile mass production tool. Finally, there came the Pennsylvanian Fay automatic. James Hartness bought the patents covering this machine and it was manufactured by the Jones & Lamson company.

Interchangeable arms manufacture produced other machine tool developments during the 1850s. Root, Howe and Lawrence between them produced an accurate profile-cutting machine between 1848 and 1852. This eliminated the trouble Blanchard had earlier experienced in fitting inaccurate lock-plates to his stocks. In 1855 Elisha Root designed for Samuel Colt a neat little vertical slotting machine for cutting the splines in the magazine of the Colt revolver through which the cartridge ejector spindle slides. Multi-spindle drilling machines appeared also. An illustration of 1859 shows a Lincoln machine with four spindles, feed being applied by raising the worktable. This could be done either by hand lever or foot treadle via a pinion and rack. The use of machines such as this led directly to two closely connected developments of great historical importance.

The need in interchangeable arms manufacture to drill many holes with speed and accuracy emphasised the deficiency, in both these respects, of the old spearpoint type of drill bit whose origins were lost in the mists of antiquity. It was in answer to this problem that the mechanics of New England evolved the twist drill such as we know today. Its overwhelming superiority was immediately obvious but its production was at first infinitely laborious and costly. One of the first firms to make these new drills was the Providence Tool Company of Providence, Rhode Island, whither Frederick Howe had transferred his services after the failure of Robbins & Lawrence. This Company was required to produce accurate twist drills for forming the holes in the percussion nipple of the new percussion lock rifle which was built in immense quantities during the civil war. One day in 1861, Howe watched a craftsman making one of these drills by patiently forming the spiral flutes on a length of tool steel rod with a rat-tail file. Howe pondered whether this tedious operation could not be done mechanically and he subsequently discussed the problem with his friend Joseph R. Brown (1810–1876) of the neighbouring firm of Brown & Sharpe. Brown's answer was to design and build the first truly universal milling machine.

The firm of Brown & Sharpe was founded by David Brown and his son Joseph in 1833. Lucian Sharpe was taken into partnership in 1850, but Joseph Brown remained the technical master of the concern throughout. For nearly 20 years the repair of clocks, watches and scientific instruments was the mainstay of the little business, but in 1850 Joseph Brown invented and built an automatic linear dividing engine for graduating rules. This proved the stepping stone to fortune. From it stemmed the steel rules, the vernier calipers, the hand micrometers and the precision gauges and measuring instruments which made the name of Brown & Sharpe familiar in the workshops and toolrooms of the world. The firm did not manufacture machine tools at all until the civil war when Howe persuaded Brown to help him re-equip the Providence Tool Company with machines to manufacture percussion lock muskets. The two men had a profound respect for each other's ability and their collaboration proved most fruitful. Howe contributed a lifetime's experience of machine tool design, whereas Brown brought to their problems a fresh eye and a mind schooled in those exacting disciplines of the instrument maker which had earlier had so beneficial an influence on Bramah, Maudslay and Clement.

The first fruit of this collaboration to be built by Brown & Sharpe was a turret lathe. The general design of this machine was Howe's, but Brown added certain features of his own; a self-revolving turret actuated by ratchet and pawl from the return motion of the slide, a reversing die holder and a device for releasing, feeding and gripping the bar stock while the machine was in motion. The problem of the twist drill and the machine which solved it came next and in this case the credit is entirely due to Joseph Brown as Howe was the first to acknowledge.

Brown's first universal milling machine and his drawings for it have been preserved by the Brown & Sharpe Company. It is of such historic importance that it merits description in some detail. Here the 'knee and column' type of milling machine which had been struggling towards birth for so many years finally emerges in a form of such classic 'rightness' and simplicity that at first glance the machine does not proclaim the genius of its maker. In other words, like all truly inspired designs, it seems obvious. The cutter spindle with its stepped pulley drive is carried in two bearings on the top of a hollow box column of strictly functional form which accommodates a tool cupboard. A knee is supported in slides on the face of this column and is adjustable vertically by the crank handle at the front through bevel gears and a lead screw. A vertical spindle parallel with the lead screw carries an adjustable stop limiting the extent to which the knee can be raised. By means of this stop, therefore, the maximum permissible depth of cut could be pre-set. On the top of the knee there is, first, a slide moving horizontally in line with the cutter spindle by means of a screw, the squared end of which accepts the same crank-handle as is used for vertical adjustment. Upon this slide a gibbed block carrying the table is mounted on a vertical axis. This enables the table to be angled horizontally through a graduated arc and then clamped firmly in position.

The table itself resembles a miniature lathe with head and tailstock units, the positions of which can be altered by sliding them along the flat guideways. Both have dead centres for mounting a workpiece, or alternatively the headstock centre can be replaced by a universal chuck. The table lead screw can either be rotated by hand or by power. The power feed is by stepped pulley driven by belt from the rear of the cutter spindle and thence by shaft to a pinion and crown wheel. The shaft has two universal joints to allow for the vertical adjustment of the knee. The headstock unit can be rotated by a hand crank, provided with an index, through mitre gears and a worm and wheel. Alternatively this motion can be derived from the table lead screw via spur wheels which engage the mitre gears. By this means the spiral flutes of twist drills could be milled automatically and their pitch varied by using change wheels. Normally the machine cut right-hand spirals, but Brown made provision for the addition of an extra wheel to the change gear train to reverse its motion so that the machine could cut left-hand spirals if desired. The headstock unit is clamped between quadrants in its housing so that it can be adjusted upwards or downwards to any degree of angularity. In this way the machine could be used to cut taper spirals or to mill the straight flutes in taper reamers. The power feed is engaged by a lever and it also has an automatic stop. Finally the machine can be used for plain milling by removing the head and tail units and substituting a simple work vice which fits in the table guideways.

This first historic machine was delivered to the Providence Tool Company on 14 March 1862, where it perfectly solved the problem which had brought about its conception. By so doing the cutting speed and precision of the drilling machine was greatly enhanced and over the following decade the now familiar twist drill appeared in engineering workshops all over the world. But it speedily became apparent to engineers that besides cutting twist drills Brown's versatile tool could do many other jobs which had hitherto required expensive hand work and that it could also be used to cut gears of many types if suitably formed milling cutters were fitted to it. Consequently the limited resources of the Brown & Sharpe works were soon taxed to the utmost to meet the demand. Ten machines had been built and sold by the end of 1862 and thereafter production steadily increased. Later and larger machines intended for heavier duty had back gearing for the cutter spindle drive and the type of cylindrical and adjustable overarm support for the end of the cutter spindle first used by Root. Adjustable braces between the end of the overarm and the knee subsequently appeared on many heavy-duty machines although this limited to some extent the advantages of the knee and column type.

Brown's universal machine did not supersede the earlier bed type of milling machine developed by Howe and popularised by the Lincoln Company. The latter was generally adequate for the plain milling operations required in routine manufacture where great versatility was not necessary and for this reason it became known as the Manufacturing Miller. The universal miller, on the other hand, quickly found its place in general engineering shops where 'short run' production was the rule and in the tool rooms of large manufacturers. In 1863, while he was at the Providence Tool Company, Frederick Howe produced an improved bed-type miller upon which, with the aid of an elaborately formed cutter, the compound curves of musket lockplates were milled in one operation. In 1868, Howe joined the Brown & Sharpe Company where he designed a somewhat similar machine which was built side by side with the universal type. It appeared in the firm's catalogue as the 'No. 12 plain milling machine', but became known in the trade as the 'Howe Miller'. Whereas his earlier miller designs had been exploited by others, this—his last—enjoyed a wide sale.

Joseph Brown followed up his masterly universal milling machine with an improved design of formed-tooth milling cutter for gear cutting which had a far-reaching influence. His work on clocks and his dividing engine had focussed his attention on the problems of precision gear cutting and in 1855 he had built a gear-cutting machine using a formed milling cutter for producing involute teeth. The blank arbor was vertical with an index plate below the table and change wheels ensured the correct divisions. This machine was built solely for the firm's own use but later, when Brown & Sharpe commenced manufacturing machine tools, it featured in their catalogue as the 'Precision' gear cutter. The facility with which his successful universal milling machine could cut gears emphasised anew the deficiency of the cutters currently used. Toothed cutters capable of cutting a substantial chip had then been in use for over 12 years but the design of their comparatively small teeth was such that to maintain the accuracy of a formed gear cutter was almost impossible. When the teeth wore down the only means of restoring their form was to anneal the cutter, raise the teeth by peaning them with a hand punch, true them in a lathe, using a templet, sharpen them with a file and then reharden. Brown's answer to this problem was to produce a cutter with segmental teeth each of which, in cross section, conformed exactly to the contour of the tooth form required. This cross section was uniform throughout the length of each tooth, the necessary cutting clearance being obtained by inclining the crown of each tooth in relation to the circumference of the cutter. Such a tool could be sharpened simply by grinding away the face of each tooth and this process could be repeated until the cutter became too weak for further use without in any way altering its formed profile. That this improvement, too, has that quality of simplicity which appears obvious is further proof of Brown's genius. It had an inspiring effect upon engineers of the time with the result that further improvements in the design of milling cutters speedily followed.

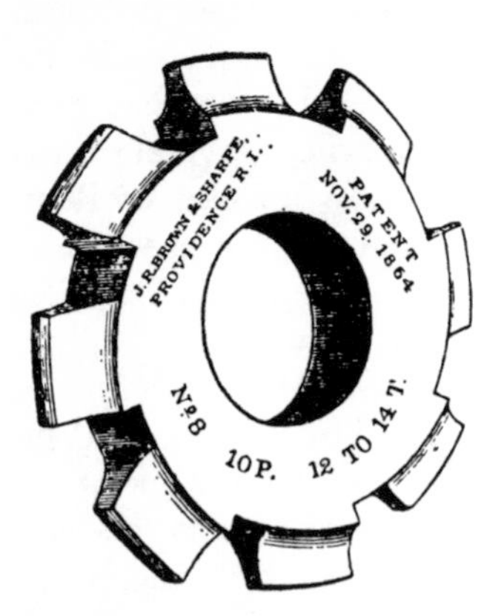

80 *Joseph Brown's improved formed milling cutter for gear cutting, 1864*

So far this chapter has been concerned solely with New England because it was, naturally enough, the cradle of American engineering and machine tool making. But in a vigorous society that was expanding so rapidly both economically and territorially New England could not long retain a monopoly. The 1850s and '60s saw the rapid industrial expansion of Philadelphia which made that city for a time the greatest centre of engineering and tool-making in America. As in New England, engineering in Philadelphia began in small workshops serving the textile trade, but thereafter development took a different course, the emphasis being on heavy engineering. A decisive influence on this development was the great Baldwin locomotive works in Philadelphia, the history of which began when Matthias W. Baldwin placed his first locomotive on the rails of the Philadelphia & Germanstown Railroad in January 1833. We have seen how the coming of railways brought about a rapid expansion of the Manchester machine-tool industry and in Philadelphia their effect was the same.

In the rise of the machine-tool industry in Philadelphia the dominating figure was William Sellers (1824–1905) who was born in Pennsylvania and opened his first small tool-making shop in the city in 1848. It grew rapidly into a great business. Sellers has been called the Whitworth of America and the contributions which the two men made to engineering and tool-making in their respective countries were indeed remarkably similar. As illustrations show, despite the ingenuity of their mechanism, the machine tools made by the earlier generation of New England mechanics appear remarkably archaic to us. This is due to the curious fact that in the design of machine beds and their supports, architectural conventions persisted longer in the new world than in the old. Machine designers appear to have been more concerned with elegance than with strength and it was Sellers who, by example, brought about the reform which Whitworth had earlier effected in England.

Writing in 1915, Joseph Roe said of him:

> Almost from the first Sellers cut loose from the accepted designs of the day. He was among the first to realise that red paint, beads and mouldings, and architectural embellishments were false in machine design. He introduced the 'machine gray' paint which has become universal; made the form of the machine follow the function to be performed and freed it from all pockets and beading. Like Bement [another Philadelphian machine tool maker] he realised that American tools then being built were too light; and they both put more metal into their machines than was the practice elsewhere. From the first he adopted standards and adhered to them so closely that repair parts can be supplied today for machines made fifty years ago.

At the Vienna Exhibition of 1873, lathes made by Sellers & Co. were awarded first place for their practical design and excellent performance.

In 1864 Sellers proposed a range of screw threads and bolt sizes which were adopted as standard by the U.S. government in 1868 and came into use throughout America within the next ten years. He rejected the Whitworth thread form with its 55° angle and rounded profile in favour of a 60° angle and a flat profile at the base and crown of the threads, arguing that this form was easier and therefore cheaper to make with accuracy. Seller's thread form was adopted as the standard for Europe at an international congress at Zürich in 1898.

In 1873 Sellers became President of the Midvale Steel Company and it was here that Frederick Taylor began, with the encouragement of Sellers, his experiments with cutting tools which went on for 26 years. As we shall see, they would have a profound effect on the art of cutting metals and on machine-tool design generally.

From 1814 onwards the methods evolved in the New England armouries were applied to the making of clocks, first of wood and later of brass, the pioneer of this movement being Eli Terry. The purpose of the 'American system' here was significantly different, the object of interchangeability being to cheapen the product and not to facilitate repair. The aim was to produce a clock so cheaply that it would cost the customer less to buy a new clock than to have his old one repaired. So speedily and successfully was this achieved that the price of a clock was reduced to less than 50 cents and by 1855 New England was producing 400,000 clocks a year, many of them being exported to Europe. By this time watches also were being produced by the new methods by the American Watch Company at Waltham, Massachusetts.

In 1846 Elias Howe invented his sewing machine and the rival designs of Wilson, Singer and Gibbs speedily followed. Here was a precision machine whose construction suited the methods evolved in the armouries and could only be produced at an attractive price by such methods. Consequently in the 1850s a number of the New England armouries and machine tool makers entered this new field, but the great demand for arms during the civil war called a temporary halt to this process. When that war was over, however, the application of the American system of manufacture was greatly extended.[1] This led to the rapid expansion of America's machine-tool industry and the application of features evolved in the New England armouries to machines of heavier calibre. Skilled mechanics in the workshops of New England and Philadelphia began to look westwards and from 1880 onwards they began to cross the Alleghenies in increasing numbers. Settling in the state of Ohio at Cincinnati, Cleveland and Hamilton they prospered so well that they soon began to rival the older eastern tool-makers and Cincinnati ultimately ousted Philadelphia to become the machine-tool-making capital of America. To quote but one example, in 1880 William Holtz began making fluted taps in his kitchen in Cincinnati, using a home-made milling machine because he was too poor to buy one. His venture became the Cincinnati Milling Machine Company which now operates the largest single machine tool building plant in the world. Later believers in the maxim 'Go west young man' leap-frogged the already prosperous industry in Ohio and founded successful machine-tool businesses in Indiana, Illinois and Wisconsin.

[1] By 1880 one American firm alone was producing 50,000 sewing machines a year as compared with a total European production of only 15,000.

Other New England mechanics, instead of taking the road to the Middle West, saw an outlet for their enterprise in the old world. One of the first of these men to leave America after the civil war was Charles Churchill, the son of an engineer, born in Hampden, Connecticut, in 1837. The purpose of his visit to England in 1861 was to instal special machines for braiding crinoline frames, but in order to assist his friend Hiram Maxim with the production problems of his machine gun, Churchill also imported some metal-cutting machine tools. The great interest aroused by these machines made Churchill realise that the importation of such tools to Britain would be a worthwhile undertaking. He founded Charles Churchill & Company in 1865 for this purpose and remained in Britain until his death in 1916. In 1906 he founded a second business, the Churchill Machine Tool Company of Manchester, to manufacture machine tools in Britain. It was through the agency of such men as Charles Churchill that American and British ideas on machine-tool design, so long divergent, began to converge. Churchill is said to have imported the first Morse twist drill, the first self-centring chuck—by Cushman—and the first hand micrometer—by Brown & Sharpe—ever seen in England.

If we could visit an up-to-date American machine shop of 1870 we should find in use in a well-developed form all the engineer's basic tools except two—the precision grinding machine and the broaching machine. The rapid evolution of the grinding machine after centuries of slumber would have a momentous effect on other machine tools and on the production techniques which made, first the bicycle and later the motor car practical manufacturing propositions. The genius of Joseph Brown and his design team played an important part in the story of the precision grinding machine which deserves a chapter to itself.

CHAPTER 9

The Precision Grinding Machine and its Influence

None of the precision metal-cutting tools so far developed could touch a hardened steel surface. The effect of the rapid development of technology during the nineteenth century was that this disability became ever more acutely and widely felt as the years went by and the speeds and stresses imposed on machines by their designers everywhere mounted. Precision components of hardened steel were what the designers needed but the engineers could not supply them. No matter how accurately such parts were machined in their soft state, some distortion inevitably occurred during the subsequent hardening process. What was needed was a tool which would give precise dimensional accuracy and perfect finish to a component *after* it had been hardened and it was obvious that the only tool to do this was a grinding wheel.

From 1830 onwards, engineers in England, Germany and America produced a number of general or special-purpose grinding machines employing either natural sandstones, segments of natural stone (Nasmyth), or emery granules used in conjunction with a leather-faced wheel or embedded in some soft metal or wood. By such means the verge wheels of clocks, loom spindles, rollers for paper mills and other purposes, needles and ball valves for pump clacks were successfully finished in the hardened state. A high finish was obtained in this way but exact dimensional accuracy was out of the question. In the production of interchangeable precision components the best-designed machine and the most skilful operator would be defeated by the unpredictably variable performance of the natural wheel or the emery lap.

Until 1856, when supplies were found in Massachusetts, the Greek island of Naxos was the chief world source of natural emery, but from 1825 onwards corundum, a much purer form of aluminium oxide, was exported to Europe and America from India, Ceylon, Burma and Madagascar. Substantial deposits of corundum were found in North Carolina and Georgia in 1871 and later in Canada. The cutting properties of corundum were eventually found to be far superior to emery, but neither could be used as a natural stone because the crystal formation was not sufficiently regular. Hence the effective use of either in a grinding machine must depend on bonding the crystals with some other material so as to make an artificial stone. Between 1840 and 1870, numerous bonding substances and techniques were tried out on both sides of the Atlantic, some of which were manufactured with fair success. The most unlikely ingredients were mixed with the abrasive powder and then bonded by adding gums, glues or cements. Vulcanised rubber (Vulcanite) enjoyed a limited success as a bond when introduced in 1857 by the Frenchman Deplangue and it is used to this day for certain purposes, notably for cut-off wheels and for the regulating wheels of centreless grinding machines.

The first attempt to produce a vitrified wheel was made in England by Henry Barclay in 1842. He pressed a mixture of Stourbridge clay and emery into moulds and fired it, but try as he would he could not prevent cracking and distortion from occurring during firing. Another Englishman, F. Ransome, was more successful in 1857, using a bond of silicate of potash or soda and firing the mixture at a lower temperature than Barclay had used. Bryan Donkin tested the cutting power of one of Ransome's stones and pronounced it to be 50 times better than the best natural sandstone wheel. Only limited progress was made at this time, however, for the difficulties confronting these pioneers were very great. The composition of the wheel must be uniform, it must run truly, be perfectly balanced and, above all, it must be strong enough to resist centrifugal forces because the bursting of a wheel at high speed could have lethal results.

In 1872 Gilbert Hart began producing silicate wheels in America, but in the following year Sven Pulson, a potter in the small shop of Franklin B. Norton, at Worcester, Massachusetts, told his master he believed he could make a better wheel than Hart out of clay. Where Barclay in England had failed 30 years before, Pulson succeeded at the third attempt, using a mixture of emery, clay and the slip clay which was used in the shop for glazing. Feldspar was later substituted for the slip clay when F. B. Norton patented the process in 1877. This was the first really successful artificial grinding wheel. It made precision grinding practicable and it led rapidly to the formation of a number of grinding-wheel manufacturing companies in New England and Philadelphia. Owing to ill health, F. B. Norton sold his business in 1885 to the Norton Emery Wheel Company, known today as the Norton Company.

The first attempts to do precision grinding work were made by the simple but unsatisfactory expedient of fixing a grinding wheel arbor to the back of the cross slide of an ordinary lathe. The wheel was belt-driven from a long roller pulley, thus enabling it to be traversed between the lathe centres, and the manual cross feed was used to apply the cut.

81 *Grinding lathe,* c. *1860* (*Rose*)

Water was sponged onto the workpiece while grinding and it was impossible to protect the guideways from the lethal mixture of water and grinding dust so formed. Although work-rests were introduced, such adaptations lacked the necessary rigidity and it was extremely difficult to prevent chatter. The fact that the choice of speeds for grinding wheel and workpiece were limited and selected empirically did not help matters. Nevertheless, plain cylindrical grinding was done in this way; also some internal grinding by chucking the workpiece and fitting a grinding wheel of small diameter on a different arbor.

In 1868, the American J. M. Poole endeavoured to finish grind some large hardened calender rolls by this method using a heavy-duty lathe and single wheel, but failed miserably to achieve the high accuracy required. By 1870 Poole had built a special heavy roll-grinding machine working on a principle never used before in a machine tool. This solved the problem with such complete success that similar machines are still being made. The lathe carriage, traversed by a lead screw, supports on vertical columns and knife-edged pivots two pendant swing frames each embodying a grinding wheel with its arbor mounted on a cross slide. These oppose each other on either side of the roller to be ground, hanging like pendulums from their pivots. With the machine at rest the positions of the two wheels on their cross slides are adjusted so that the distance between their peripheries is exactly equal to the required finished diameter of the roll. When the machine is started and the traverse engaged, the mechanism acts like a giant pair of calipers, sizing the roller throughout its length. So long as the roller is true to size there will be no cut, but any inaccuracy will bring pressure to bear on one or both grinding wheels, force the swing frames out of the vertical and cause cutting to take place until dimensional accuracy restores the equilibrium. Thus, instead of accurately machined guideways, Poole's ingenious machine utilised the inertia of a pendulum to achieve a result which proved to be accurate within 0·000025 of an inch, a degree of precision never before achieved on a heavy production machine tool.

For small-scale cylindrical grinding operations Poole's method was not applicable and in order to mitigate the defects of the lathe adaptation, Pratt & Whitney and other American tool-builders produced a special grinding lathe. This had a heavily weighted carriage in an attempt to achieve solidity and so prevent chatter, a quick reversible drive to the carriage by stepped pulleys giving three speeds, and guards on the carriage extending over the ways to protect them from abrasive dust. Such lathes were frequently fitted with a special attachment for grinding tapers.

Between 1860 and 1870 a very similar grinding lathe was developed by Brown & Sharpe for the purpose of grinding needle bars, foot bars and spindles for the Wilcox & Gibbs sewing machine which the firm had undertaken to manufacture. Although some of these lathes were built for sale, practical experience in his own shop made Joseph Brown well aware of their shortcomings. To produce consistently accurate work called for the greatest skill and care—so much so that Thomas Goodrum, the firm's first grinder operator, commanded a wage of seven dollars a day in 1867 and was the only man on the place, other than the two managing partners, who assumed as of right the dignity of a tall silk hat. It was said that Goodrum's art consisted in knowing just where to stand and how to lay a judicious hand on the machine at precisely the right place and moment. So subtle an artistry could not be hurried and consequently grinding operations became a serious bottle-neck in manufacture.

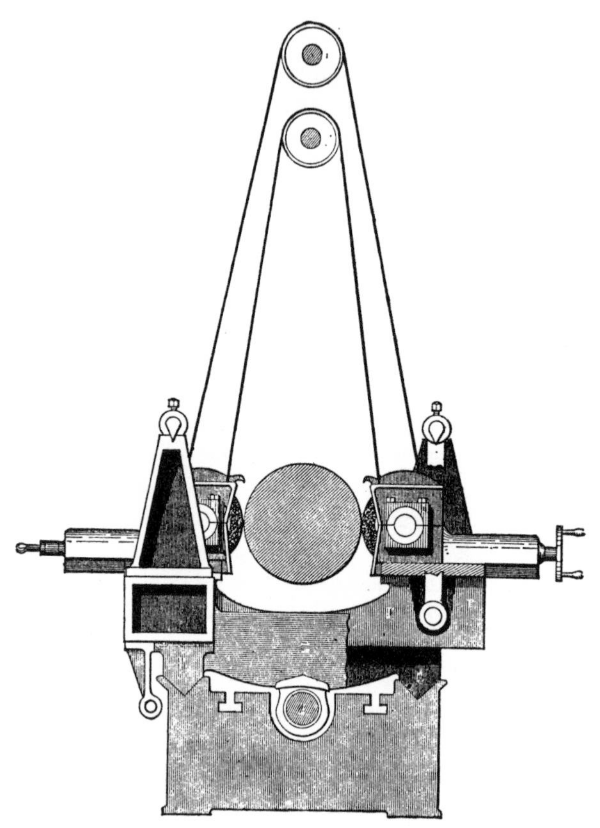

82 *J. M. Poole's precision roll-grinding machine, 1870* (*Rose*)

To overcome this difficulty, Joseph Brown conceived an improved 'Universal Grinding Machine' in 1868, but owing to pressure of other concerns the drawing incorporating his ideas was set aside. The scheme was not revived until 1874 when Brown himself appears to have played little active part in it but to have left the design and construction of the first machine in the hands of his staff. The prototype Universal Grinder was installed in the Brown & Sharpe machine shop and was set running a few days after the death of Joseph Brown in July 1876.

Although Joshua Rose, in his *Modern Machine Shop Practice*, describes this new Brown & Sharpe tool as a 'Universal Grinding Lathe' it bore little resemblance to its makeshift predecessors. To begin with, the mode of operation was reversed; instead of the wheel traversing along the workpiece, the workpiece now travelled past the wheel. In the way the head

83 *First Universal Grinding Machine by Brown & Sharpe, 1876* (*Rose*)

and tailstock units are mounted on a traversing table, the machine is more closely akin to Brown's universal milling machine than to the lathe. The length of travel of the table is automatically controlled by adjustable trips at the front of the machine and for taper grinding the upper table slides can be angled by means of an adjusting screw at one end of the traversing table. The table is so designed that the guideways are well protected from abrasive dust, although on this machine the danger of so fouling the ways was reduced by feeding coolant water from a nozzle and conducting it away into a bucket at the back of the bed. On this first machine it would appear from the illustration that the tailstock originally had a live centre driven, like the headstock, by belt from a drum pulley on an overhead countershaft. Later a spring-loaded dead centre would become recognised as the best method of ensuring precision.

The grinding-wheel spindle runs in double taper bearings of hardened steel. The wheel arbor is mounted on a cross slide or saddle and the wheel is drawn into cut by the indexed hand wheel at the front. The cross-saddle slides can be adjusted to alter the angle of the feed in relation to the work table. The arbor can be removed and replaced by a special attachment for internal grinding. For this purpose a chuck can be fitted to the headstock and the headstock itself angled for grinding internal tapers.

It has been said that this machine exhibited defects of detail which would have been avoided if Joseph Brown had concerned himself directly with its construction. Nevertheless, the inspiration was his and, shortcomings notwithstanding, the result was an immense advance on anything built before and the parent of all precision grinding machines. Like Maudslay's lathe and Brown's universal miller, this was a definitive design, for despite many detail refinements the universal grinder of today is recognisably the same tool.

It was obviously not a coincidence that the construction of this first precision grinder followed so closely upon the appearance of Sven Pulson's vitreous emery wheel in 1873. No doubt it was the improved performance of this wheel that persuaded Joseph Brown to take his 1868 idea out of cold storage. The combination of the new wheel and the new machine was so speedily successful that plain and surface grinders of many different types were soon being built in America by Brown & Sharpe and other tool-builders. The planer type, the post type and the face type, they had ancestors, but none had appeared in *precision* form before.

At the time the first universal grinding machine was being developed a young man named Henry Leland was working as a foreman in the Brown & Sharpe shops, having earlier served his apprenticeship there. He evidently had no doubt about the significance of the new tool, or of the part played in its development by Brown himself, for, many years later, when he had become President of the Cadillac Motor Company, Leland recalled those early days and wrote:

> What I consider Mr. Brown's greatest achievement was the Universal Grinding Machine. In developing and designing this machine he stepped out on entirely new ground and developed a machine which has enabled us to harden our work first and then grind it with the utmost accuracy ... If all these machines should be suddenly taken away, it is hard to imagine

84 *The first Brown & Sharpe universal milling machine, 1862*

85 *The first Fellows gear-shaping machine, 1897*

86 *Corliss bevel-gear-cutting machine at the Centennial Exhibition, Philadelphia, 1876*

87 *Brown & Sharpe heavy-duty universal milling machine with overarm support,* c. *1870*

what the results would be. It would be impossible to make any more hardened work for the best parts of our machinery and tools, that would be round, true and accurate in every detail to the closest possible limits. This in my judgement is one of the most remarkable inventions and too much cannot be said in its praise, or in acknowledgement of Mr. Brown's perseverance, wonderful initiative and genius . . . I know of none who deserves a higher place, or who has done so much for the modern high standards of American manufacture of interchangeable parts as Joseph Brown.

By the time Henry Leland wrote these words the grinding machine was fast becoming an indispensable production tool in the automobile engineer's machine shop, but this is a later story. Initially, the technique of precision grinding exercised its greatest influence on production indirectly through the tool room. In Brown & Sharpe's own shops and elsewhere precision grinding vastly improved and facilitated the production of precision gauges and measuring instruments of all kinds. On the shop floor precision tools and precision measuring instruments interacted vigorously during the 1880s to produce far higher standards of accuracy. Whereas James Watt, in 1776, referred to a thin sixpence as a measure of accuracy and Joseph Clement referred in a similar context to a sheet of paper, the mechanic of the 1880s used a thousandth part of an inch as his yardstick. His son would soon be thinking in terms of a tenth of a thousandth.

Precision grinding machines also made infinitely easier the production of accurate hardened-steel cutting tools of all kinds: drills, taps, reamers and, above all, milling cutters. The high cost and difficulty of making and maintaining the cutters had hitherto checked the development and application of the milling machine and limited its use as a manufacturing tool to those plain milling operations which could be performed with the simplest type of cutter. Now that precision grinding made available better cutters in a great variety of forms, new types of horizontal and vertical spindle milling machines soon began to proliferate in the machine shops. Many of the jobs which had previously been done on planers, shapers, vertical lathes or boring machines were now performed with far greater speed and efficiency by the new milling machines. For example, a workpiece requiring machining on one face and four sides would need to be set up five times on the table of a shaping machine, whereas on a vertical spindle milling machine it could be machined far more rapidly at one setting and with only one change of cutter.

Gear cutting by means of formed milling cutters came into wider use owing to the greater ease with which the hardened cutters could be produced and maintained by grinding, and Brown & Sharpe marketed Brown's patent formed cutter from 1864 onwards. The first recorded fully automatic gear-cutting machine was of the formed milling cutter type and was built by the firm of Gage, Warner and Whitney of Nashua, New Hampshire about 1860. This made ingenious use of the ancient principle of the weighted tumbling bob to throw a clutch and so reverse the cutter feed. When the cutter returned to its starting point the tumbling bob was thrown again and at the same moment the gear blank was automatically indexed to the next tooth.

At the Paris Exhibition of 1867, William Sellers exhibited a machine of the same type in which the sequence of automatic motions was so controlled by stops that it was impossible for the cutter to advance unless and until the gear blank had been correctly indexed for the next tooth. When all the teeth on the blank had been cut, the machine stopped automatically.

In 1877 the three firms of Craven Brothers in Manchester, England, Gould & Eberhardt and Brown & Sharpe in America all marketed similar gear-cutting machines and from this date forward the use of such automatic tools for producing involute straight-cut spur or bevel gears of small or medium size extended very rapidly. The teeth of very large gears were planed by a single-point tool controlled by templet to produce the correct profile, and machines of this type also appeared in automatic form in the 1880s. The most celebrated maker of templet gear-cutting machines at this time was the Gleason Company of Rochester, New York, who produced machines to cut gears up to 15 feet in diameter. Such very large wheels were generally cast to standards of accuracy which left the minimum amount of metal to be removed by the machine.

Certain cycloidal tooth forms could not be produced by any type of formed cutter. The alternative was a gear-cutting machine operating on the generating principle whereby, instead of indexing the gear blank, the cutter and the gear blank are given synchronous motions, so that, in effect, the two are correctly meshed together. The moulding generating cutter may be either a straight-toothed rack or a gear which does literally engage the blank and although the describing generating machine uses a single-point tool it operates upon the same principle. In the late nineteenth century the describing generating method became popular, particularly in small shops, because it required no elaborate and expensive cutters but used a simple cutting tool and could be adapted to the shaping machine.

Although, as we saw in an earlier chapter, the American Joseph Saxton had demonstrated the describing method upon a small scale in London in the 1840s, the first two production designs of this type were the work of German engineers, E. Hagen-Thorn in 1872 and Gustav Hermann in

1877. Germany, indeed, was rapidly becoming a force to be reckoned with in machine-tool design. Hagen-Thorn did not construct a machine but indicated clearly how a competent engineer could adapt an ordinary shaping machine to cut involute gears using a double-pointed tool for cutting each flank of a tooth alternately. Hermann's method was even more easily adaptable to the ordinary shaping machine. It used a single-point tool to cut either involute or cycloidal spur gears.

In America Ambrose Swasey and George Grant designed machines of this type and the former, using a small cylindrical cutter in a machine based on a lathe, was built for sale by Pratt & Whitney. But the method was more popular at this period in Europe than in America. This is understandable because, though accurate, the describing generating method was slow and therefore better suited to European short-run production methods than to the American system.

In 1884, Hugo Bilgram of Philadelphia produced a gear shaper working on the moulding generating principle for the express purpose of machining the small bevel gears for the chainless bicycle which was then enjoying a great vogue in America. In doing so he introduced a new tooth form known as the octoid. This was followed in 1885 by a most ingenious machine designed by Swasey to cut spur gears on the moulding principle by means of a rotating milling cutter. This cutter passed across the circumference of the gear blank, the axes of the two being at right angles to one another. Since both were given synchronous motion the effect was that of a gear and a straight rack in mesh.

The gear-cutting machine which represents the climax of this phase of development did not appear until 1897. This was the Fellows gear shaper, one of the classic machine-tool designs. This machine, too, is of the moulding generating type, but instead of the straight rack principle as used by Swasey, Fellows adopted a complete gear with hardened and sharpened teeth. This cutter was used in what is essentially a specialised slotting machine. The gear blank is mounted on a vertical arbor and the cutter reciprocates vertically as the blank and the cutter slowly revolve synchronously. The machine could cut either external or internal spur gears but not bevel gears. Fellows designed the teeth of his cutter in such a way that one cutter could be used to produce gears of any diameter provided the pitch was the same, but their teeth must be of the specific helix angle which the cutter was designed to produce.

Although the Fellows gear shaper speedily found its way into the workshops of the world, the most significant feature of the invention was not the shaping machine itself but the machine which Fellows devised to make the hardened cutters for it. The success of his shaping machine depended absolutely on his ability to produce with great accuracy a hardened-steel cutter gear. Fellows first cut the gear a little oversize on a gear shaper. After hardening, it was then finished to exact size on a gear-grinding machine. This worked on the describing generating principle using an emery wheel instead of a steel cutting tool. This precision gear-grinding alone made the Fellows gear shaper possible; it also foreshadowed the not far distant day when the grinding of hardened gears would become a routine production operation.

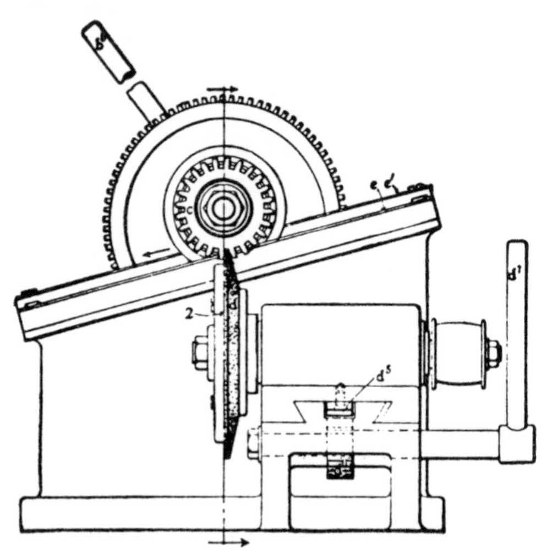

88 *Fellows gear-cutter grinding machine and bevel-gear generator, 1897* (American Machinist)

The remarkable thing about E. R. Fellows is that he was comparatively inexperienced at the time he designed his machine tools. He was not trained as an engineer but worked as a window dresser in a drapery and carpet shop until he was 22 years old. James Hartness must have realised that the young man possessed latent engineering talent for he brought Fellows with him when he joined the Jones & Lamson Machine Company in 1889. After only one week in the shops, Fellows was transferred to the drawing office where he at once displayed that extraordinary flair for design which, only a few years later, enabled him to produce these two outstanding machines. Their success was such that Fellows was able to found his own Company to exploit them, the Fellows Gear Shaper Company of Springfield, Vermont.

So much for the indirect influence of the precision grinder as a toolroom machine. As a production tool its application was limited during the period covered by this chapter. Production engineers looked upon it as a means of prolonging the life of machined components which were subjected to hard wear. Such components were machined in exactly the same way as heretofore except that they were finished slightly oversize. They were then hardened and ground to size. By 1891, railway-wheel tyres and axle journals were being hardened and surface ground; so were the valve motion pins, links and similar hard-wearing parts of locomotives.

Yet for some years this application of the grinding machine was largely confined to America. Elsewhere, particularly in England, the machine had to overcome the quite erroneous belief that its use on bearing surfaces was undesirable because the ground surface absorbed abrasive particles from the wheel.

In production, therefore, precision grinding was at first an additional finishing process. It seemed that engineers were so dazzled by the fact that they now had a tool which could finish a hardened part to the most precise limits that they could not see beyond it. The man who convinced them otherwise, who first demonstrated the fact that the precision grinder could be a heavy production metal-cutting tool of great efficiency and capability, was the American, Charles H. Norton. Norton's work was only one aspect of a remarkable revolution which began in the closing years of the nineteenth century and radically changed the design of every type of metal-cutting machine. It coincided almost exactly with the birth of the motor car and the conjunction was most fortuitous. History repeated itself. A hundred years earlier the future of Watt's steam engine and Stephenson's locomotive had lain in the hands of the tool-makers; now the success of the internal combustion engine, the motor car and the aeroplane depended no less on their ability to produce the tools for the job. Had they failed to do so, the motor car might have remained an inventor's dream or, at best, a costly toy and Wilbur Wright would never have made his historic powered flight at Kittyhawk in 1903.

CHAPTER 10

Metal Cutting becomes a Science

An engineer of today, looking back over a long lifetime of experience as did William Fairbairn in 1861, could recall a revolution in engineering technique just as momentous. The term of Fairbairn's life covered the invention and wide application of self-acting machine tools. A century later, in a similar term of years, the performance of these tools has been completely transformed. In the earlier revolution the steam engine supplied the incentive, first directly to enable the engine itself to be built and later indirectly by creating a demand for power-driven machinery in the textile and other trades. Of the second revolution the internal combustion engine was the spur, particularly in its application to the road vehicle. It would be true to say that from 1895 to the present day, the motor industry has been the biggest consumer of engineering machine tools and has brought to bear upon the tool-builder the greatest pressure to improve and develop his designs.

When the automobile engineers and the machine tool makers first put their heads together they started one of those closely interacting sequences of development that have been so marked a feature of the industrial revolution ever since the days of Thomas Newcomen. The machine tool maker's new tools enabled the automobile designer to introduce better bearings and better gears and so to produce more efficient, refined and compact transmission systems. The machine tool maker quickly perceived that he could adopt the new bearings and gears to great advantage in, say, a lathe headstock with its built-in change-speed mechanism. The new lathe was supplied to the motor industry and so initiated another similar sequence.

This influence of the motor industry was so important that this chapter might have been called 'machine tools and the motor car'. It might equally well have been titled 'the application of electric power' because the marriage between the electric motor and the machine tool was of crucial significance. It was the most important event in the machine shops since the steam engine had superseded the foot treadle or the waterwheel. More fundamental than either of these factors, however, was the improvement of the metal-cutting tools used in the machines. The most expert wood-carver could not work with blunt chisels and similarly the performance of the finest metal-cutting machine is dependent on that of the tool it uses whether it be a single-point tool, a milling cutter or a grinding wheel. It follows from this that the cutting capacity of the tool must be the starting point of machine-tool design and that the most efficient machine will be that which will enable its operator to utilise that capacity to the full. There is, however, a big snag to this seemingly simple proposition. The machine tool designer cannot take the cutting tool as his starting point and build round it the most efficient machine unless he has accurate knowledge of the potential performance of the tool, any more than an automobile engineer could design the chassis and transmission system of a motor car without knowing the power output curve of the engine to be fitted to it.

As the motoring historian knows, by no means every designer succeeded in building a satisfactory vehicle round the internal combustion engine, although the problems are simple compared with those confronting the designer of machine tools. There are so many variable factors involved that it is very difficult to make a true assessment of the optimum performance of a cutting tool. Yet it is upon such an assessment that the designer must base the strength of his machine, the proportions of its parts and the selection of the gear ratios for the work spindle and feed drives. Here we reach the real crux of the matter. Because so many variables affect the result, a valid basis for assessing the capabilities of cutting tools could only be determined by systematic and intensive scientific study. Hitherto organised studies had been almost exclusively confined to the realm of pure science. The successful application of the fruits of scientific research to technology had been due to brilliant individuals who had been able to bring their scientific knowledge to bear upon the practical problems of the workshop. It was only during the last two decades of the nineteenth century that the methods of scientific research were intensively applied under commercial sponsorship to the study of such processes as the cutting of metals. It was a novel concept and it speedily yielded spectacular results. The rapid development of machine tools over the last 70 years, along with the progress of technology generally, has been due more to the adoption of scientific methods of study than to any other single cause.

An earlier chapter of this book emphasised that the achievements of Henry Maudslay and the other great British tool-makers were only made possible by Benjamin Huntsman's crucible steel-making process which gave them the carbon steel cutting tool. Despite the efforts of the British Government to prevent the export of technical knowledge and skill to America, emigrants from Sheffield very soon brought the secret of crucible steel making to the new world.

The world's first improved tool steel was produced in 1868 at a little iron works near Coleford in the heart of Gloucestershire's Forest of Dean. Its inventor was Robert Forrester Mushet (1811–1891), the son of a pioneer Scottish ironmaster, David Mushet, who had moved south to Coleford in 1810. Robert Mushet had earlier made the Bessemer process of cheap steel making practicable by proposing the addition of Spiegeleisen, a Prussian iron ore rich in manganese. Like his father before him, Mushet was a great experimentalist—too much so to achieve commercial success—and it is doubtful whether, at this time, any other practical ironmaster in England knew more about the properties of iron and steel and their alloys.

Alloy steels had already been produced by 1868, but the effects of the addition of alloys on the properties of steel were not clearly understood and it had not dawned on anyone that alloys might improve the performance of carbon steel cutting tools. As early as 1819 Michael Faraday had made experiments with alloy steels in the laboratory of the Royal Institution with the assistance of a Sheffield cutler named James Stodard. Faraday succeeded in producing chrome steel but not in sufficient quantity to enable mechanical tests to be made.[1] It was not until 1877 that chrome steel was produced commercially by Jacob Holtzer at Unieux in France. Faraday is also said to have produced nickel steel at the Royal Institution, but the invention is commonly credited to Johann Conrad Fischer who first produced it at his steel works at Schaffhausen in Switzerland in 1824–5. It was first marketed on a large scale by the celebrated Schneider steel works at Le Creusot. Tungsten steel was invented in 1855 by the Austrian chemist Franz Koller and produced at a special works at Reichraming on the river Ems in Austria.

Mushet's little concern in the Forest of Dean was known by the grandiose title of the Titanic Iron & Steel Company. It was equipped with crucible melting furnaces where Mushet made many experiments with chromium, manganese and tungsten alloys. In 1868 Mushet was

[1] It should be recorded, however, that cutlery was made from Faraday's alloy steels by the Sheffield firm of Green, Pickslay & Co.

approached by a Glasgow manufacturer named J. P. Smith with the proposal that Mushet should manufacture a new 'Adamantine' cast steel tool of Smith's invention. This was just the kind of project to appeal to Mushet but it proved a failure, the new tools being far too brittle. This disappointment acted as a challenge to Mushet who continued to experiment on his own account to see if he could not produce a tool steel of superior cutting quality. In the crucial experiment an iron pig cast from an ore rich in manganese was pulverised and to it was added a proportion of wolfram ore (tungsten) finely powdered. The mixture was then placed in a crucible furnace and the molten mixture subsequently poured into an ingot mould. Part of this historic ingot [1] was forged up under a tilthammer into a bar of tool steel by Mushet's faithful assistant George Hancox and it was speedily apparent that they had made a discovery of the first importance, exceeding their most optimistic hopes. Not only was the cutting performance of the new alloy steel far superior to that of carbon steel but, unlike the latter, it proved to be *self-hardening*, a characteristic Mushet had never conceived possible. Whereas the carbon steel tool had to be hardened by heating and then quenching in water, the success of the result being dependent on the practical experience and skill of the toolsmith, this new material hardened itself correctly, simply by being left to cool in air after forging.

For reasons not directly connected with his great discovery, Mushet's Titanic Steel Company subsequently failed, but an arrangement was made whereby 'R. Mushet's Special Steel' was produced and marketed by Samuel Osborne & Co. of Sheffield. Its superiority as a tool steel was so great that its success was immediate and world-wide. One of the earliest of many testimonials which Mushet received came from John Fowler & Co., the famous steam-plough builders of Leeds, who informed him that they could now turn iron shafts in the lathe at the rate of 75 feet per minute and that in machining steel wheels in their boring mill they could take a roughing cut half an inch deep.

Instead of taking out a patent, Mushet decided to keep his process secret and the most extraordinary precautions were taken. For some time after the melting was transferred to Sheffield, the processing of the ingredients and their mixing was done by Mushet and a few picked men in the seclusion of the Dean Forest Steelworks in great secrecy. The wolfram ore and other ingredients were always referred to by cyphers and were ordered through intermediaries so that their destination should not be traced. The mixture, packed in barrels, was consigned from the Forest to Sheffield

[1] The remainder has been preserved by Samuel Osborne & Co. Ltd. of Sheffield.

by different and devious routes, likewise through intermediaries. So effective were these security arrangements that although samples of 'R.M.S.', as it was called for short, were subsequently analysed, the actual production technique used by Mushet remains a secret to this day.

The rapid introduction of the Bessemer and the Siemens Martin processes of steel making on both sides of the Atlantic led equally swiftly to the use of manganese steel for railway wheel tyres and axles. For the economic machining of this tough material Mushet's tool steel was considered essential. Indeed many engineers tended to regard Mushet's steel in the same light as the precision grinding machine—as a means of cutting a tough material rather than as an improved means of carrying out ordinary metal-cutting operations. The characteristics and potentialities of the material as a cutting agent were not fully grasped even by Mushet himself and his invention had no effect on machine-tool design. On both sides of the Atlantic the basis of machine-tool design was still empirical being founded simply on an accumulated fund of practical experience in the art of metal cutting.

In 1876 an event of outstanding importance in the history of technology took place when Alva Edison opened his new laboratory at Menlo Park near New York. This was an establishment of an entirely new kind—the world's first 'inventions factory' in which a team of research workers under Edison's direction undertook to investigate promising new ideas and develop them to a practical commercial stage. The spectacular results achieved by Edison at Menlo Park deeply impressed American industrialists and nowadays every large industrial organisation has its research and development division. Given the necessary funds it is obvious that such an organisation can complete in a few years a research programme which an individual would be unlikely to achieve in a long lifetime. Hence the extraordinarily rapid progress of technology in our century—the second industrial revolution as it has been called. But, like every other manifestation of material progress, organised invention has its debit side. Hitherto, enterprising commercial organisations had exploited inventions, often in ways unforeseen by the inventors, but the inventors themselves had remained free. Now inventive talent became no longer a free agent. To use socialist jargon, it was 'collectivised', absorbed in the production organisation and ordered to achieve prescribed commercial objectives. Much must inevitably be lost when inventive talent, hitherto free to flow where it will, is pooled and then canalised in this way. Inevitably, too, the historian of technology finds his chronicle becoming increasingly impersonal as he approaches the present, because so much development work is due to anonymous teams and not, as in the past, to a few dedicated and inspired individuals.

So far as this book is concerned the influence of Edison was indirect. He carried out no notable work in connection with machine tools at Menlo Park, but he succeeded in convincing American business men and engineers that industrial research was a worthwhile investment and one of these men was William Sellers, President of the Midvale Steel Company in Pennsylvania.

The Midvale Steel Company specialised in the production of manganese-steel locomotive tyres and railway axles. The Company ran a small machine shop where these tyres and axles were machined and where, needless to say, Mushet's special steel tools were in use. In 1880, a young man named Frederick W. Taylor (1856–1915) was appointed foreman of this machine shop. Taylor speedily became convinced that the output of the machines was far too low, but he realised that he could not hope to convince others of this because he could not produce any factual data to substantiate his beliefs. A series of methodical experiments with cutting tools was the only answer and here Taylor was fortunate in three respects; the material used in the shop was of uniform quality, he was able to use a powerful machine, a 66-inch boring mill, for his first experiments and, most important of all, his President, William Sellers, was sympathetic to the idea. Not only did Sellers give the project his financial blessing but he provided Taylor with a team of five assistants, technical graduates from the Stevens Institute of Technology.

Little did Sellers, or even Taylor himself, realise in 1880 that these experiments would extend over a period of 26 years and cost over $200,000. In 1889 Taylor left Midvale but continued his experiments elsewhere, most notably at the nearby Bethlehem Steel Works where his latest and most important work was done with the assistance of Maunsel White, a Bethlehem metallurgist. Such a costly and protracted research programme did not go unopposed, but Taylor had his way thanks to the unwavering support of old William Sellers who was undoubtedly the most influential of American machine tool builders. Sellers lived to see his confidence in Taylor justified by remarkable results, but he died in 1905, a year before Taylor summarised his labours in his classic address *On the Art of Cutting Metals* to the American Society of Mechanical Engineers in New York. Six years before this, however, visitors to the Paris Exhibition of 1900 had been given a spectacular demonstration of the results of Taylor's work. They were astounded to see shavings peeling away at blue heat from an American lathe and to discover that the tip of the cutting tool was visibly red hot.

Taylor's historic paper would have been more aptly titled *On the* Science *of Cutting Metals* since it was based on the results of 50,000 experiments in the course of which 800,000 pounds of metal were cut with experimental tools. The earlier experiments were made with tools of Mushet steel and in the first year Taylor established that a round-nosed tool could be run at higher speed than the old diamond-point type and that coarse cuts at low speeds removed more metal in a given time than fine cuts at high speed. Next, Taylor found that a constant stream of water directed at the point of chip removal so increased the cutting speed that the output of the experimental machine rose by from 30 to 40 per cent. This was a discovery of the first importance which contradicted Mushet who insisted that his self-hardening tools must be run dry. To prevent rusting the water was saturated with carbonate of soda to form what we now call 'suds'.[1] When, shortly after this, a new machine shop was laid out at Midvale all the machines were equipped with suds tanks. The suds drained into a single sump whence it was returned by pump to an overhead supply tank. Although no secret was made of this installation, it was not copied elsewhere until 1899, 14 years later.

That the new self-hardening tools should be reserved for use on hard metals was another fallacy which Taylor exploded. He proved that they showed the greatest gain in cutting time on soft metals—a 90 per cent improvement on soft cast iron compared with 45 per cent on hard steel or chilled cast iron. This led to the use of the new tools for all roughing work.

A highly significant discovery made by Taylor in 1883 was that all the machine tools in use at Midvale had quite inadequate feed power. He showed that if a lathe tool became dull as much power was needed to feed it as was required to drive the cut, and as a result all the machines at Midvale were redesigned so that their feed power was equal to their drive power.

In these, as in many other valuable findings, the secret of Taylor's success—and the reason why his experiments were so protracted—was that he truly distinguished all the variable factors involved in metal

[1] Notwithstanding Mushet's strictures, 'suds' was in use as a coolant in England in the 1870s. The Rev. Francis Kilvert, curate of Clyro, is the unlikely witness of this. Visiting Laird's shipyard at Birkenhead in June 1872, he wrote: 'The lathe too was wonderful, peeling off the outer rusty skin of great iron cylinders and leaving them bright and shining while the peeled thin pieces curled up and dropped into a receptacle to be smelted again, and all the while there was a constant drip of soap and water upon the cylinder which was being peeled by the lathe.' (*Kilvert's Diary*, ed. William Plomer, 1939, Vol. II, p. 216.)

cutting by machine and then applied the golden scientific rule of only varying one factor at a time. In the same period similar tests were carried out in Manchester[1] but yielded little of value due to a failure to observe this golden rule. For example, in Manchester the area of the cut was treated as a single factor whereas Taylor realised that it was the product of two variables, thickness of cut and depth of cut of which the first, determined by feed, was the more important. Had he not made this vital distinction Taylor could not have established the need to increase feed power.

Taylor distinguished no less than 12 variable factors in metal cutting and he found that his most difficult problem was mathematical when it came to expressing his results as formulae. However, he succeeded in devising a form of slide rule for the use of production engineers and these substituted scientific control of the machine shop for the rule of thumb methods of the machine operators.

The most spectacular results of all were achieved when Taylor began to vary the composition of his steel tools and the degree of heat applied to them before letting them harden off in air. From the experience of 14 years of experimental work he concluded that the best comparative basis of tool performance was the exact cutting speed in feet per minute which would cause the tool to be ruined after a 20-minute run, all the other factors being held constant. These tool tests were the climax of Taylor's long years of experiment and were carried out in collaboration with Maunsel White in the Bethlehem steelworks. Analysis of Mushet steel showed that it contained 7 per cent tungsten, 2 per cent carbon and 2·5 per cent manganese and Taylor and White succeeded in proving that it was the manganese content which gave the steel its self-hardening characteristic. In 1892 Henri Brustlein began producing a chromium tool steel at the steel works at Unieux where Jacob Holtzer had earlier pioneered the use of chromium. In 1894 Brustlein sent two samples of chrome tungsten steel to the Midvale Company and these were tested and analysed by Taylor and White at Bethlehem. In the process they discovered that, so far as the self-hardening property was concerned, chromium was an effective substitute for manganese while it gave a better performance. White then increased both the chromium and tungsten contents, the latter to a figure as high as 14 per cent. He also added silicon and found that it improved shock resistance. It was when these experimental tools were heated to different temperatures that Taylor and White

[1] The experiments were jointly sponsored by the Manchester Association of Engineers, the Manchester School of Technology and Armstrong Whitworth, Ltd. Their best feature was the use of a dynamometer to measure tool pressures.

made a discovery that astonished the engineering world, themselves included.

Up to this time all the recognised authorities on steels had insisted that the new alloy tool steels must not be heated above 1550°F. (cherry-red heat) or their cutting properties would be impaired or destroyed. Taylor and White confirmed that the Mushet steel tended to crumble if it was overheated, but in the case of the tungsten chrome tool they found that performance continued to improve with heating until fusion point was reached. When such a tool was brought to cherry-red heat before cooling in air a cutting speed of 30 feet per minute was sufficient to cause failure in the prescribed period of 20 minutes. When a similar tool was heated to 2000°F., this being just below fusion point, cutting speed could be increased to 80 or 90 feet per minute before failure occurred. The lathe which caused such a sensation at the 1900 Paris Exhibition was equipped with one of these Taylor-White chrome tungsten tools.

Not content with this spectacular success, Taylor and White continued to experiment with other alloys after 1900. Molybdenum and titanium were tried and rejected as too costly, but the addition of 0·3 per cent of vanadium produced a further improvement and this proportion was gradually increased to 0·7 per cent. This addition of vanadium marked the end of a remarkable series of experiments which gave the world high-speed tool steel. 'Consciously the machine builders, unconsciously the whole world, have derived great benefit from the invention of the high speed tool', wrote one engineer in 1914,[1] but the first reaction of the engineering world was one of dismay, for the capabilities of the new steel made every existing machine tool obsolete overnight. Soon after the Paris Exhibition demonstration, one of the most reputable of German machine-tool builders, the Ludwig Loewe Company, A.G., of Berlin, tested the new steel tools in a lathe and a drilling machine of their manufacture, running them in such a way that the tools gave their maximum performance. In four weeks both machines were reduced to scrap metal. The keys fell out of the gears and shafts; cast gears were broken and the main drive spindles twisted; thrust bearings were destroyed and it was obvious that the lubrication system of both machines was totally inadequate.[2]

The moral of this destructive experiment was obvious. In order to reap the full advantages of the new tools the machines using them must be completely redesigned. They must be much more robust; both feed power and drive power must be increased; hardened steel gears must replace

[1] G. Schlesinger in *Zeitschrift des Vereins deutscher Ingenieuren.*

[2] *Die Geschichte de Ludwig Loewe, A.G., Berlin,* 1689–1929, Berlin, 1930. Both sources quoted from Karl Wittmann (see Bibliography).

cast gears in both drives; lubrication must be improved and finally the speed range of both drives must be greater and as nearly infinitely variable as was practicable in order to obtain optimum cutting speeds for different materials, different diameters of workpiece and different depths and thicknesses of cut. In other words machines must be redesigned round the new Taylor-White tools by a process no longer empirical. For Taylor had not only given the machine designer the tool but also the formulae by which its performance could be translated into terms of feed, speed and tool pressure.

Where the question of speed range was concerned the effect of the high-speed tool was to make an old problem much more acute. Ever since Joseph Clement produced his classic facing lathe with infinitely variable speed drive in 1827 the problem of machine-tool drives in general and the feed drive on lathes in particular proved almost as attractive to aspiring inventors as the idea of perpetual motion. An account of their efforts would fill a large book. Here we can only trace briefly the ancestry of the device which was first popularised by the introduction of the high-speed tool.

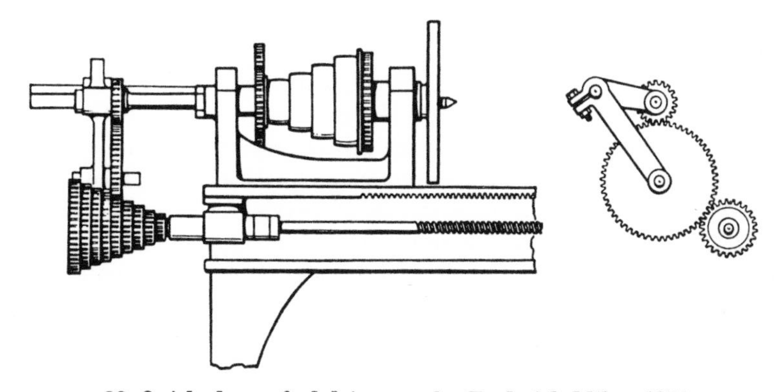

89 *Quick change feed drive gear by Frederick Miles, 1871*

Frederick B. Miles of the Ferris & Miles Machine Tool Works in Philadelphia is best-known in America for his improvements to the steam hammer, but in 1871 he patented a feed drive for a screw-cutting lathe. An illustration of this device shows a cluster of nine stepped gears on the end of the lead screw. An idler gear to engage any one of these stepped gears is mounted on a rocking arm, the axis of which is an extension of the lathe spindle. The idler gear engages a drive pinion on the lathe spindle and both the rocker arm and this drive pinion can slide along the spindle in order to effect a change of speed. Although Miles was almost certainly unaware of the fact, this was simply a new application of a device which Henry Maudslay had adopted as main drive for a lathe nearly 60 years before.

Although Miles' invention was a time-saver compared with the orthodox arrangement of change wheels it did not become popular; indeed, it seems to have dropped into the limbo of lost causes until Rankin Kennedy[1] discovered it in 1907 and drew attention to its significance. This had by then become apparent. That another American, Wendell P. Norton, succeeded in 1892 where Miles had failed 20 years before can only have been due to the advent of the new tool steels of Mushet and Taylor. Norton's feed drive gear did not differ in principle from those of Maudslay and Miles. But Norton came forward at precisely the right moment in history and the Norton Quick Change Box has been in world-wide use on machine-tool feed drives down to the present day

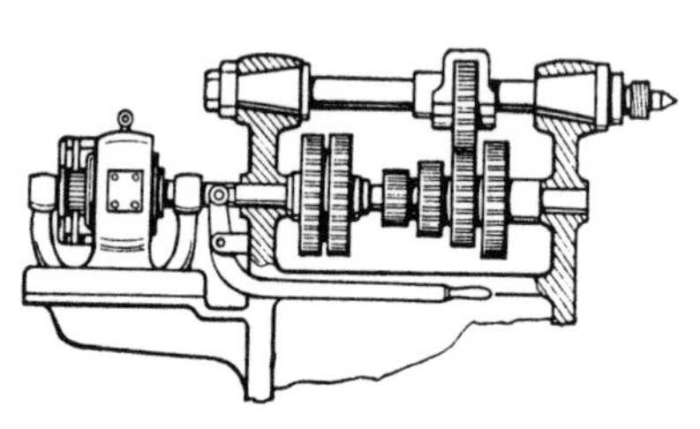

90 *W. P. Norton's tumbler gear drive, 1892*

In the improvement of machine-tool main drives, Frederick Taylor himself pointed the way forward. His early experiments with Mushet tools at Midvale convinced him of the inadequacy of the current practice of belting up machines to counter-shafts and line shafting and we are told that for his latest series of experiments at Bethlehem he used a machine powered by an electric motor and equipped with an infinitely variable speed drive of undisclosed design. The commonest form of infinitely variable drive then in use was still cone pulleys as used by Clement and Whitworth, but for heavy duty it was unsatisfactory because the combination of cone pulleys and flat belts is inherently unsound mechanically. Of the many alternatives which were tried, that of a vee belt running between expanding and contracting vee pulleys as patented by the American M. O. Reeves in 1897 was the most promising. For the power demands now being made by heavy machine tools, however, no variable speed drive relying solely on friction could be entirely satisfactory. A positive drive was essential. Nevertheless, where perfection of finish was the aim the machine tool designer soon found that he could not afford to dispense altogether with the chatter-free smoothness of belt drive. Consequently as the flat leather belt was banished by the electric motor, so the

[1] Rankin Kennedy, *The Modern Machine Shop*, 1907, p. 190.

91 *Frederick Lanchester*

92 *Lanchester's worm-gear-hobbing machine, 1896*

93 *Charles H. Norton*

94 *Norton's first heavy production grinding machine, 1900, now in the Ford Museum*

vee rubber belt, latter-day equivalent of the 'gut bands' of the pioneers, took the place which it holds to this day.

The fact that Taylor was able to use an electric motor to drive his experimental machine from 1894 onwards emphasises a very important aspect of the history of technology. This is the fortunate—one might almost say fortuitous—way in which parallel but quite separate lines of development reach a stage when they suddenly became indispensable to each other and therefore converge. It is extremely unlikely that the development of electrical power generation and transmission systems entered at all into the calculations of Mushet or Taylor when they began to experiment with high-speed steels, yet the results of their labours could never have been fully exploited in the machine shop had it not been for the advent of the electric motor. Similarly, when Gottlieb Daimler and Karl Benz were building their first 'horseless carriages' in Germany, they were not aware of the fact that on the other side of the Atlantic engineers were rapidly perfecting the tools which would make 'motoring for the million' possible.

The Frenchman Théophile Gramme (1826–1901) first demonstrated an electric motor driving a machine at the Vienna Exhibition of 1873 and in the following year he installed a motor to drive the line shafting at his own works in Paris. This appears to have set a precedent. Strange though it may seem, remembering the pioneer work of Murdock and Nasmyth with their little vacuum and steam motors, the immense possibilities of the electric motor in the machine shop were not recognised for over 20 years. It promised to rid the machine shop of a clutter of belts and line shafting, obscuring light and hampering crane movement, but it was not until the last few years of the century that the motor was used to power individual machine tools. In 1901 the first attempts were made to combine motor and tool as one unit. That these were very clumsy was partly due to the size of the early motors, but as techniques developed and reduced the size and weight of motors of a given power, more successful marriages were achieved. Attempts were made to substitute variable-speed direct-current motors for mechanical variable-speed gears but these were seldom successful because only a motor of excessive size could produce sufficient power for heavy cuts at low speeds. Where a wide range of speeds was required a combination of variable-speed motor and a mechanical form of gear change was found to be the best solution. This gives a very wide and closely stepped speed range. In modern machine tools which are so equipped the electrical steps and the mechanical steps are automatically co-ordinated, the mechanical shifts being performed by electrically operated clutches.

Before the first world war another important development had appeared —the use of auxiliary motors to power the feed motions of machine tools. In the process of building the skill into the machine the problems of deriving such motions mechanically from the main drive spindle had taxed the ingenuity of engineers ever since the days of Maudslay, and as the machines became more powerful and standards of precision higher, so their solutions necessarily became more complex. It was not easy to reconcile such mechanical complexity with that speed and simplicity of control by the operator which is the aim of every machine tool designer. The auxiliary electric motor provided a way out of this impasse at precisely the right moment in history. The motor offered many advantages: simplified and conveniently grouped controls, the elimination of a great deal of complex mechanism, and the independence of feed speeds from spindle speeds. In most cases, too, it was a better mechanical solution. For example, on a large heavy-duty lathe the orthodox method of driving the carriage by means of a long lead screw or shaft, which must necessarily be unsupported throughout the length of the traverse, was obviously objectionable and a number of ingenious mechanical methods of relieving the lead screw or shaft of the power load were devised. Yet none of these could be so simple or satisfactory as the installation of an auxiliary motor on the carriage. Again, the use of such motors made it a far simpler matter to speed up unproductive motions such as the idle return of a carriage after completion of a cut. Finally, by the use of the motor it became possible to use standard units, a number of powered work-heads for example, in order to build up a special-purpose machine tool designed to perform a number of operations on a workpiece either simultaneously or successively.

Following Taylor's example, both the milling cutter and the grinding wheel were made the subject of similar scientific studies leading to rapid improvement of the cutting tools themselves and of the machines using them. The research work on milling cutters was carried out by A. L. De Leeuw of the Cincinnati Milling Machine Company. The results of his studies and the new designs of cutter based on his findings appeared in 1904. De Leeuw's experiments had shown that the cutters then in use were inferior to the machines and would fail before the maximum power of the machine was reached. His improved cutters had fewer and coarser teeth which were much more widely spaced than their predecessors. The rake angles of the teeth were the outcome of careful study and so were the adoption of spiral teeth or staggered teeth for certain types. One of the first of the new cutters to be made was a face mill which removed 50 per cent more metal per horsepower.

It was recognised that in order to utilise the performance of a milling cutter to the full, cutting speed should not be affected by the differing diameters of the cutters used and that it should be possible to vary the speed of the feed without altering the speed of the cutter spindle. Except that in this case it was the diameter of the cutter and not that of the workpiece which had to be allowed for, the problem of ensuring constant optimum cutting speed and feed was the same as on the lathe or the boring machine and its solution was similar. The first miller to have an all-gear constant speed drive from an individual electric motor, and feed speeds which could be rendered independent of spindle speeds at will, appeared in 1901. This was the No. 2 universal milling machine designed by John Parker for Brown & Sharpe and it is the prototype of the constant speed milling machine of today. The only notable addition on the latter is a flywheel on the cutter spindle necessitated by the greater cutting power of modern carbide cutters.

Before turning to the grinding machine and its wheel it is appropriate at this point to consider the effect of the high-speed steel on the gear-cutting machine. High-speed tools enabled the output of existing machines to be speeded up and so to keep pace with a rapidly increasing demand for precision gears. But this speeding-up process created a new problem. With the sole exception of the Fellows shaper, the machines then used, no matter whether they employed a single-point tool or a rotating cutter, cut one tooth at a time successively round the periphery of the blank. At the higher rate of cut this caused local heating of the blank and consequently deformation of the finished gear. In an attempt to mitigate this, machines were modified so that, instead of cutting each tooth successively, it became customary to cut one tooth and then pass several before taking the next cut, proceeding in this way until the gear was complete, the object being to spread the heat more evenly. But the trouble focussed attention on the moulding generating method of gear cutting which uses a rotating cutter or hob in the form of a worm. Instead of cutting one tooth at a time, the hob progressively excavates all the teeth on the blank as the two are meshed together by the feed mechanism while they rotate synchronously. Hence there is an even distribution round the blank of the heat generated in cutting. The Fellows gear shaper also cuts progressively, but whereas the design of the shaper cutter fixes the helix angle of the gear, a hob can be used to produce gears of any helix angle from 0° to 180°.

The principle of the gear hob is extremely simple and we have the evidence of Bodmer's hob in the Science Museum in London to show that the idea was by no means new. The successful application of the principle to precision gear cutting is not nearly so simple, however, and this explains why, despite the efforts of Bodmer, Whitworth and Christian Schiele (1856), so many years passed by before the hobbing machine came into its own. The angular relationship and alignments of the axes and centres of the cutter and the blank were critical and were difficult to determine. Moreover, the necessary accuracy of the hardened steel hob was only achieved by the continuing development of precision grinding technique. Jüngst and Reinecker in Germany and Frederick Lanchester in England produced specialised gear-hobbing machines in 1893, 1894 and 1896 respectively, while in 1897 another German engineer, Hermann Pfauter, produced the first universal machine of this type. Once the practical difficulties had been overcome it was found that, providing the design of the hobbing machine was sufficiently robust, full advantage could be taken of a high-speed steel cutter to cut precision gears at a far faster rate than had been possible before without any heat deformation. The success of the method was such that by 1909 no less than 24 manufacturers were making gear-hobbing machines, mainly to meet the demands of the young automobile industry. The gear-hobbing machine also played a vital part in the success of the steam turbine. The hob was as essential to the production of turbine reduction gears as Wilkinson's boring machine had been to the production of cylinders for Watt's steam engine. Despite its spectacular performance, Sir Charles Parsons' little experimental craft *Turbinia* proved that the shaft speed of the turbine was too high for direct ship propulsion and in this application his great invention might have been still-born had not the machine tool makers, once again, come forward with the tools for the job.

In 1884, Gilbert Hart of the Detroit Emery Wheel Company carried out an exhaustive series of tests with emery and corundum grinding wheels which proved that the latter was a vastly superior abrasive. By 1895 corundum had practically superseded emery but its variable quality, scarcity and high cost concentrated the attention of manufacturers upon the possibility of producing a synthetic abrasive of controlled quality. In 1891, the American Edward G. Acheson produced, by fusing a mixture of carbon and clay in an electric arc furnace, crystals of a hardness then surpassed only by the diamond. The crystals were in fact silicon carbide. This had been produced as a laboratory curiosity earlier in the century, but Acheson did not know this and christened his discovery carborundum. The recipe for producing silicon carbide was simple, but Acheson's invention could not have been exploited at any earlier date because the 'cooking', on a commercial scale, entailed a prodigious consumption of electric power. In 1895, Acheson's Carborundum Company was established at Niagara Falls where the necessary hydro-electric power could be produced and carborundum wheels were marketed in the following year.

In 1897, another American, Charles B. Jacobs, succeeded in producing artificial corundum, or alundum as it was called, by fusing a nearly pure aluminium oxide (bauxite) with small quantities of coke and iron borings. The Norton Emery Wheel Company acquired the rights in the process and soon shortened its name to the Norton Company because the new synthetics rapidly superseded the use of natural emery and corundum. Jacob's process, like Acheson's, required an immense amount of electric power, so Niagara Falls was again the site of the first commercial plant to begin producing alundum wheels in 1901.

The man who did for the grinding wheel what Taylor had done for the single-point tool and De Leeuw for the milling cutter was Charles H. Norton. He was also chiefly responsible for the development of the production grinding machines which applied the new synthetic abrasive wheels to such good purpose. Somewhat confusingly, Charles Norton was in no way related to Franklin B. Norton, the founder of the Norton Company.[1] Charles Norton (1851–1942) was a native of Worcester, Mass. He received his engineering training at the Seth Thomas Clock Company of Thomaston, Connecticut, where he worked for 20 years, succeeding his uncle, N. A. Norton, as master mechanic. The firm's production included large tower clocks and Norton, who was responsible latterly for tooling the plant, gained experience of the light grinding techniques then current. In 1886, Norton left Thomaston and joined the Brown & Sharpe Company as assistant to their chief engineer, Edward Parks.

Norton's first task at Providence was to make a careful study of the firm's universal grinding machine with a view to its improvement. Although, as we saw in the previous chapter, this machine was a great advance on the makeshift grinding lathes that preceded it, experience had shown that there was plenty of room for improvement. The machine had proved a great asset in the tool room, but as a production tool it was far from satisfactory. Its output was extremely low, mainly because the production of uniformly accurate work still called for great skill and patience on the part of the operator. Norton first studied the behaviour of the wheel itself in collaboration with Charles Allen of the Norton Company.[2] His research in this field continued until 1905. It accompanied,

[1] The original small pottery firm from which the Norton Company stemmed was founded by Franklin Blackmer Norton in 1858. F. B. Norton did not long remain with the Company after grinding-wheel manufacture began.

[2] The shortened title of this company is used here and subsequently for the sake of simplicity.

and was a vital factor in, his development of the grinding machine, but here it will be most convenient to summarise first the results of Norton's work on abrasive wheels.

Norton first discovered that the wheels used on the Universal machine were not perfectly balanced and that they were being run at too high a speed. Subsequently, he would invent a machine for dynamically balancing grinding wheels. A microscopic examination of the grinding dust revealed to Norton that in running at too high a speed the wheel burnt the metal away and by so doing dissipated much power uselessly in the form of heat. When he reduced the speed to a point where burning ceased, his microscope showed that the wheel was now cutting the metal into minute chips as did other forms of metal-cutting tool. This was the first of a long series of experiments with wheels of different grades used at varying speeds on different classes of work. These extended into the era of synthetic abrasive wheels and they enabled Norton to specify the correct choice of wheel and speed for a particular grinding operation.

Norton also investigated the processes of dressing and truing the grinding wheel and distinguished between them. The former operation was generally carried out with a roller studded with hardened steel points, its purpose being to remove the surface layer of abrasive, which had become dulled by use, in order to expose fresh cutting points. Norton showed that while this barbarous technique might be necessary on the wheels used for fettling in foundries, it should not be applied to precision grinding wheels where it was unnecessary provided the grade of wheel and its speed were correctly selected. Truing, on the other hand, was essential from time to time in order to maintain the accurate contour of the wheel. At the time Norton's investigations began it was customary for operators to true their wheels by hand, using a piece of an old grinding wheel for the purpose, but he condemned this practice as a form of dressing rather than truing and insisted that wheels should only be trued by means of a diamond point. Even so, there was a tendency for operators to play safe by truing wheels too frequently and by 1925 machines had been equipped with diamond gauging points indicating when truing was necessary. On many modern machines, wheel truing is now carried out automatically at regular intervals, any reduction in the size of the wheel being compensated automatically in the cross-feed mechanism.

Turning now from the wheel to the machine, Norton found that, even with a balanced wheel running at the right speed, the Brown & Sharpe Universal machine had inadequate bearings and was far too lightly constructed for production work. He therefore redesigned it in the more robust form which it retains to this day. The new machine proved far more accurate than its predecessor but its productivity was limited by the proportions of the wheel. It was only half an inch wide and the operators persistently trued even this width away to leave no more than a cutting edge, insisting that an accurate result depended on such treatment. Performance was therefore extremely limited. Norton became convinced that much wider wheels could be used to enormous advantage on production machines, but for the present his was a voice crying in a wilderness of prejudice.

In 1890 Norton left Brown & Sharpe along with their shop foreman, Henry Leland, and the two men moved to Detroit where they founded the Leland-Falkner-Norton Company. Norton stayed for six years in Detroit and it was during this period that he first became interested in the problems of motor car manufacture. The brothers Charles and Frank Duryea built their first 'gasoline automobile'—to use American parlance—at Springfield, Massachusetts, in 1893 and American engineers rapidly became alive to the possibilities of the new vehicle. The Leland-Falkner-Norton Company were pioneers in this new field and so helped to make Detroit the centre of America's automobile industry under the changed title of the Cadillac Company.

In 1896, Charles Norton returned to Brown & Sharpe where, against the weight of much prejudiced opposition, he designed a heavier type of plain grinding machine. By the following year he had reached certain firm conclusions on production grinding and these he now endeavoured to put into practice. It must be emphasised once more that at this date the grinding machine was still universally regarded as a super-finishing tool. Components would be finished to within 0·002 inch of the required dimension before being passed to the grinding machine no matter whether the material was surface hardened or not. Norton, on the other hand, had concluded that a production grinding machine ought to be capable of reducing a component to finished dimensions from the rough machined stage with great speed and accuracy, thus eliminating the need for the slow, fine finishing cut on the lathe or other metal-cutting machine of like kind. The success of this conception depended on the use of wide grinding wheels and here Norton's ideas had advanced considerably. Given a machine of sufficiently robust construction he was now thinking in terms of wheels a foot or more in width so that, if possible, their width would exceed the length of the workpiece. By the use of such wheels, he argued, it would no longer be necessary to traverse the wheel along the workpiece or vice versa but only to feed it into the work. Thus Norton had conceived the technique which is known today as plunge grinding.

He realised, too, that it was not only applicable to plain grinding but made possible form grinding by the use of wheels specially shaped by diamond point to the contours required.[1] Finally, Norton conceived that such a machine could be its own micrometer, that it could, in other words, size the work to extremely fine limits so that the operator could adjust an index 0·00025 inch and the machine would then reduce the workpiece by precisely that amount.

By implementing Norton's revolutionary ideas, Brown & Sharpe could have made history yet again, but unfortunately they were ridiculed and frustrated by the works Superintendent, Richmond Viall. Viall stubbornly maintained the prevailing view that it was impossible to obtain accurate results with a wide grinding wheel. He also insisted that the first cost of a machine such as Norton envisaged would be so high that it would outweigh the labour-saving advantages claimed for it. So implacable was Viall's opposition to his ideas that in 1899 Norton gave up the struggle and sought the help of the Norton Company where he found a sympathetic and influential supporter in his old friend Charles Allen who had helped him in his early experiments. The upshot of this was the formation of the Norton Grinding Company[2] with Charles Norton as chief engineer.

In March 1900 Norton designed his first heavy production grinding machine and by November of that year the first two machines had been built. The first to be sold went to a firm of printing-press manufacturers in New York where it worked continuously for nearly 30 years. This historic machine is now in the Ford Museum. It shows that Norton wisely decided not to attempt to run before he had learned to walk, for it is a plain cylindrical grinding machine with traversing worktable. Yet so massive are its proportions that there is as great a difference between this machine and the first Brown & Sharpe Universal Grinder as there is between a Whitworth lathe of 1850 and an eighteenth-century pole lathe. Like Whitworth before him, Norton had realised that the key to precision is absolute rigidity. The machine is designed for a wheel two feet in diameter and two inches wide, an unprecedented size in 1900, and in order to utilise its full performance the worktable has a quick travel, moving two inches for each revolution of the workpiece so that the full width of the

[1] Today such wheels are 'crush formed' by rotating them under pressure against rolls of the required form. Thread-grinding wheels are produced in this way.

[2] Although sponsored and financed by individual members of the Norton Company, the two concerns remained entirely separate until 1919. There was then a merger, though the two Companies retained their separate identities.

wheel is continuously in cut. A built-in suds tank and a pump capable of circulating 50 gallons of coolant a minute is evidence of the fact that Norton appreciated the need to avoid heat deformation at high cutting rates. The machine represents an historic milestone of the greatest significance for from it there quickly stemmed all those special-purpose production grinding machines which alone made 'motoring for the million' possible.

CHAPTER 11

Tools of the Twentieth Century

When Frederick Taylor discovered his high-speed tool steel he prophesied that its introduction would be slow. Taking a world view of the engineering industry we could say that Taylor prophesied truly and that his forecast might have been extended to the work of De Leeuw and Charles Norton. There is always a time lag in the application of new techniques and the lag will be longer if the application involves heavy capital expenditure. Taylor's lathe tools, De Leeuw's milling cutters and Norton grinding wheels might be inexpensive commodities, but costly new machines could alone exploit their full potential and no industrialist could be expected to scrap his entire machine shop overnight. Yet the new tools required such a ruthless policy because, in a production machine shop, the functions of the different machines are so interdependent that the piecemeal introduction of one or two high-performance machines can show only a very limited advantage. They may only cause the work to pile up against older and slower machines.

Because of the profound difference between the social and economic philosophies of the two countries, the rate of introduction of new machines and new methods tended to be most rapid in America and slowest in England. Throughout the first three decades of the twentieth century and despite the upheaval of the first world war, British engineers still excelled in what might be called bespoke engineering and tended to look askance at American production methods. Not that British machine-tool builders lagged far behind. For example, in 1906 the Churchill Machine Tool Company of Manchester produced the first of a range of heavy production grinding machines which were no whit inferior to their American counterparts, but the rate of introduction of such tools in Britain was relatively slow. As late as 1930 the average British production machine shop was still a dense jungle of leather belts and line-shafting where a few modern tools jostled machines so antique that American engineers would have consigned them to the scrap heap years before. On these veterans carbon-steel tools were still used since there was little advantage to be gained by adopting high-speed steel. The writer, who served part of his apprenticeship in such a shop in 1929, can recall taking his lathe tools along to the toolsmith to be tempered as generations of machinists had done before him. The general tendency in Britain up to this date was to introduce new machine tools only as a solution to some new and novel production problem and not because they could carry out more rapidly and efficiently operations which existing tools could do.

From 1900 onwards the fact that Germany had taken the lead in machine-tool design and manufacture in the old world became increasingly apparent. Reviewing the Paris Exhibition of 1900, the Frenchman M. G. Richard concluded that German machine-tool construction had overtaken the French and that whereas the Germans had been copying American machines a few years before, they were now exporting machines and ideas to the United States. Again, Thomas Shaw of Manchester, after a visit to German plants in 1903 remarked: 'It is a pity that there are no such excellently ordered and equipped machine tool factories found on English soil.' Nevertheless, despite these European rivalries and distinctions the development of the motor industry throughout the old world followed a similar pattern which contrasted sharply with the new world and typified their differing philosophies.

In addition to purely financial considerations, man's natural conservatism, his tendency to cling to old and well-tried methods of doing a job, contributes to a reluctance to replace his tools by better ones. Hence it is always in new industries that we first find new tools and new methods for in them there is no capital locked up in old tools and fewer prejudices. As we have seen, the new industry in this case was the motor industry where, in America, the new tools were eagerly grasped.

So successfully was the American system applied to the manufacture of the bicycle that between 1890 and 1897 national output rose from 40,000 to 1,000,000 bicycles a year. The extension of the system to the manufacture of motor cars followed logically and in this new field some of the techniques developed in bicycle manufacture proved valuable, notably the production of hardened gears[1] and ball bearings. When an American

[1] See previous reference to the American chainless bicycle.

manufacturer turned from bicycles to motor cars his philosophy of production did not change. Because the new motor car would inevitably be a much more elaborate and therefore costly machine to produce he did not aim it deliberately at a small and exclusive luxury market. On the contrary, living as he did in a new democracy which prided itself on the fact that it recognised no traditional social hierarchies, his one concern was how to reduce his production costs so that his cars would find the widest possible market. In other words, in the United States the concept of 'motoring for the million' was implicit from the beginning.

In Europe, and particularly in Britain, the motor car was born into a totally different world where the traditional social hierarchy was still intact. Moreover, the financial gulf between rich and poor in Europe had never been wider than it was during the formative years of the motor car from 1890 to 1914. Whereas at the bottom end of the scale 'the labouring poor' were little better off than they had been a century earlier, the upper and middle classes enjoyed a purchasing power such as they had never commanded before and will never see again. This situation influenced the European motor manufacturer profoundly. He regarded his product as the successor to the gentleman's carriage. His chief concern was to improve the quality and performance of his cars so that they would appeal to the sophisticated tastes of the moneyed classes and the reduction of manufacturing costs was a secondary consideration. Hence in what we call the Edwardian era before the first world war, the European and American automobile industries and their products present a revealing and in some ways paradoxical contrast. First Germany, then France and finally Britain led the world in automobile design, producing magnificent motor cars by means of machine tools and methods which were archaic by American standards. Meanwhile on the other side of the Atlantic American engineers were using the most advanced machine shop techniques to produce cars of a crude simplicity quite unacceptable by European standards. The extreme manifestations of these contrasting philosophies were, of course, the 'Silver Ghost' Rolls Royce and the Model T Ford, the one a consummate example of conservative engineering craftsmanship and the other the product of the most advanced machine tools in the world at that time.

Owing to obstructive legislation, Britain's motor industry made a belated start. It was established first in Coventry in 1894 and a little later in Birmingham. Earlier, the foundation of the sewing-machine trade in 1859 and of the cycle trade in 1869 had helped to offset the decline in Coventry's ribbon-weaving industry. Coventry claims to have produced the first machine for grinding the hardened balls for cycle bearings, although the first ball-grinding machine was patented in 1853 by Hiram Barker and Francis Holt of Manchester and was used to produce hardened balls for locomotive clack valves. Just as in earlier days the machine-tool industry had grown with the growth of the textile trade in the North of England, so now it developed alongside the cycle and motor trade in the English Midlands. An example of this trend was the business of Herbert & Hubbard, a small shop opened in Coventry in 1889 to make machinery for the cycle and ribbon trades. As a result of the advent of the motor industry this business grew rapidly, under the name of Alfred Herbert Ltd., into one of the largest and most famous machine-tool plants in the world.

It was this accompanying growth of the machine-tool industry which enabled the British motor manufacturers to overcome their initial handicap and so speedily to overtake their European rivals. The first cars built in Britain were inferior copies of Continental models. The first engineer to design and build a truly British car was Frederick Lanchester and the story of his achievement reveals that Britain was not only handicapped by a late start but by the conservatism of her engineering methods. Lanchester's difficulties were comparable with those which confronted Watt in building his first steam engine and they would have defeated an engineer of less versatile genius. Having designed the car, Lanchester had to design the machines and the jigs and plan the production methods to make it. To cut the 'hour-glass' worm and wheel for the final drive unit, Lanchester designed the special hobbing machine which was mentioned in the previous chapter. The machine produced the entire output of worm gears for Lanchester cars for 25 years and is now preserved in the Birmingham Industrial Museum. In the epicyclic gear-box and in the rear axle, Lanchester pioneered the use of roller bearings and because no manufacturer of ball bearings would undertake to produce these for him, he evolved his own methods and machined the first sets with his own hands. In lengths of five or six, the hardened steel rollers were ground between centres to a tolerance of 0·0002 inch, the individual rollers being then parted off with a thin flexible grinding wheel. No range of screw threads then extant in Britain would suit Lanchester's purpose; the Whitworth range was too coarse, while although the cycle trade used fine threads there was no standardisation, each manufacturer following his own ideas. Lanchester therefore designed his own range of 'M' threads, as he called them. These differed very little from, and were in some respects better than, the B.S.F. (British Standard Fine) range designed by Clement and Crompton eight years later and not widely adopted until after the first world war.

To produce his ten-horse-power car of 1903 Lanchester adopted throughout the interchangeable system. This had never before been applied in

England to the manufacture of so large and complex an assembly involving over a thousand parts. In this he once again displayed his original genius by rejecting the bilateral system of plus or minus tolerances for each dimension which had been evolved in American interchangeable manufacture. Instead he used the unilateral system which he had originated in 1895 at his Birmingham laboratory. Every dimension given represented the ideal fit with minimum clearance and carried a single tolerance figure with a plus sign for internal dimensions and a minus sign for external dimensions. The tolerance figure therefore indicated the maximum permissible machining error in every case and also, in the case of working parts, the maximum tolerable wear. This Lanchester system proved much simpler in use. It was much easier to check the compatibility of matching dimensions with the effect that trouble with interference fits was eliminated in the Lanchester machine shops.

Compared with Lanchester's difficulties, the task of the American automobile pioneer was relatively simple. Not only was he the heir to a long tradition of interchangeable manufacture, but he was able to take immediate advantage of the new techniques evolved by such men as Taylor, De Leeuw and Norton. In his insistence upon interchangeable parts, Lanchester was mainly concerned with the convenience of the users of his cars in an England where garages staffed with competent fitters did not exist. To his American counterpart this convenience of the customer was a useful by-product of a system whose prime importance was to reduce production costs. In the pursuit of this goal the grinding machine in its many forms played a decisive role, more than fulfilling all that Charles Norton had forecast.

Production grinding was introduced in locomotive building and other branches of engineering after 1900 as an improvement upon older methods, whereas in the case of the new motor industry the grinding machine was absolutely essential to success. It has been estimated that more than three hundred different grinding operations go to the making of a modern car, so it will be appreciated that a survey so broad as this can do no more than skim the surface of this prodigious development where the grinding machine, or indeed any other type of machine tool, is concerned. As Professor Woodbury very rightly points out: 'A volume should be written about machine tools and the automobile industry. In no industry has the technical development of tools been so crucial in all its aspects, and no industry has had such a great effect on the far smaller machine tool industry. Not only did the automobile industry after 1900 become the largest single customer of the machine tool industry, taking 25 to 30 per cent of the output, but it actually increased its volume consistently.'

By 1903 Charles Norton had produced a special crankshaft-grinding machine using a wide wheel capable of reducing a journal to finished diameter in a single plunge cut. It performed in 15 minutes an operation which had previously required five hours of turning, filing and polishing. At first the American car builders sent their crankshafts to the Norton Company to be ground, but in 1905 both Nortons and the A.B. Landis Tool Company marketed these special machines. The Locomobile Company was the first to buy one, but other makers soon followed and finally Henry Ford ordered no less than 35 for his new 'Model T' production plant.

In 1911–12 both Norton and Landis produced camshaft-grinding machines and these were accepted by the motor industry with even greater alacrity. Previously it had been necessary to grind the hardened steel cams individually on a plain cylindrical machine fitted with a special hand-operated attachment. The finished cams were then threaded on a plain shaft and secured in their correct positions, usually by taper pegs. Now it became possible for designers to specify one-piece camshafts of hardened alloy steel.

In the heart of the internal combustion engine—the cylinder and piston—the grinding machine proved vital. The internal grinding of large steam and gas engine cylinders proved relatively simple but the small, thin-walled bores of a multi-cylinder block for a car proved a far more difficult proposition. Throughout the earliest years of the motor car this problem was not solved and orthodox practice was to machine cylinder bores in three operations: boring, reaming and hand lapping. This method was far from satisfactory. Inevitably hard and soft spots in the iron casting caused the cutting tool of the boring machine to be deflected in one part of the bore and to dig in in another part. The very costly reamers then used did not eliminate such defects because they tended to follow the irregularities, while the final lapping operation only gave a delusively fine finish. It was the American James Heald (1864–1931) who overcame this difficulty in 1905 when he produced his planetary grinding machine. It is so called because, while the small grinding wheel revolves at a high speed, its spindle also describes a circle at a much slower rate. This planetary motion of the wheel is obtained by carrying the wheel spindle in an eccentric bush which, in its turn, is mounted eccentrically in the main drive spindle of the machine. By adjusting these two eccentricities, the planetary motion of the grinding wheel can be most finely and accurately indexed from nil up to a predetermined maximum diameter. It is possible, however, to increase the range of the machine beyond that provided by this indexed adjustment merely by using a grinding wheel of larger size.

In practice Heald's invention fulfilled all that he claimed for it. The wheel exerted a very light pressure on the work and was not affected by hard or soft spots. With his prototype of 1905 Heald proved that from the rough bored state he could produce finished cylinders perfectly straight and parallel to within 0·00025 inch. The machines used for this purpose today do not differ in principle from Heald's first machine and the only significant subsequent development in this sphere has been the introduction of the cylinder-honing machine in the 1920s to provide that superfine finish which could only be achieved earlier by laborious hand lapping. The hone head on its vertical spindle consists of abrasive segments which can be forced outwards by mechanical or hydraulic means as it simultaneously rotates and reciprocates within the cylinder. It is the modern equivalent of Leonardo da Vinci's prophetic design described in Chapter 1 and does not differ in principle from its remote ancestor.

There was little value in a precision-ground cylinder bore unless the piston could be fitted with rings of comparable accuracy. By the aid of a special mandril the wearing face of a piston ring could be finished on a plain cylindrical grinder, but it was essential that the top and bottom faces should have a ground finish also to ensure a precise fit in the ring grooves of the piston. In 1902 Reinecker of Germany produced a machine for grinding the sides of the large rings used in steam and gas engines and two years later Heald designed a smaller machine for the automobile industry. In both the grinding wheel was mounted on a horizontal axis, while the piston ring was held on the worktable by a magnetic chuck. The worktable was rotated while the periphery of the grinding wheel was brought to bear. The machine also proved useful for grinding thrust washers and similar precision parts, while the magnetic chuck has since been widely applied as a great time and labour saver when parts have to be machined which would be difficult to secure by mechanical means.

James Heald established his Heald Machine Company at Barber's Crossing, close beside the Norton Grinding Company's plant on the outskirts of Worcester, Massachusetts. The conjunction was appropriate, for it was James Heald and Charles Norton who, above all others, made 'motoring for the million' possible. Heald's machines were as essential to the success of the modern high-speed internal combustion engine as was Wilkinson's boring bar to that of the steam engine. But just as Watt's name is remembered and Wilkinson's forgotten, so one may search the pages of popular motoring histories in vain for the names of Heald or Norton. Like all the great toolmakers, their fame has never penetrated far beyond the four walls of the machine shop.

By 1914 the great Ford plant at Detroit was producing over a million

95 *Landis crankshaft-grinding machine, 1905*

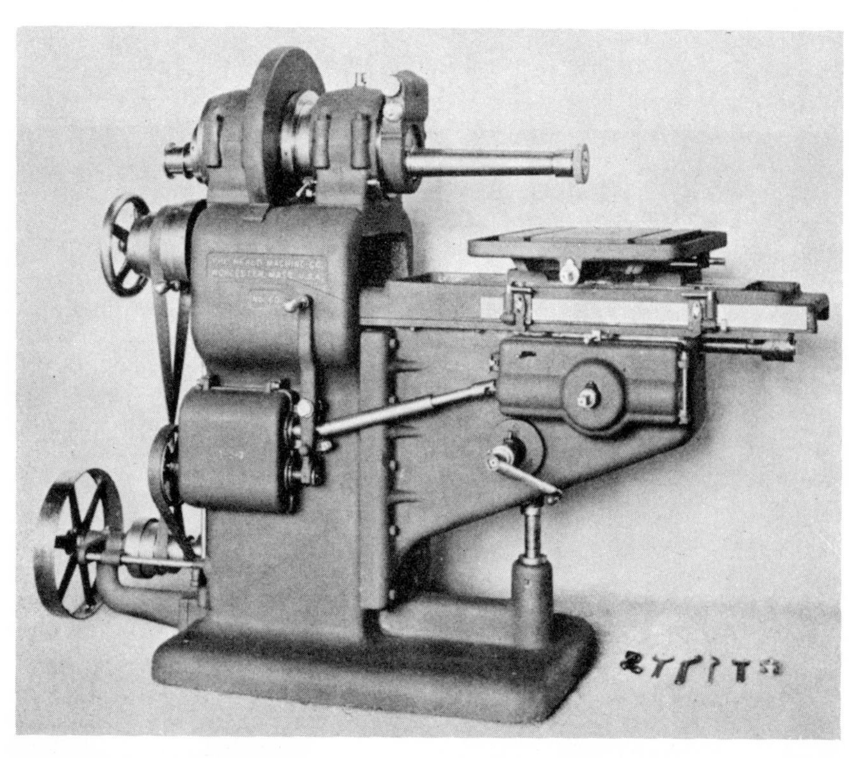

96 *Heald planetary cylinder-grinding machine, 1905*

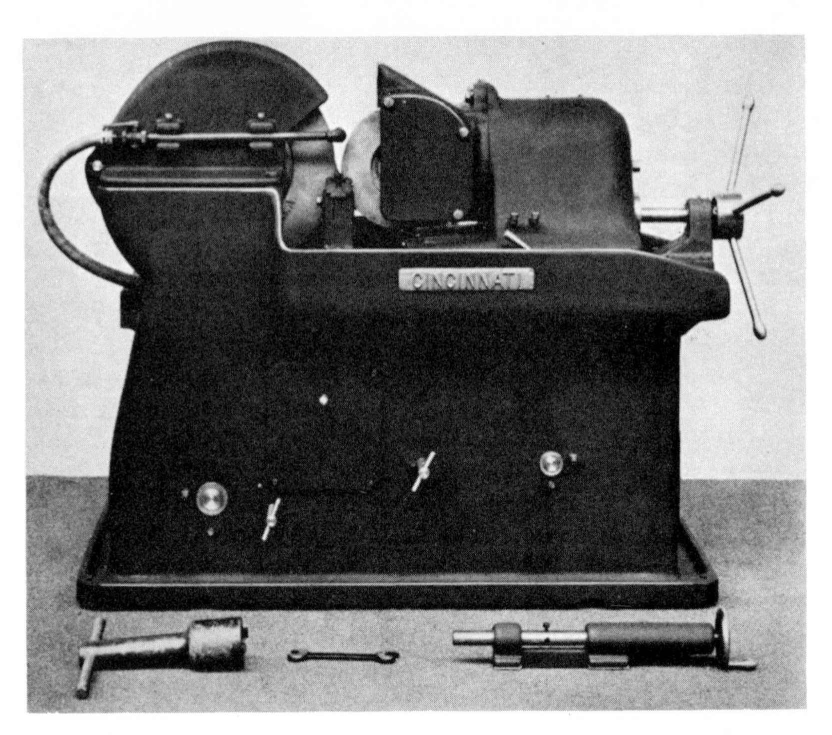

97 *First production Cincinnati centreless grinding machine, 1922 (L. R. Heim's patent)*

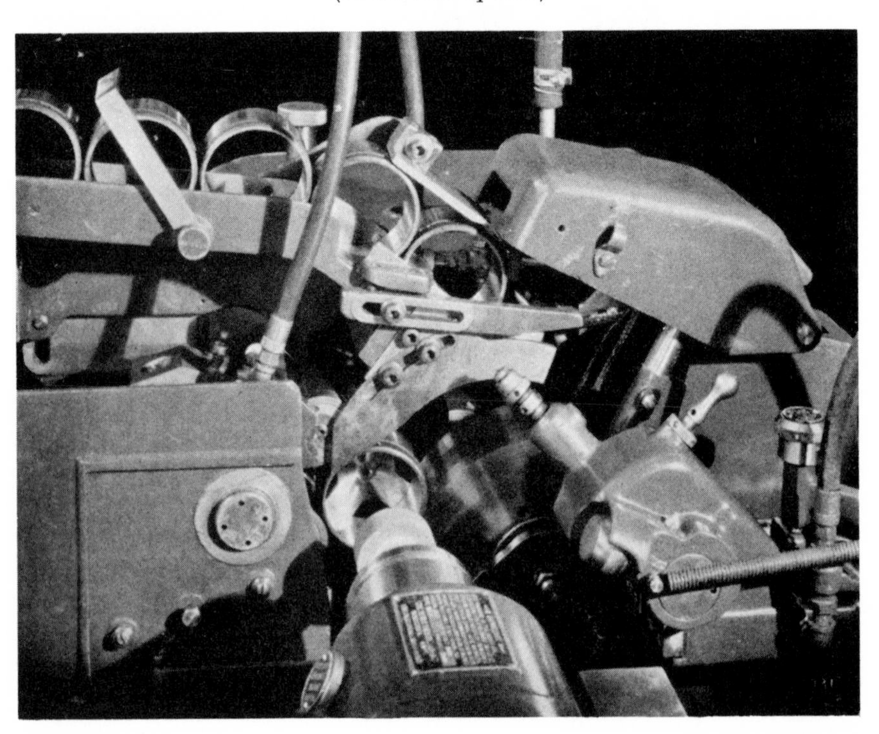

'Model Ts' a year. It was at that time the ultimate manifestation of American machine-tool expertise and of that American system which had been codified and reduced to cold scientific terms by Frederick Taylor in his book *Principles of Scientific Management*, published in 1911. So successfully had the skill been built into the whole production process that the name of Ford had become anathema to the skilled craftsman. But Henry Ford did not want craftsmen. 'As to machinists,' wrote two of

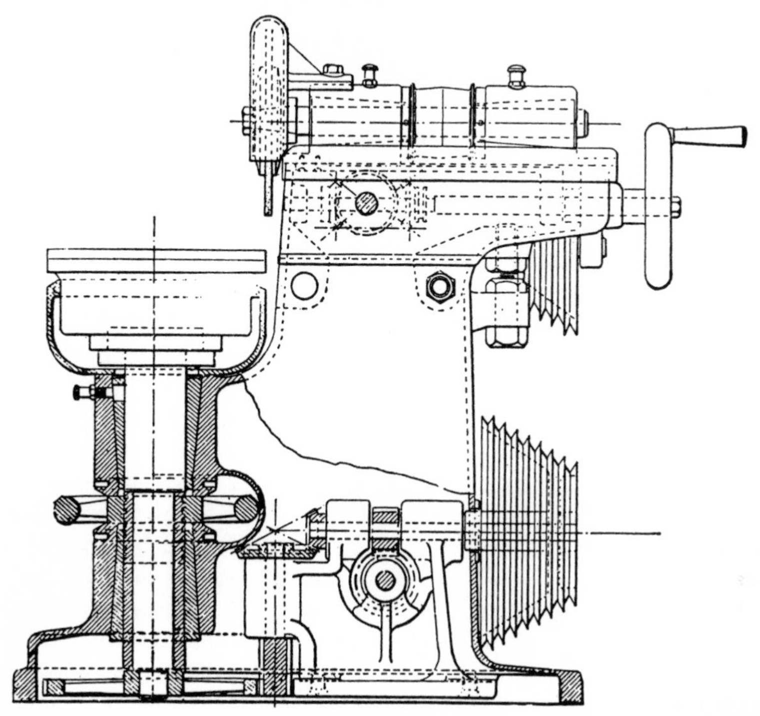

99 *James Heald's piston ring grinding machine with magnetic chuck, 1904* (American Machinist)

Ford's disciples,[1] 'old time, all-round men, perish the thought! The Ford Company has no use for experience, in the working ranks anyway. It desires and prefers machine-tool operators who have nothing to unlearn, who . . . will simply do as they are told to do, over and over again, from bell-time to bell-time. . . .' This was a bleak philosophy, but it was by no means novel. Eli Whitney had said the same thing, albeit in less trenchant

[1] Arnold and Faurote, *Ford Methods and Ford Shops*, quoted by Burlingame, *Henry Ford*, p. 74.

terms, a hundred years before. Its financial outcome now shook the world's economists. The price of the Ford car was progressively reduced until by 1913 it had come down to 600 dollars. This was a figure with which no other motor manufacturer could compete, for although the appearance and behaviour of the 'Model T' had made it the butt of innumerable jokes, it had proved itself a rugged machine of unfailing reliability. Yet, having so drastically cut the price of his car, in the very next year Ford more than doubled the minimum wage of his employees by raising it to five dollars a day. Many of his rivals seriously believed that Henry Ford had gone mad and were disconcerted to find that his business went on flourishing. The high wages not only helped to make the working conditions tolerable; more important still from the point of view of Ford's philosophy, they turned his own workers into potential customers for his cars.

It was, above all, the tools provided by such men as Norton and Heald that enabled Ford to put his revolutionary business theories into practice, but despite the spectacular success of his methods they were not widely emulated in Europe for a decade or more. To say that the first world war was responsible for this hiatus would be misleading. The war certainly deflected the normal course of technological development by bringing motor car production practically to a standstill in Europe. But it is arguable that had there been no war the old extremes of wealth and poverty might have survived much longer than they did. As it was, the great financial slump which followed the brief post-war boom of the early twenties forced European industrialists to face the fact that they had been living in a dream world and that pre-war economic conditions would never return. Motor manufacturers realised that their conception of the car as the vehicle of a moneyed class would no longer hold and that they must embrace the Ford philosophy of motoring for the million or perish. This brought about a radical change in the structure of the industry. So long as cars were built for the fortunate few, simple general-purpose machine tools plus a great deal of skilled fitting would suffice for their production. Consequently, in England especially, a great many small engineering firms with very limited capital resources became motor manufacturers either before or immediately after the war. The great depression drove the weaker and smaller firms to the wall, while of those strong enough to survive many pooled their resources by amalgamation. In this way there emerged in the 1930s a few much larger organisations commanding the necessary capital to equip new plants modelled on the American system as exemplified by Henry Ford.

This reorganisation of the motor industry typifies the general pattern of industrial development in Britain and in Europe from that day to this. The effect of this development has been progressively to reduce the hitherto striking disparity between production methods in the new and the old worlds until, at the present time, it no longer exists. The cosmopolitan collection of British, American, German, French, Swiss and Italian machine tools which may be found in a typical modern machine shop is the evidence for the revolution which has taken place in the last thirty years.

While the rapid expansion of Germany's machine-tool industry has been the most remarkable feature of the present century in this context, reference should here be made to two outstanding Swiss-built machines which have found their place in the world's workshops, the Swiss-type automatic lathe or screw machine and the Société Génévoise Jig Borer.

Switzerland's machine-tool industry was founded to meet the needs of her manufacturers of watches and precision instruments. Both the machines with which we are here concerned originated in this way but proved so successful that they were developed in heavier forms for general engineering use. The Swiss-type automatic screw machine developed quite independently and followed a different evolutionary course to that of the American-type automatic pioneered by Spencer. Its sire was a machine built by Jacob Schweizer at Bienne in 1872. Whereas the first American automatic was an adaptation of the turret lathe and its descendants to this day display evidence of this origin, Schweizer's machine was a completely original conception. The whole of the mechanism was carried on a broad rectangular table. It had a single hollow-spindle headstock with an arrangement for gripping the bar stock, and the bar passed through a steady rest before being attacked by one or other of the two opposing tools mounted on a common cross slide. But the most significant feature of Schweizer's invention was that the headstock, mounted to the right of the table, was free to slide in the direction of its spindle axis in order to provide lateral feed motion and present the work to the tools. This important provision has remained to this day a distinguishing characteristic of the Swiss automatic. It makes possible a versatility and speed of operation not to be equalled by fixed headstock automatics of the American type.

On Schweizer's pioneer design the screwing operation was carried out by a rotating diehead with the headstock spindle stopped, retraction being achieved by stopping the diehead spindle and starting the headstock. Instead of Spencer's large 'brain wheels', all the motions of this Swiss machine were controlled by cams of small size on two camshafts at each end of the table and at right angles to the axis of the headstock.

It would be out of place here to describe in technical detail the subsequent evolution of the Swiss automatic, the multiplication of tools and spindles, the provision for easy cam changing and for carrying out screwing operations without stopping the headstock. These developments have been accompanied by a progressive increase in the speed of operation. The P.7. Petermann, the best-known modern Swiss automatic, has a spindle speed of 10,000 r.p.m. and a drilling speed exceeding 20,000 r.p.m.

The Société Génévoise d'Instruments de Physique was founded in Geneva by Auguste de la Rive in 1862. Its purpose was the improvement and production of extremely accurate instruments for scientific measurement of every kind, including linear and circular dividing machines, micrometer microscopes and comparators. In this field it built up a world-wide reputation but it also, understandably, became the guide, philosopher and friend of the Swiss watch-makers. In 1912 the watch-makers invoked the Society's aid on the problem of how to drill the fine holes in watch plates with greater accuracy. The Society's answer was a small 'pointing machine' incorporating high precision measuring devices. This did not drill the holes but was fitted with a centre punch to mark the centre of the hole to be drilled and a miscroscope to inspect the mark.

This 'Polar Co-ordinate Pointing Machine', to give it its full title, was essentially a scientific instrument, but so successful was it that a more substantial version capable of drilling holes was produced for the watch trade. The next step was to scale up the machine for general engineering use as a jig borer whilst still retaining the ten-thousandth of an inch standard of accuracy of the original instrument. With these first large machines the practice was to 'pop' the hole as on the small prototype, then rough bore the hole on another machine and finally use the jig borer for a finishing cut to exact size. Soon, however, more massive machines of the double-column planer type were produced which obviated the use of a second machine for heavy cuts. At first, lead screws with correction devices to compensate for wear, were used for traversing and measuring against fine scales, but in 1934 the Society introduced its Hydroptic Jig Borer with hydraulically operated work-table and optical scale reading system. Today, a Société Génévoise jig borer has become an essential feature of every well-equipped tool room.

By the time the British motor industry began to re-equip itself in the 1930s, considerable advances had been made both in metal-cutting tools and in the machines using them. Twentieth-century development had, in fact, become a race between the makers of cutting tools and the makers of machines comparable to that between the makers of projectiles and armour plate. Frederick Taylor's work was continued by others in America, the ultimate development being 'Stellite'. This cobalt-chromium-tungsten alloy first appeared in 1917 but was subsequently much improved. It was produced by melting the three ingredients in a furnace with the addition of a small percentage of carbon and casting it in graphite moulds. The result has neither the hardness nor the tensile strength of the high-speed steels developed by Taylor and White, but it is more heat resistant, its cutting performance being quite unimpaired at red heat.

The next advance came from Germany and was so great that it brought about changes in machine-tool design even more radical than those that had followed the introduction of high-speed steels. This was the tungsten-carbide tool. The technique of manufacture is to pulverise tungsten carbide, mix it with cobalt and mould it into the required shape under hydraulic pressure before sintering in a furnace. The material was first produced by Krupps of Essen for the German Osram Company who used it for the drawing dies required in making tungsten filaments for lamp bulbs. It is said that its value as a cutting tool was first discovered in 1926 by a workman at Krupps who tried a piece of the material in a lathe. Be this as it may, Krupps decided to develop and market it as a cutting tool and after extensive trials in the factory it was exhibited under working conditions at the Leipzig Fair in March 1928 where it caused as great a sensation in the machine tool world as had Taylor's high-speed steels at the Paris Exhibition of 1900. The material was thereafter manufactured by Krupps and distributed in the U.K. by A. C. Wickman Ltd. under the trade names 'Widia', and 'Wimet'. In America it was marketed as 'Carboloy'.

So hard was the tungsten-carbide tool that no existing abrasive wheel could cut it, but in 1934 the Norton Company produced a small diamond-bonded wheel capable of dealing with it and with the other carbide tools such as Molybdenum-Titanium Carbide or Tantalum Carbide which followed it. Though extremely hard, these carbides, like Stellite, have a very low tensile strength. For this reason, and because of their high cost the new tools were produced in composite form, a small cutting tip being brazed onto a steel shank. This practice of brazing the tip onto the shank is today giving way to the detachable tip tool.

In order to appreciate what this metallurgical advance meant to the machine-tool designer it is only necessary to quote comparable performance figures. Using a workpiece of medium-quality cast iron and with all other factors constant as in the earlier tests carried out by Taylor, the results are: high-speed steel, 75 feet per minute; Stellite, 150 feet per minute; tungsten carbide, 400 feet per minute.

Before considering the effects of this astonishing performance in general, mention must be made here of the new machining technique of fine boring which the introduction of tungsten-carbide tools popularised. It consists of running a fine finishing cut at an extremely high speed but at a very low rate of feed, the result being a bore of such accuracy and high finish that the necessity for grinding or any further finishing operation is avoided. In 1928 the Automatic Machine Company of Bridgeport, Connecticut, produced a machine called the Coulter Diamond Borer. Using a diamond tool and a maximum spindle speed of 4,000 r.p.m. this machine could finish bore with great accuracy, but its use was restricted to non-ferrous metals. It was the German, Ernst Krause of Berlin, who successfully demonstrated that the tungsten-carbide tool had made it possible to apply the same technique to the boring of iron cylinders and other ferrous parts. Kraus patented his process in Germany in 1931 and subsequently in other countries. He first produced a range of machines for reboring car cylinders, but the fine boring technique was subsequently adopted by the motor industry generally and in many applications it has now supplanted the planetary grinding machine.

The tungsten-carbide tool could not only save time in machining traditional materials, but it could deal speedily and efficiently with new tough alloys of steel and aluminium. These were being used to an increasing extent in the motor and aircraft industries owing to the designers' concern to save weight without sacrificing strength.

The characteristics of the carbide tool are such that it requires much higher spindle speeds with a very close range of speeds in the upper ratios and the elimination of vibration and chatter by ensuring absolute rigidity. If speed is too low, not only is its potential performance lost but its cutting edge is soon dulled; if vibration occurs the cutting edge is speedily destroyed. Because maximum cutting performance has to be achieved at high speed, a machine designed for carbide tools requires from three to four times more nominal horsepower than a machine of the same dimensions designed for high-speed steel. To ensure stability and rigidity the modern machine is likely to be 75 per cent heavier than its predecessor. Yet it was not, as the uninitiated might infer from these facts, simply a matter of adding mass to the machine and applying brute strength. The carbide tools presented the machine-tool designer with some difficult problems, but it was at this point in history that the motor industry began to pay back its technological debt to the machine-tool trade. It was a handsome dividend. In the solution of his problems the machine-tool designer was able to adopt and adapt to his special purposes features of car design and manufacture which the machines of his predecessors had made possible.

In the design of machine-tool gear-boxes this fruitful interchange was particularly apparent. The range of speeds required on the machine was much wider and closer than was needful on a motor car, but the problems created by higher shaft speeds and stresses were not dissimilar to those the automobile engineer had already met and solved. Long unsupported shafts tend to deflect and vibrate under load, so automobile-type gears of hardened nickel-chrome steel were now adopted on machine tools. The high tensile strength of such gears enables their face widths to be greatly reduced so making possible short stiff shafts, splined where sliding gears or clutches are employed. In order to reduce friction at high speeds and loads the use of ball or roller bearings to support such highly stressed shafts was essential. As we have seen, Frederick Lanchester pioneered the use of roller bearings on the motor car at the beginning of the century and by 1930 the use of ball or roller bearings in the motor industry had become universal. That they were not so rapidly adopted on machine tools was not due to conservatism but to requirements so exacting that it was many years before bearing manufacturers could meet them satisfactorily. The earliest known application of this type of bearing to a machine tool appears to have been made by L. Schuler of Germany who fitted a ball thrust bearing to a lathe spindle in 1899. Such applications soon became commonplace, and by the 1920s ball and roller bearings were widely used for transmissions; but to entrust the whole support of the work spindle of a precision tool to bearings of this type was a very different matter and even in the 1930s the normal tolerances adopted by specialist bearing makers would not satisfy the machine tool designer. However, his need was then met by a special pre-loaded bearing which, with less than 0·0001 inch of eccentricity in the races, ensured complete freedom from vibration and chatter. Henceforward various combinations of ball and roller bearings, mounted in precision-bored housings, would be used to carry both the journal and thrust loads of work spindles.

On the heavier non-automatic turret lathes it had become customary to use a power-operated turret and this was the source of many accidents to operators. By using the new frictionless bearings on the turret spindle it was now possible to eliminate such accidents by reverting to manual rotation of the turret from station to station without loss of time or increased physical effort.

The new machines focused attention once more upon the question of lubrication and here again automobile practice was adopted. The high-speed steels had earlier revealed the inadequacy of exposed gears and of bearings lubricated on a total loss basis by oil can or, at best, by an oil cup. The enclosed oil bath foreshadowed by Joseph Clement took the place of this haphazard system, but the new gear-boxes required something better still in the shape of pressure lubrication by filtered oil circulated by pump. Elsewhere on the machine first grease nipples and later 'one-shot' lubrication systems banished the oft-neglected oil hole. These new methods of lubrication demanded oils of stable and enduring quality, but the machine-tool builders were able to take advantage of the improved mineral oils which the motor car had brought into being.

Because the cutting speeds of the new carbide tools were so critical it was essential that the machine tool designer should make the process of speed changing as quick and as simple as possible. This was not only a question of saving time. It had been found by experience that many machine tool operators displayed as much reluctance to change speed as an inexperienced motorist faced with a 'crash' gear-box. The preselector gear-box offered one solution to this problem. It proved a temporary success on the motor car and a permanent one on the machine tool. Preselector gear-boxes for machine tools were patented by F. A. Schell of Berlin in 1929 and by Alfred Herbert and Lloyd of Coventry in 1932. The latter was marketed in 1934 as the Herbert 'Preoptive' headstock and is a feature of the Herbert turret lathe today. The required speed is selected on a dial and engaged by pressing a central button. Owing to the 'limited slip' design of the friction clutches which effect the speed changes, speed can be changed while the machine is in full cut with such smoothness that the point of change is not detectable on the workpiece.

Another approach to the problem of fine, accurate and simple speed control for the new machine tools was by way of our old friend the infinitely variable gear which eliminates even the smallest steps in the speed range. The most ingenious and popular of these solutions is the so-called P.I.V. gear (Positively Infinitely Variable). This uses the old idea of a vee belt running in an expanding vee pulley in a new and positive way. Instead of a belt, the P.I.V. gear employs a special chain whose individual links incorporate plates with cross adjustment. These plates can adapt themselves to engage positively the radial grooves on the cones of the expanding and contracting vee pulleys. This simple, compact gear has a range of one to six and can transmit up to 30 horsepower. It has found a great variety of applications on machine tools but is particularly favoured for jig-boring machines and gear hobbers. Some mystery has surrounded its origin. Credit for the invention has been awarded to America by some and to Germany by others. The German attribution is understandable because it has been manufactured and popularised by the German firm of Werner Reimers K.G. of Bad Homburg. In fact, however, the P.I.V. gear was invented by the English engineer, G. J. Abbot of London, and patented by him in Germany in 1924.

The tremendous cutting power of the carbide tool presented the machine designer with a new and serious problem—how to deal with the swarf. Gone were the days when turners could vie with each other in producing the longest unbroken length of swarf. The heavy chip curling away at near red heat from the tip of a carbide tool under heavy cut was a potential source of injury to the operator and damage to the guideways of the machine. Chip breakers were introduced to break up the swarf as it left the tool. Special attention also had to be paid to the rake angles of the cutting tool and its angle of presentation to the work in order to ensure that the chip flowed away in an even cork-screw form and in a direction as nearly as possible at right angles to the axis of the workpiece. Above all, it was necessary to design machine beds and guideways of such a form that they could provide the necessary rigidity under heavy cutting loads and yet at the same time offer no lodgement to the damaging swarf but allow it to fall freely into bins under the bed. No form of flat bed could meet those two requirements and the solution was a bed with guideways of a very deep inverted vee section completely protected from chip damage by accurately fitting covers on the carriage slides. This change coincided with the introduction of a new method of finally bedding guideways and slides by machine instead of hand scraping. Various methods of hardening guideways were evolved, the hardened surfaces being then finished on slideway grinding machines of high precision. This technique was originated in Germany by Dr. R. Schonherr in the late 1920s and the first slideway grinding machines were produced there by Billeter and Klunz. It was rapidly adopted on the Continent and in Britain for finishing, first cast iron, and later hardened ways, but in America it was not widely used until the introduction of hardened ways made the use of grinding machines essential.

These revolutionary changes in the older types of metal-cutting tools were accompanied by the further development of grinding wheels and grinding machines. In 1914–15 James Guest in England and George Alden in America advanced the pioneer work of Charles Norton by carrying out research which placed the choice of wheel, speed and feed on a scientific basis. In other words, by distinguishing and studying the many variable factors involved, they did for the grinding wheel the work that Taylor had done for the single-point tool. Guest's results confirmed Norton's belief in the value of large and wide wheels and he also emphasised the importance of coolants in grinding, both to increase cutting power and to improve finish. These studies had a rapid and most beneficial effect on grinding machine design, but it is only in the last 20 years that modern methods of scientific study and control have brought about a major improvement in grinding wheels. By control of the production process it has been possible to produce crystalline grains with more cutting points and of such a structure that, as soon as they become dulled, the points break off and, in doing so, form fresh ones. Moreover, these improved crystals can be produced in a predetermined range of grain sizes. This facility, coupled with improved methods of mixing and moulding with the bond, has resulted in the production of a wide variety of grinding wheels closely adapted to meet the multifarious requirements of the modern machine shop. These modern wheels are at once safer and more accurately balanced than their predecessors. How far removed they are from the sandstone grinding wheel of the medieval swordsmith or his scythe-grinding successor!

The most important development in grinding technique to follow the work of Norton and Heald was the appearance of the centreless grinding machine. It was eagerly welcomed by the motor industry as a great time-saver in the production of gudgeon pins, king pins and similar cylindrical components requiring a precision finish to fine limits after hardening. The principle of the machine is an ancient one. It was employed by the first man to hold a cylindrical object against the face of a grindstone with a block of wood and allow it to rotate through the action of the wheel. A number of nineteenth-century engineers produced machines working on this principle, David Wilkinson among them, but these used a stationary block to hold the work against the wheel and none had the quality of precision.

It was the American L. R. Heim who added precision to the centreless principle in his patent of 1915. For the stationary block Heim substituted a powered regulating wheel with a bonded vulcanite face and instead of the worktable of the older machines he used a narrow workrest or work blade with an angled top to support the workpiece in a position a little above the parallel axes of the two wheels and, by virtue of this angled top, to hold it against the face of the regulating wheel. The latter rotates at a speed lower than that of the grinding wheel and in the opposite direction, the actual grinding speed being the difference between the two rates. Like the gear-hobbing machine, the simplicity of the centreless grinder is deceptive because, in practice, its precision depends upon a most exact relationship between the grinding wheel, the workpiece, the regulating wheel and the work blade. The position of the last-named and the angle of its top are particularly critical. Provided these relationships are correctly established the machine can produce work with great speed to an accuracy of 0·0002 inch.

Heim's invention was taken up by the Cincinnati Milling Machine Company who produced the first production centreless machine in 1922. Its capabilities immediately impressed the motor industry and its development in automatic form was extremely rapid. By 1925 automobile valve stems were being finished ground on centreless machines at the rate of 350 an hour. By slightly inclining the face of the regulating wheel a plain cylindrical component such as a gudgeon pin or a bearing roller could be fed through the machine, but in the case of a headed part such as a valve it was necessary to plunge cut and then to retract the regulating wheel and work blade to release the workpiece. Although on the automatic machine this operation was performed very speedily it was not fast enough to satisfy the insatiable time-saving demands of mass production. Accordingly, between 1932 and 1935 the Cincinnati Company developed the cam-type regulating wheel. With this arrangement the machine finishes a component in one revolution of the cam wheel. While that portion of the periphery of the wheel which represents the base of the cam is opposite the face of the grinding wheel a finished part is released and another workpiece introduced from a magazine to be held against the grinding wheel by the rising cam profile.

In 1933 the Heald Machine Company introduced an internal centreless grinding machine. Because it eliminated the chucking problems of the orthodox internal grinding machine, it proved a much faster method of machining small bearings and bushes. In this type of machine the workpiece is positioned between three rollers, a large-diameter regulating roll, a small pressure roll above and a small support roll below. By the 1930s centreless machines, like the other, older types of precision grinding machine, had been fitted with automatic size control.

The latest addition to the ranks of centreless machines is the thread grinder using a crush-formed grinding wheel to produce headless hardened steel set-screws such as those used for tappet clearance adjustment in the rockers of automobile engines. Machines of this type were first produced by the Landis Machine Company in 1947, but the relevant patent was filed in America by the Englishman, A. Scrivener of Birmingham in 1944.

Another type of modern tool in which the workpiece is not centred or fixed upon a worktable is the vertical spindle lapping machine used for exceptionally fine and accurate finishing work on plain or external cylindrical surfaces. The work is passed between two bonded abrasive discs, but for the finest finishes laps of cast iron are used in conjunction with abrasive grains of a very fine and even quality suspended in lubricant. Used for gauge making, machines of the latter kind can work to an accuracy of 0·00001 inch. Lapping machines using abrasive tape have been used to give a fine finish to the crankshaft journals and cams of internal combustion engines.

To sum up, the modern production grinding machine achieves all that

Charles Norton forecast for it. As he predicted, it has usurped many of the operations previously carried out on the older types of machine tool, executing them far more speedily and with much greater accuracy. For example, a modern surface grinder can complete in 3½ hours a job which would take 40 hours to plane and scrape. Not only has such a machine reduced the need for final hand-scraping, but in many cases the need for a preliminary rough cut on another machine has been obviated also. The greater accuracy of modern metal *forming* techniques in forge and foundry has increased the number of components which can be finished ground from the blank.

The motor industry's demand for stronger, quieter gears led during the 1930s to a greatly increased use of precision gear-grinding machines using formed wheels to give a precision finish to gears after hardening. It will be recalled that E. R. Fellows had pioneered this process at the beginning of the century as a means of finishing his gear shaper cutters. At the same time the process of shaving as a means of giving a fine finish to unhardened gears was pioneered by the Michigan Tool Company of Illinois. The first gear-shaving machines used a rack-type cutter but modern machines are of the rotary type using a helical gear form of cutter, with serrated teeth, in crossed-axes relationship to the blank. Such a cutter produces fine, hair-like shavings and leaves an extremely smooth and accurate finish on the tooth. The tendency today is for gear shaving to supersede the grinding of hardened gears. Modern metallurgy has made possible the production of material in which the amount of deformation occurring during hardening is accurately predictable. Consequently, a shaving cutter can be designed to produce a gear form which will be inaccurate in the soft state but correct after hardening. Machines are now being produced which apply the shaving technique to splined and serrated shafts.

The need of the motor industry for a variety of components having internal teeth, splines or serrations of many forms brought about the birth—or rather the rebirth—of the process known to the pioneer English tool-makers as drifting. It was first introduced by Joseph Whitworth as a more rapid method than the slotting machine of cutting internal keyways. Holtzapffel's description[1] of this Whitworth tool cannot be bettered. He writes:

> The cutter is a cylindrical rod of steel, through which are made about ten or a dozen rectangular mortises, placed at equal distances and in right line. Every mortise is fitted with a small steel cutter, the sides of which are made exactly true in the engineer's planing machine; the first cutter is

[1] Charles Holtzapffel, *Turning and Mechanical Manipulation*, Vol. II, p. 990.

sharpened so as scarcely to project beyond the surface of the cylindrical bar, the second projects a little more than the first, and so on to the last the projection of which equals the full depth of the key-way. When used, the bar is first put into the hole of the wheel, and which it should exactly fit, and the bar is steadily pushed quite through the hole of the wheel or pulley, by aid of the steady movement of an appropriate screw-press. . . . From the subdivision of the work amongst the many cutters, the work is well done, and almost without injury to the cutters, which should be sufficiently close together, that the succeeding cutter may enter the groove, before the previous one has passed through the same.

Although this method of keyway cutting was extremely rapid, the tool was highly specialised so perhaps it is not surprising that the technique did not come into its own until the age of mass production was fairly under way. It seems to have been forgotten and to have been re-invented in America by Anson P. Stephens in 1873. Stephens' method of drifting was the same as Whitworth's, but instead of using a simple vertical screw-press his rack-and-pinion machine was more advanced mechanically in the way it held, pushed and guided the tool. Most unfortunately, Stephens called the tool a broach and the process broaching. This was very confusing because, in traditional English usage, a broach is a rotative tool for forming taper holes whereas the drifting tool is reciprocating, not rotative, and consequently the one thing it cannot do is to cut tapers. However, the use of the word broach in this context, though a gross misnomer, has become part of the engineer's vocabulary so it must perforce be accepted here.

Stephens' device evidently failed to win popularity, for the only method of broaching described by Joshua Rose (*c.* 1890) is a curiously primitive device for cutting cotter slots and the like. The area of the slot having been previously drilled out, the slot is completed by pushing through it under a vertical press a series of rectangular cutter blocks in ascending order of size. Rose refers to these blocks as 'a set of broaches'. They were provided with teats and indentations on their upper and lower faces respectively so that they located positively with one another when placed successively under the press. This technique probably derived from that of Richard Lawrence, of Robbins & Lawrence, who in 1853 pushed serrated balls through heated gun barrels in order to size them.

It is obvious that so long as the broach was *pushed* through the hole in the workpiece the technique was severely limited by the mechanical strength of the broach under compression. By pulling the broach instead of pushing it, thus putting the tool in tension, far wider applications of the process at once became possible. Much longer and more elaborate broaching tools could be used upon which a variety of operations and successive roughing, fine shaving and finishing cuts had all been 'built in' in the tool room. As a result, a complicated internal machining operation could be speedily completed in a single pass of the broaching machine.

The pioneer of pull broaching was John N. Lapointe, a foreman in the Pratt & Whitney machine shop at Hartford, Connecticut, who patented the first horizontal pull broaching machine with screw-and-nut action in 1898. In 1902 John Lapointe founded his own business, the Lapointe Machine Tool Company, at Atlantic Avenue, Boston, Massachusetts, to manufacture his broaches and broaching machines. The American Rolls Royce Company of Springfield was among the early users of his machines which soon proved their value in the automobile industry. In 1903 John Lapointe opened a larger plant at Hudson, Massachusetts, but in 1914 he sold out his interest to J. J. Prindiville and started a second business of his own at New London, Connecticut. At the same time his son, Frank Lapointe, broke away from his father to start his own business, the American Broach & Machine Company of Ann Arbor, Michigan. Thus the three major firms responsible for broaching development stemmed from one family.

Special form-grinding machines for broach production were developed in 1918 to bring greater precision to the process and in 1921 the first hydraulic broaching machine was produced by the Oilgear Company. For a time there was controversy between the advocates of screw and hydraulic machines, for although the latter were swifter and smoother in action they were of the water-powered type dependent upon hydraulic mains and accumulators. Then came the modern oleo-hydraulic system with its compact 'power pack' to put an end to the argument.

External or surface broaching was introduced in 1934.[1] Today, the face of a cylinder head or cylinder block may be finished machined by the single rapid pass of a giant broach equipped with teeth of tungsten carbide. More recent developments are the spiral broach, which enables such parts as internal helical gears to be cut by this method, and the turret broaching machine with automatic indexing on which multiple operations can be carried out. Like Charles Norton's grinding machine, John Lapointe's broaching machine has speedily become an essential tool in the modern production machine shop.

So successful was hydraulic actuation on the broaching machine that its

[1] Patents for surface broaching date from 1882 but the date given is that of successful commercial manufacture and application.

application to the traverses of grinding machines, where freedom from vibration was supremely important, very speedily followed. Today, hydraulic operation is practically universal on grinding machines. The machine itself initiated this development because the manufacture of compact hydraulic equipment of this kind, depending as it does on very close machining tolerances, was only made possible by precision cylindrical grinding.

The most striking feature of machine-tool engineering in the twentieth century has been the rapid and widespread adoption of powered control systems—hydraulic, pneumatic, electric, electronic, either singly or in combination—on all but the simplest and smallest general-purpose tools. A device such as an hydraulic or pneumatic actuating jack controlled by a solenoid-operated valve and micro-switch represents an extension of the human hand far more sensitive, precise, rapid and safe than the straight mechanical systems that taxed the ingenuity of earlier designers and not infrequently harassed machine-tool operators. Such control systems combined with separate motor drives to spindles and feed motions through modern variable-speed transmissions enable the designer to attain the ideal of simple, effortless centralised control by the operator of the largest and most elaborate machine. Alternatively, they make complete automation of the tool very much easier to achieve. A good example of modern technique is the power operation of chucks or work-holding fixtures either by compressed air or by electromechanical means. Such devices are an essential feature of automated machines, while on operator-controlled machines they save time and eliminate a potential accident risk.

Though working principles remain the same, the contrast between the smooth exterior of the modern machine tool and the exposed wheels and shafts of its skeletonic ancestor is very striking. It resembles the transformation which the motor car has undergone over the same period of time, but the analogy is a false one. For whereas fashionable styling is largely responsible for the motor car's 'new look', the design of the machine tool is still strictly functional. Its changed appearance is due to the fact that by the use of power controls all its moving parts can be more fully enclosed and shrouded. This protects the operator from the hazards inseparable from the need for direct manual intervention in machining processes and it protects the machine itself from swarf or abrasive dust.

Modern methods of power control may be used to manipulate a workpiece automatically throughout a whole sequence of machine operations and it is this technique which is now popularly known as automation. The first manifestation of this sytem was, in effect, a single huge special-purpose machine performing successive operations, the workpiece being transferred from one stage to the next by some automatic means—an hydraulic transfer arm being the device currently favoured. Such an installation is only justified where mass production conditions apply and even so some of the earliest efforts in this direction suffered from lack of flexibility. Ford's pioneer plant at Detroit exhibited this defect of being too highly specialised. Behind the corny old joke to the effect that a Ford customer could have his car finished in any colour provided it was black there lurked a sober truth, while it is notorious that Henry Ford clung to his 'Model T' until long after it had been outmoded because he was reluctant to scrap the over-specialised plant which produced it. No manufacturer can afford to ignore the changing needs of his customers or bid the technical development of his product stand still throughout the lifetime of his tools. Consequently the modern designer of machines for mass production must endeavour to combine maximum output performance with adaptability to design changes, two attributes not easily reconciled.

The link-line system is one example of the efforts which are being made to make mass production processes more flexible. In this arrangement, instead of a single highly specialised transfer machine, a series of standard production machine tools are automated and linked together by a conveyor system, the workpieces being moved between the worktables and the conveyor by hydraulic transfer arms. This does not mean to say that the link-line will supersede the transfer machine. In deciding which system to adopt the production engineer has to be guided by the shape and dimensions of the workpiece and the machine operations required on it.

As a consumer of machine tools the aircraft industry has risen to a position second only to the motor industry, but its requirements are different. Batch production rather than mass production is the rule in the aircraft builder's machine shop, the quantities involved being small by the standards of the motor manufacturer. Most of the components of the modern high-speed aircraft are made of high-duty alloys of steel or aluminium and are of a form and specification which require the performance of a complex sequence of machine operations to extremely accurate standards. To apply orthodox mass production techniques to the machining of such parts in small quantity is out of the question. At the other extreme, the employment of simple general-purpose tools for such work would involve an unwarrantable expenditure on jigs and fixtures and an equally great expenditure of time by many highly skilled and highly paid machinists. The machine-tool designer's answer to this type of production problem has been the widespread introduction of the copying principle.

100 *Lapointe broaching machine with screw feed,* c. *1903*

101 *Modern Cincinnati-Weatherley broaching machine for connecting rods*

102 *Eight Churchill Rigidhobbers forming part of the Churchill Gear Machine Company's link-line system for the fully automated production of automobile layshaft gears*

103 *Cincinnati Hydrotel milling machine arranged for numerical control*

The idea of using the profile of a templet or a master component to control the motions of a cutting tool on a machine is a very ancient one. It could be said to date back to the templet used by Jacques Besson on his sixteenth-century ornamental lathe and, as we have seen, it was employed successfully by Thomas Blanchard on his gun-stocking lathe of 1818. These were wood-turning applications, however. To apply the same principle to a heavy-duty metal-cutting machine by any straight mechanical means would be out of the question because of the load imposed on the stylus which must follow the templet or master. Modern power-control systems removed this difficulty. On the copying lathe or copy-milling machine of today the stylus exerts no more than finger-tip pressure, yet its movement over the master profile accurately controls the motions of the machine by hydraulic or electrical means or by a combination of both. Actual machining time is not reduced in this way, yet overall time may be reduced by more than 50 per cent, the reason being that the operator need no longer stop the machine frequently to check the workpiece for dimensional accuracy, take trial cuts, check again, and refer repeatedly to drawings.

It is at this stage in the evolution of machine tools that the new branch of engineering known as cybernetics has been introduced in the past few years. It is so called because it exploits the similarities between physiological and machine control systems by electronic means. Functionally, a cybernetic machine-control system consists of three elements, a receptor, a comparator and an effector. The receptor monitors the positions of the machine controls and transmits them in the form of electrical signals to the comparator. As its name denotes, the function of the comparator is to evaluate these signals, compare them with the required co-ordinates and initiate the appropriate responses in the machine. This is done by transmitting electrical signals to the effector. The effector, by means of transistor amplifiers, converts these signals into direct-current voltages suitable for driving the motors which operate the slide motions of the machine. The required co-ordinates may be either pre-set on dials on the comparator unit or they may be fed into it by means of a punched tape.

Where it is appropriate, a simplified form of this system can be used for direct copying by using a tracer head moving over a templet or a photo-electric reading head moving over a drawing of the required profile. But for certain complex operations the tape control system using electrical scale receptor units appropriately positioned on the machine has great advantages. The best sequence of machine operations can be planned beforehand and translated onto a master tape, copies of which are quickly made on a modern tape-perforating machine. The alternative would be to issue working drawings to the machine shop. These would have to be studied by highly skilled operators, the sequence of operations decided, jigs made and the machine set up for the successive operations. In the course of this the machine would be standing idle for a high proportion of the total time. The widespread introduction of tape control has so far been somewhat inhibited by the high cost of the electronic equipment, but notwithstanding this handicap it has already proved its value, particularly in the aircraft industry where highly complex components have to be machined with great accuracy in small batches. Here tape control has the added advantage that it can be applied to machines such as the horizontal boring machine on which, owing to the nature of the operations it performs, no physical copying method is feasible.

In order to machine with precision the bearing housings of a gear-box casing on the older type of horizontal boring machine it was necessary to bore them in line. This involved careful setting up and the use of jigs to support the boring spindle. On the modern boring machine, however, the relative positions of the spindle and the worktable are electrically co-ordinated with such accuracy that 'in line' boring, with all that it entails, is no longer necessary. Instead, when one end of a gear-box casing has been bored and faced the table can be indexed through 180° and the other end machined with such precision that opposite bores will correspond within limits as close as 0·0001 inch. Moreover, such machines have compound rotary tables which can present the workpiece in varying angular relationship to the axis of the spindle. Such a machine lends itself to tape control whereas its predecessor did not. On a machine of this type with tape control an aircraft auxiliary gear-box has been machined on ten faces in varying angular planes from a solid block of Dural. The machine operations included drilling, boring, counterboring and tapping; slotting, recessing, grooving and undercutting, chamfering and radiusing. This involved more than 130 automatically co-ordinated settings of the table and spindle head but only two settings of the workpiece. Tool changes were simplified by press-button power tool locking and tool ejection.

This is the present end of the process of building the skill into the machine which we have followed through successive chapters of this book. It conjures up a vision, not of a single machine, but of an entire machine shop under the control of the coldly calculating synthetic brain of a computer, a consummation such as Henry Maudslay never dreamed on, and one which should give sociologist and philosopher furiously to think.

Where the machine tools themselves are concerned, progress continues.

Ceramic tools have appeared with a cutting performance greater than the carbides and for some years experiments have been going forward on a process of electro-discharge machining which could supersede many of the orthodox methods of cutting metal by single- or multiple-point tool or grinding wheel. Upon the other hand it seems likely that the need for heavy machining operations will diminish in the future. It is obviously uneconomic and wasteful to employ one set of machines to form metal into certain shapes and then to instal a second set of machines in order to cut a great part of those shapes away. Already more precise methods of metal forming including the rapidly developing technique of cold extrusion are reducing the need for heavy machining on many components. Then, too, there are the machines that do not come within the scope of this book which form metal instead of cutting it. Thread rolling as opposed to thread cutting is the oldest example of this machine process and now machines exist which can form splines in the same way. Other things being equal, a formed component is generally stronger than its equivalent produced by metal cutting because the forming process tends to densen the molecular structure of the metal.

By the standards of our modern industrialised society the world's machine-tool industry is a small one, but it is of vital importance. For good or ill it has made possible the world in which we live today and in this sense it is the arbiter of tomorrow. It is nearly 200 years since James Watt discovered that the greatest invention is of no practical value unless the maker of tools can supply the tools for the job. It is a far cry from John Wilkinson's boring machine to the tape-controlled boring machine of today, but this fact has not changed. Nor has the skill and resource of the tool-maker. The policy of building the skill into the machine which he has pursued with such spectacular results ever since the days of Henry Maudslay has not had the effect of diminishing his own skill. The reverse is true. His is a craft industry and it is likely to remain so. Not long ago it was suggested that the machine tool maker should swallow some of his own medicine and reorganise his own production methods on mass production lines. The demands made upon him are too varied and too specialised for that and his customer is less interested in what his machine will cost than in what it will save him by its speed and economy of operation.

Because machine tool making is a craft industry its financial rewards are generally lower than those which can be won in many of the industries it serves. But for the man who, like Maudslay, Clement, Roberts or Nasmyth, regards mechanical engineering as a vocation there are rewards of another kind. Summing up a long lifetime of experience, one of the greatest of latter-day British machine tool makers, the late Sir Alfred Herbert, wrote: 'There are few branches of engineering which offer greater attraction to the mechanical enthusiast, and though monetary reward may be inadequate, the continual overcoming of constantly increasing difficulties introduces an element of excitement and even of sport into the trade, which encourages the machine tool maker never to faint. As Robert Louis Stevenson aptly wrote: "It is a better thing to travel hopefully than to arrive and the true reward is to labour." ' To a man, the great pioneer engineers would agree with him.

Bibliography

Abell, S. G., with Leggatt, John, and Ogden, W. G., *A Bibliography of the Art of Turning and Lathe Machine Tool History*, London, New York: the Society of Ornamental Turners, 1956.

Baillie, G. H., Clutton, C., and Ilbert, C. A., *Britten's Old Clocks and Watches and their Makers*, London: Spon, 1956.

Benson, W. A. S., 'The Early Machine Tools of Henry Maudslay', London: *Engineering*, Jan./Feb. 1901.

Bergeron, L. E. (Salivet, Louis George), *Manuel du tourneur*, 2 vols., Paris, 1792–96.

Berthoud, Ferdinand, *Essai sur l'horlogerie*, Paris, 1763.

Besson, Jacques, *Theatrum Machinarum*, Lyon, 1578.

Buchanan, Robertson, *Practical Essays on Millwork* (3rd ed.), ed. Rennie, George. London: John Veale, 1841.

Bulleid, A., and Gray, H., *The Glastonbury Lake Village*, Glastonbury Antiquarian Society, 1911.

Burlingame, Roger, *Machines That Built America*, New York: Harcourt, Brace, 1953.

———, *Henry Ford*, London: Hutchinson, 1957.

Churchill Machine Tool Company, The Story of, Manchester: C.M.T. Co., 1956.

Davies, W. O., *Gears for Small Mechanisms*, London: N.A.G. Press, 1953.

Derry, T. K., and Williams, T. I., *A Short History of Technology*, Oxford: Clarendon Press, 1960.

Dickinson, H. W., *John Wilkinson, Ironmaster*, Ulverston: Hume Kitchin, 1914.

———, and Jenkins, Rhys, *James Watt and the Steam Engine*, Oxford: Clarendon Press, 1927.

———, 'Joseph Bramah and his Inventions', London: *Newcomen Society Transactions*, vol. XXII, 1941–2.

———, 'The Origin and Manufacture of Wood Screws', London: *Newcomen Society Transactions*, vol. XXII, 1941–2.

———, 'Richard Roberts, His Life and Inventions', London: *Newcomen Society Transactions*, vol. XXV, 1945–47.

Edwards, E. Percy, 'Broaching Machines, Tools and Practice', London: *Proceedings of the Institution of Production Engineers*, 1946.

Ffoulkes, Charles, *The Gun Founders of England*, Cambridge: the University Press, 1937.

Forward, E. A., 'The Early History of the Cylinder Boring Machine', London: *Newcomen Society Transactions*, vol. V, 1924–25.

French, Sir James Weir, *Machine Tools*, 2 vols., London, 1911.

Gale, W. K. V., 'Some Workshop Tools from Soho Foundry', London: *Newcomen Society Transactions*, vol. XXIII, 1942–43.

Gill, J. P., *Tool Steels*, Cleveland, Ohio: American Society of Metals, 1944.

Habakkuk, H. J., *American and British Technology in the Nineteenth Century*, Cambridge: the University Press, 1962.

Hadfield, Sir Robert A., Bart., *Faraday and his Metallurgical Researches*, London: Chapman & Hall, 1931.

Hancock, H. B., and Wilkinson, N. B., 'Joshua Gilpin, an American Manufacturer in England and Wales', London: *Newcomen Society Transactions*, vol. XXXII, 1959–60.

Henry Maudslay and Maudslay, Sons & Field, a Commemorative Booklet, London: the Maudslay Society, 1949.

Hogg, O. F. G., 'The Development of Engineering at the Royal Arsenal', London: *Newcomen Society Transactions*, vol. XXXII, 1959–60.

Holtzapffel, Charles, *Turning and Mechanical Manipulation*, vol. II, London: Holtzapffel & Co., 1875.

Hulme, E. W., 'The Pedigree and Career of Benjamin Huntsman', London: *Newcomen Society Transactions*, vol. XXIV, 1943–45.

Kingsford, P. W., *F. W. Lanchester, the Life of an Engineer*, London: Arnold, 1960.

Lanchester, G. H., 'F. W. Lanchester, LL.D., F.R.S., His Life and Work', London: *Newcomen Society Transactions*, vol. XXX, 1957–58.

Lloyd, A. H., 'A History of Machine Tool Development', *Heaton Works Journal*, 1951.

MacCurdy, Edward (ed.), *The Notebooks of Leonardo da Vinci* (5th imp.), London: Jonathan Cape, 1948.

Machine Tools, Illustrated Catalogue of the Collection in the Science Museum, London: H.M.S.O., 1920.

Machine Tool Industry, The, A Report by the Sub-Committee of the Machine Tool Advisory Council, London: H.M.S.O., 1960.

Matschoss, C., *Great Engineers*, London: Bell, 1939.

Nasmyth, J., *Autobiography*, ed. S. Smiles, London: John Murray, 1882.

Nicolson, J. T., and Dempster, *Lathe Design for High and Low Speed Steels*, London: Longmans, 1908.

Osborne, F. M., *The Story of the Mushets*, London: Nelson, 1952.

Pater, Walter, *The Renaissance*, London: Macmillan, 1915.

Petree, J. F., 'Maudslay, Sons & Field as General Engineers', London: *Newcomen Society Transactions*, vol. XV, 1934–35.

Pressnell, L. S. (ed.), *Studies in the Industrial Revolution*, London: Athlone Press, 1960.

Raistrick, A., *A Dynasty of Ironfounders*, London: Longmans, 1953.

Ramsden, J., *Description of our Engine for Dividing Straight Lines*, London, 1777.
Roe, Joseph W., *English and American Tool Builders*, New York: McGraw-Hill, 1916 (repr. 1926).
———, 'Interchangeable Manufacture', London: *Newcomen Society Transactions*, vol. XVII, 1936–37.
Rose, Joshua, *Modern Machine Shop Practice*, 2 vols., London: J. S. Virtue, n.d. (*c.* 1890).
Scott, E. Kilburn (ed.), *Matthew Murray, Pioneer Engineer*, Leeds: Edwin Jowett, 1928.
Smiles, S., *Lives of Boulton and Watt*, London: John Murray, 1865.
———, *Lives of the Engineers*, vol. II, London: John Murray, 1862.
———, *Industrial Biography*, London: John Murray, 1882.
'Soho Foundry', London: *The Engineer*, Sept.–Oct. 1901.
Taylor, F. W., 'On the Art of Cutting Metals', New York: *Proceedings of the American Society of Mechanical Engineers*, 1906.
Thiout, Antoine, *Traité d'horologerie méchanique et pratique*, Paris, 1741.
White, George, 'A History of Early Needle Making', London: *Newcomen Society Transactions*, vol. XXI, 1940–41.
Williams, Alfred, *Life in a Railway Factory*, London, Duckworth, 1915.
Wittmann, Karl, *Die Entwicklung der Drehbank*, Berlin, 1941 (consulted in original typescript translation).
Woodbury, Robert S., *History of the Gear-cutting Machine*, Cambridge, Mass.: the Technology Press, 1958.
——, *History of the Grinding Machine*, Cambridge, Mass.: the Technology Press, 1959.
———, *History of the Milling Machine*, Cambridge, Mass.: the Technology Press, 1960.
———, *History of the Lathe*, Cleveland, Ohio: the Society for the History of Technology, 1961.
———, 'The Legend of Eli Whitney', *Technology and Culture*, Vol. I, No., 3, Wayne State University Press, 1960.
Young, J. R., 'Recent Developments in the Application of Machine Tools', Glasgow: *Proceedings of the Institution of Engineers and Shipbuilders of Scotland*, 1954.

Index

The numerals in **heavy** type refer to the figure numbers of illustrations.

Index

Index